D0648714

Linear Systems of Ordinary Differential Equations

With Periodic and Quasi-Periodic Coefficients

MATHEMATICS IN SCIENCE AND ENGINEERING

A SERIES OF MONOGRAPHS AND TEXTBOOKS

Edited by Richard Bellman
University of Southern California

1. Tracy Y. Thomas. Concepts from Tensor Analysis and Differential Geometry. Second Edition. 1965
2. Tracy Y. Thomas. Plastic Flow and Fracture in Solids. 1961
3. Rutherford Aris. The Optimal Design of Chemical Reactors: A Study in Dynamic Programming. 1961
4. Joseph LaSalle and Solomon Lefschetz. Stability by Liapunov's Direct Method with Applications. 1961
5. George Leitmann (ed.). Optimization Techniques: With Applications to Aerospace Systems. 1962
6. Richard Bellman and Kenneth L. Cooke. Differential-Difference Equations. 1963
7. Frank A. Haight. Mathematical Theories of Traffic Flow. 1963
8. F. V. Atkinson. Discrete and Continuous Boundary Problems. 1964
9. A. Jeffrey and T. Taniuti. Non-Linear Wave Propagation: With Applications to Physics and Magnetohydrodynamics. 1964
10. Julius T. Tou. Optimum Design of Digital Control Systems. 1963
11. Harley Flanders. Differential Forms: With Applications to the Physical Sciences. 1963
12. Sanford M. Roberts. Dynamic Programming in Chemical Engineering and Process Control. 1964
13. Solomon Lefschetz. Stability of Nonlinear Control Systems. 1965
14. Dimitris N. Chorafas. Systems and Simulation. 1965
15. A. A. Pervozvanskii. Random Processes in Nonlinear Control Systems. 1965
16. Marshall C. Pease, III. Methods of Matrix Algebra. 1965
17. V. E. Benes. Mathematical Theory of Connecting Networks and Telephone Traffic. 1965
18. William F. Ames. Nonlinear Partial Differential Equations in Engineering. 1965
19. J. Aczél. Lectures on Functional Equations and Their Applications. 1966
20. R. E. Murphy. Adaptive Processes in Economic Systems. 1965
21. S. E. Dreyfus. Dynamic Programming and the Calculus of Variations. 1965
22. A. A. Fel'dbaum. Optimal Control Systems. 1965

MATHEMATICS IN SCIENCE AND ENGINEERING

23. A. Halanay. Differential Equations: Stability, Oscillations, Time Lags. 1966
24. M. Namik Oğuztöreli. Time-Lag Control Systems. 1966
25. David Sworder. Optimal Adaptive Control Systems. 1966
26. Milton Ash. Optimal Shutdown Control of Nuclear Reactors. 1966
27. Dimitris N. Chorafas. Control System Functions and Programming Approaches. (In Two Volumes.) 1966
28. N. P. Erugin. Linear Systems of Ordinary Differential Equations. 1966
29. Solomon Marcus. Algebraic Linguistics; Analytical Models. 1966
30. A. M. Liapunov. Stability of Motion. 1966

In preparation

A. Kaufmann. Graphs, Dynamic Programming, and Finite Games

Minoru Urabe. Nonlinear Autonomous Oscillations

A. Kaufmann and R. Cruon. Dynamic Programming: Sequential Scientific Management

George Leitmann (ed.). Optimization: A Variational Approach

Y. Sawagari, Y. Sunahara, and T. Nakamizo. Statistical Decision Theory in Adaptive Control Systems

Masunao Aoki. Optimization of Stochastic Processes

F. Calogero. Variable Phase Approach to Potential Scattering

J. H. Ahlberg, E. N. Nilson, and J. L. Walsh. The Theory of Splines and Their Application

Harold J. Kushner. Stochastic Stability and Control

Linear Systems of Ordinary Differential Equations

With Periodic and Quasi-Periodic Coefficients

(with revisions by the author for the English edition)

Nikolay P. Erugin
ACADEMY OF SCIENCES OF THE BSSR, MINSK

Translated by SCRIPTA TECHNICA, INC.

Translation Editor
RICHARD BELLMAN
UNIVERSITY OF SOUTHERN CALIFORNIA, LOS ANGELES, CALIFORNIA

1966

ACADEMIC PRESS New York • London

COPYRIGHT © 1966, BY ACADEMIC PRESS INC.
ALL RIGHTS RESERVED.
NO PART OF THIS BOOK MAY BE REPRODUCED IN ANY FORM,
BY PHOTOSTAT, MICROFILM, OR ANY OTHER MEANS, WITHOUT
WRITTEN PERMISSION FROM THE PUBLISHERS.

ACADEMIC PRESS INC.
111 Fifth Avenue, New York, New York 10003

United Kingdom Edition published by
ACADEMIC PRESS INC. (LONDON) LTD.
Berkeley Square House, London W.1

LIBRARY OF CONGRESS CATALOG CARD NUMBER: 66-23935

Originally published as:
"Lineynyye Sistemy Obyknovennykh
Differentsial'nykh Uravneniy s Periodicheskimi
i Kvaziperiodicheskimi Koeffitsiyentami"
Press of Acad. Sci. BSSR, Minsk, 1963

PRINTED IN THE UNITED STATES OF AMERICA

Library
I.U.P.
Indiana, Pa.

517.382 Er91
c. 1

Author's Comments

In 1956 a monograph by the author, *The Lappo-Danilevskiy method in the theory of linear differential equations*, was published (University of Leningrad Press). It was written* exactly twenty-five years to the day after the death of the outstanding Russian mathematician I. A. Lappo-Danilevskiy in commemoration of that event.

It was assumed that this work would be published in the periodical *Uspekhi matematicheskikh* nauk or in the series *Problemy sovremennoy matematiki*, which is published under the direction of the preceding periodical. Therefore, the exposition was extremely brief and in many places almost sketchy. The present monograph is a revision of that work. Here, the material is expounded in much greater detail and the content of the book has been considerably supplemented. Therefore, even its name has been changed.

The author is aware that even now greater detail might be in order in certain portions of the exposition, for example, in Sections 1, 37, 43, 44, and others. However, the reader can find greater detail on the subject of Section 37 in the work by Lyapunov. Here, we needed this only for the validity and completeness of the solution of problems on the bounded solutions of the equation $\ddot{x}+p(t)x=0$ with periodic function $p(t)$ of varying sign. We have not dealt with other methods of solving this problem but refer the reader to the survey article by V. M. Starzhinskiy.

*The monograph was written in 1954. An address on the subject in question was presented April 20, 1954, at the Scientific Section of the Physico-mathematical sector of the Academy of Sciences of the Kazakh SSR [66].

Contents

Introduction

In Section 1 the fundamentals of the theory of functions of a single matrix are expounded along the lines of Lappo-Danilevskiy. A method based on Lappo-Danilevskiy's formulas is presented for constructing Lagrange's minimum polynomial from a matrix A, where this polynomial is a function of the matrix A. We show that the analytic continuation of $f(A)$, which is obtained by using Lagrange's formula, produces all possible values of $f(A)$ including irregular ones if $f(A)$ is a multiple-valued function. We give the general representation of the function $Y = \ln X$, we show when this function can possess real values, and we indicate the form of the principal and regular value.

In Section 2 we study the problem of expanding a matric function $f\left(\sum_{k=0}^{\infty} X_k \varepsilon^k\right)$ (where the X_k are matrices) in a series of powers of ε. Here, we treat both regular and irregular values of $f\left(\sum_{k=0}^{\infty} X_k \varepsilon^k\right)$.

In Section 3 we treat functions of several matrices, following Lappo-Danilevskiy.

In Sections 4 and 5 we give some classes of systems of differential equations that are integrable in closed form. These classes of equations can be of significance in the construction of approximate solutions of systems of linear differential equations.

In Section 6 we present some general theorems on the series expansion of an integral matrix of a linear system of differential equations with respect to a parameter ε that appears in the coefficients of the system. Basically, we follow the procedure of Lyapunov.

In Section 7 we give certain results concerning the solution of the Poincaré—Lappo-Danilevskiy problem that are obtained from the analytic theory of linear systems of differential equations. Specifically, we shall present methods of constructing an exponential matrix W that characterizes the multivaluedness of the integral matrix $X(z) = (z-a)^W \cdot N(z-a)$ in a neighborhood of a singular point $z=a$, where $N(z-a)$ is a single-valued matrix in a neighborhood of the point $z=a$.

We present the general representations of W for the case in which $z=a$ is a regular singular point (Lappo-Danilevskiy) and also for the case of an irregular singular point [5, 29]. We give Lappo-Danilevskiy's expansions of W in a series with respect to small parameters that appear in the coefficients of the system of differential equations. As mentioned elsewhere, all this is of significance in the theory of linear systems with periodic coefficients.

In Section 8 we pose certain problems in the theory of linear systems of differential equations with real periodic coefficients. The problem is that of constructing an integral matrix $X(t)$ in the form (Floquet's problem) $X(t) = \exp At \cdot N(t)$, where A is a constant matrix and $N(t)$ is a periodic matrix. Here, we show when it is possible to have A and $N(t)$ real. We also show what the period of the function $N(t)$ is and under what conditions A is a regular value of $\ln X(2\pi)$, where $X(2\pi)$ is an integral transformation, that is, a matrix by which we multiply the integral matrix $X(t)$ that is normalized at the point $t=0$ when we increase t by the period 2π of the coefficient matrix.

In Section 9 we give the general solution of the problem posed in Section 8. Specifically, we exhibit the procedure for constructing W with the aid of formulas that are found in [5, 29] for the general representation of $\ln X$ and are listed in Section 1.

We give an example in which we obtain a real matrix for W and a matrix $N(t)$ with period twice as great as the period of the coefficient matrix of the given system of differential equations. For a system of the form

$$\frac{dX}{dt} = XP(t)\lambda$$

(where λ is a parameter), we present a procedure for finding the matrices W and $N(t)$ in the form of series in powers of the parameter λ. A bound is given for the radius of convergence of these expansions in terms of the maximum absolute values of the elements of the coefficient matrix and for the region of convergence of the series constructed by Lappo-Danilevskiy which represent an exponential transformation (see Section 7). It turns out that, in seeking the invariants of the matrix A (see Section 8), we can use the expansion obtained by Lappo-Danilevskiy for a certain singular exponential matrix $W=H$. We shall present certain inequalities of a general form concerning a 2×2 matrix A for which the characteristic numbers possess specified properties.

In Sections 10 and 11 we present various methods of constructing matrices A and $N(t)$ (Sections 8) for a system of the general form

$$\frac{dX}{dt} = X \sum_{k=0}^{\infty} P_k(t) \varepsilon^k$$

in the form of series in terms of the parameter ε.

In Section 12 we give approximate methods of constructing an integral matrix. These methods are based on the fact that, in the representation of the integral matrix

$$X(t) = \exp At \cdot N(t),$$

where

$$A = \sum_{k=0}^{\infty} A_k \varepsilon^k, \quad N(t) = \sum_{k=0}^{\infty} N_k(t) \varepsilon^k,$$

we take segments of the series for A and $N(t)$. It turns out that we can sometimes, as a preliminary, represent the given system of differential equations in a form such that, for $\varepsilon = 0$, we obtain a system that is integrable in closed form and in which A and $N(t)$ are easily found. Here, the systems studied in Sections 4 and 5 are of significance.

In Section 13 we study separately the case in which the first $m+1$ matrices $P_0(t), P_1(t), \ldots, P_m(t)$ in the system studied in Section 10 are constants. We also present systems in which the coefficient matrix of the system of differential equations is not a holomorphic function of the small parameter ε.

In Section 14 we examine the case in which P_0 is a constant matrix and the matrix $\exp P_0 t$ is periodic.

In Section 15 we give an example of a system of two equations (illustrating Section 14) in which the matrix is $P_0 = \left\|\begin{smallmatrix} 0 & 1 \\ -1 & 0 \end{smallmatrix}\right\|$. We consider various methods of representing the integral matrix $X(t)$ in the form

$$X(t) = \exp At \cdot N(t)$$

including the method of taking $2\pi A$ in the form of an irregular value of $\ln X(2\pi)$, where $X(2\pi)$ is an integral transformation of the matrix $X(t)$.

In Section 16 we study canonical systems of linear differential equations

$$\frac{dX}{dt} = X\left(P_0 + \sum_{k=1}^{\infty} P_k(t) \varepsilon^k\right)$$

with periodic matrices $P_k(t) = P_k(t + 2\pi)$ and constant matrix P_0. We give the conditions (of N. A. Artem'yev) under which the integral matrix $X(t)$ of such a system will be bounded.

In Section 17 we examine the system studied in Section 16, this time under the condition that $P_0 = P_1 = \ldots = P_{m-1} = 0$.

In Section 18 we consider Artem'yev's problem on the conditions for boundedness of the integral matrix of the canonical system

$$\frac{dX}{dt} = XP(t, \mu_1, \ldots, \mu_\nu, \varepsilon),$$

where

$$P(t + 2\pi, \mu_1, \ldots, \mu_\nu, \varepsilon) = P(t, \mu_1, \ldots, \mu_\nu, \varepsilon)$$

and $\mu_1, \ldots, \mu_\nu, \varepsilon$ are parameters. Here, the problem concerns the region of values of the parameters $\mu_1, \ldots, \mu_\nu, \varepsilon$, in which the integral matrix $X(t)$ is bounded.

In Section 19 we find that the entire set of real matrices $Z(t)$ that, together with $Z^{-1}(t)$, are bounded and that map the system

$$\frac{dX}{dt} = XP(t), \quad P(t + 2\pi) = P(t)$$

into the system

$$\frac{dY}{dt} = YB$$

with real canonical matrix B according to the formula $X = YZ(t)$.

In Sections 20 and 21 we study a system of the form

$$\frac{dX}{dt} = X\left[P_0 + \sum_{k=1}^{\infty} P_k(t)\, \varepsilon^k\right] = XP(t), \tag{20.1}$$

where the matrices $P_k(t)$ are quasi-periodic:

$$P_k(t) = \Sigma\, C^{(k)}_{\mu_k} e^{i\mu_k t}.$$

Here, the $C^{(k)}_{\mu_k}$ are constant matrices and the μ_k are real numbers. Such systems were first considered by I. Z. Shtokalo [10, 38]. In these two sections we also study Shtokalo's method of finding the conditions under which the integral matrix $X(t) \to 0$ as $t \to \infty$ (Theorem 24.1).

In Sections 22–24 Shtokalo's method is used to obtain certain approximate integral matrices (20.1). Bounds for the error in the approximations of these solutions are given. We construct approximate solutions and conditions for the asymptotic stability of solutions of certain nonlinear systems of differential equations. We pose certain problems for nonlinear systems of differential equations in Section 24. A criterion found by A. E. Gel'man [40] is given for the reducibility of a linear system with quasi-periodic coefficients.

In Section 25 we obtain other approximate forms of solutions (and under different hypotheses) based on methods of Shtokalo and N. N. Bogolyubov [79, 80].

In Section 26 we look at a problem of B. P. Demidovich for finding the conditions for boundedness, for small values of ω, of the integral matrix of the system

$$\frac{dX}{dt} = XP(t),$$

where the matrix $P(t)$ is periodic with period ω and where

$$\lim \frac{1}{\omega} \int_0^\omega P(t)\,dt = M \quad \text{as} \quad \omega \to 0.$$

In Section 27 we consider in detail a particular problem of Artem'yev and we present a second problem (considered by various authors [49]), another formulation of which leads to Artem'yev's problem.

In Section 28 we show the connection between the Poincaré-Lappo-Danilevskiy problem and the Floquet problem on the representation of an integral matrix of the system

$$\frac{dX}{dt} = XP(t), \; P(t+2\pi) = P(t)$$

in the form

$$X = \exp At \cdot N(t),$$

where A is a constant matrix and $N(t)$ is periodic. We show how it is possible to solve the Floquet problem in certain cases by using the methods of solving the Poincaré—Lappo-Danilevskiy problem by using certain general considerations pointed out by Lyapunov. Here, certain formulas obtained by Lappo-Danilevskiy are simplified. We show that in these questions, the exponential transformation of a special integral matrix obtained by him can be of value.

In Section 29 we give some general tests for boundedness or unboundedness and periodicicity of solutions of linear systems of two differential equations with periodic coefficients.

In Section 30 we look at the problem of boundedness and periodicity of solutions of systems of the differential equations studied in Sections 3 and 4.

In Section 31 we investigate questions of boundedness and periodicity of solutions of a system of two differential equations and consider an example. With the aid of a singular exponential transformation of Lappo-Danilevskiy, we show the connection between the parameters of the system under which there exists a periodic solution with specified period (equal to or a multiple of the period of the coefficient matrix). An approximative form of this periodic solution is constructed.

In Section 32 we find more conditions of periodicity of solutions of the system considered in Section 3.

In Section 33 we study the equation

$$\ddot{x} + p(t)x = 0, \quad p(t+1) = p(t). \tag{33.1}$$

Following Lyapunov, we shall study the question of the boundedness of the solutions of this equation. For the case in which there is a one-parameter family of solutions possessing the property that $x \to 0$ as $t \to \infty$, we find the entire set of initial values $x(0)$, $x'(0)$ of such solutions. We find the characteristic numbers of solutions of this equation.

In Section 34 we establish the conditions under which all solutions of Eq. (33.1) are bounded and the conditions under which there are periodic solutions. We find the set of all initial values of the periodic solutions.

In Section 35 we find the region of values of the parameters ε, μ, and λ that appear in the equation

$$\ddot{x} + P(t, \varepsilon, \mu, \lambda)x = 0,$$

corresponding to which there are periodic solutions with periods commensurable with the period of the function $P(t, \varepsilon, \mu, \lambda)$. Methods of constructing these solutions are given. We show that the periodic solutions of the system of n equations

$$\frac{dX}{dt} = XP(t, \varepsilon), \quad P(t + 2\pi, \varepsilon) = P(t, \varepsilon)$$

can be represented in the form of series of positive powers of ε that converge in the same region in which the series

$$P(t, \varepsilon) = \sum_{k=0}^{\infty} P_k(t)\, \varepsilon^k$$

converges. From this, we obtain the region of convergence of the series representing periodic solutions of the system of n equations

$$\frac{dX}{dt} = XP(t, \mu, \varepsilon),$$

where μ is defined as a function of ε in such a way that periodic solutions exist.

In Section 36 we show that the system of two linear differential equations

$$\frac{dx}{dt} = xP(t)$$

with periodic matrix $P(t) = P(t + \omega)$ does not have solutions with period incommensurable with the period of ω. This shows that all periodic solutions of the equation were found in the preceding sections. We show that this assertion does not hold for a system of n equations when $n > 2$. We show how one may find for such a system conditions under which it does or does not have periodic solutions with period incommensurable with the period of the matrix $P(t)$. We consider the question of periodic solutions of linear systems with nonperiodic coefficient matrix.

In Section 37, following Lyapunov, we present methods of solving questions on the existence of bounded and periodic solutions of the equation

$$\ddot{x} + p(t)x = 0$$

with a periodic function $p(t)$ of variable sign.

In Section 38 we describe a transformation introduced by V. M. Starzhinskiy that maps a system of two linear homogeneous differential equations with periodic coefficient matrix into the equation $\ddot{x} + p(t)x = 0$ where $p(t)$ is a nonnegative periodic function.

In Sections 39 and 40 we construct a transformation of a system of two linear differential equations with periodic coefficient matrix that maps this system into a canonical system with periodic coefficient matrix.

In Section 41 a remark is made on the transformation of a system of n linear equations into a canonical system.

In Section 42 we find necessary and sufficient conditions for the roots of a polynomial with real coefficients to lie on the unit circle. We present a method for showing the existence of roots of this polynomial inside the unit circle.

In Section 43 we study the behavior of roots of a polynomial as functions of a parameter ε appearing in the coefficients of the polynomial. We find conditions under which the roots of the polynomial will lie on the unit circle for small values of ε if they lie on the unit circle for $\varepsilon = 0$. We give a method for finding the entire region of variation of ε on the real axis that will allow these roots to remain on the unit circle.

In Section 44 we consider the system of linear differential equations

$$\frac{dX}{dt} = XP(t, \varepsilon), \quad P(t, \varepsilon) = \sum_{k=0}^{\infty} P_k(t)\,\varepsilon^k, \tag{44.1}$$

where the matrices $P(t + 2\pi) = P(t)$. We present methods for finding the conditions under which the integral matrix of the system (44.1) possesses the property that $X(t) \to 0$ as $t \to \infty$ or that $X(t)$ will undergo bounded oscillations. We shall study the canonical and noncanonical systems (44.1). These questions are solved on the basis of the integral matrix; that is, their solution will not involve an exponential transformation as was the case in the preceding sections. Therefore, all the series in powers of ε with the aid of which all these questions are solved converge in the region in which the series in the system (44.1) converges.

In Section 45 we use these same methods to answer the question as to when the integral matrix $X(t) \to 0$ as $t \to \infty$. Here, we also use the paper of I. S. Arzhanykh [70] on finding conditions that the parameters of the system of differential equations

$$\frac{dX}{dt} = XP(t, \mu_1, \ldots, \mu_\nu, \varepsilon),$$

where the matrix

$$P(t + 2\pi, \mu_1, \ldots, \mu_\nu, \varepsilon) = P(t, \mu_1, \ldots, \mu_\nu, \varepsilon),$$

must satisfy for the integral matrix $X(t)$ to have bounded oscillations. Here, we assume this system to be canonical. The method of solving this question is the same as in Sections 44 and 45.

In Section 46 we give a second method of solving Artem'yev's problem.

In Section 47 we draw certain conclusions from [32] regarding the theory of implicit functions. Specifically, we study the implicit function $y = y(x)$, defined by the equation

$$P_m(x, y) + P_{m+1}(x, y) + \ldots = 0, \tag{47.40}$$

where $P_k(x, y)$ are kth-degree homogeneous polynomials with real coefficients and the series (47.40) converges in a neighborhood of the point $x = 0$, $y = 0$. We find necessary and sufficient conditions for the existence of real functions y satisfying the equation that approach 0 as $x \to 0$. We shall find all such solutions. We determine the entire region of convergence of series representing such functions. We show that none of functions $y = y(x)$ defined by equation (47.40) have singular points $x = \overset{*}{x}$ in the region of convergence of the series (47.40) with the property that the function $y(x)$ does not have a limit as $x \to \overset{*}{x}$.

In Sections 48 and 49, implicit functions $x = x(z), y = y(z)$ defined by Eqs. (48.4) and (48.5) are studied in detail.

Implicit functions $x(z), y(z)$ defined by the equations

$$\Phi(x, y, z) = 0, \ F(x, y, z) = 0,$$

where the functions $\Phi(x, y, z)$ and $F(x, y, z)$ are not holomorphic in a neighborhood of the point $x = y = z = 0$, are studied, for example, in Sections 2 and 5· of [32]. We do not go into this question here, although these cases are related to the content of the present book in the study of differential equations the right-hand members of which satisfy certain relevant hypotheses.

In the present book we have not touched on the questions of exact expansions (for example, as in [76-78]) or questions of the asymptotic behavior of solutions of linear differential equations (as, for example, in [45]).

1. Functions of a Single Matrix

In the present book, we shall use matrix calculus. Therefore, we shall begin by explaining certain facts related to the theory of functions of a matrix.* We assume that matrix algebra and the reduction of matrices to canonical form is already known to the reader. We shall consider only square matrices.

A function $f(A)$ of a matrix A is said to be *analytic* if it can be represented in the form of a Taylor series with numerical (scalar) coefficients in a neighborhood of a matrix of the form aI, where a is a number and I is the unit matrix (of appropriate dimensions), that is, if it can be represented in the form

$$f(A) = \sum_{k=0}^{\infty} \alpha_k (A - aI)^k, \tag{1.1}$$

where the α_k are numbers (possibly complex). The function $f(A)$ is called an *entire function* if the series (1.1) converges for all finite values of the matrix A. If A is a matrix, the expression $\exp A = e^A$ means, by definition, the sum of the matrix series

$$\exp A = \sum_{k=0}^{\infty} \frac{1}{k!} A^k. \tag{1.2}$$

We note that the series (1.2) converges for every matrix A whose elements are complex numbers. In other words, the function defined by the series (1.2) is an entire function.

An analytic function $f(A)$ possesses the property that

$$f(SAS^{-1}) = Sf(A)S^{-1}, \tag{1.3}$$

where S is an arbitrary matrix with nonzero determinant $D(S)$. This follows from

$$[SAS^{-1}]^k = SA^kS^{-1} \quad (k = 0, 1, 2, \ldots).$$

---

*See also [1-3].

We write the characteristic equation of the matrix A of order n

$$(-1)^n D(A-\lambda I) = \lambda^n + a_1 \lambda^{n-1} + \ldots + a_n = 0. \quad (1.4)$$

Here, the a_k (for $k = 1, 2, \ldots, n$) are the basic symmetric functions of the characteristic numbers $\lambda_1, \ldots, \lambda_n$ of the matrix A. (These functions are known up to sign from algebra.) At the same time, the a_k are polynomials in the elements of the matrix A.

We know that the characteristic equation of the matrix SAS^{-1} coincides with (1.4) for an arbitrary matrix $S \subset D(S) \neq 0$.

We shall call the basic symmetric functions of $\lambda_1, \ldots, \lambda_n$ the *invariants* of the matrix A.

If the α_k and a in the series (1.1) are symmetric functions of $\lambda_1, \ldots, \lambda_n$, then $f(A)$ obviously possesses the property (1.3).

However, if the α_k and a depend on $\lambda_1, \ldots, \lambda_n$ but are not symmetric functions, then, in general, $f(A)$ in formula (1.1) is defined only when we state how the characteristic numbers $\lambda_1, \ldots, \lambda_n$ are numbered. This numbering may be such that the property (1.3) will be conserved even for nonsymmetric functions $\alpha_k(\lambda_1, \ldots, \lambda_n)$. For example, this will be the case if the numbers $\lambda_1, \ldots, \lambda_n$ are numbered in accordance with some numerical properties that they possess. However, if they are numbered in order of their position in the canonical form of the matrix $A = SJS^{-1}$, their numbering will depend on the choice of the matrix S and the matrix $f(A)$ will no longer possess the property (1.3).

Lagrange's formula, which makes it possible to represent an analytic function of a matrix $f(A)$ in the form of a polynomial in the matrix A, is familiar to us. In the case in which the characteristic numbers $\lambda_1, \ldots, \lambda_n$ of the matrix A are distinct, this formula takes the form

$$f(A) = \sum_{k=1}^{n} \frac{(A-\lambda_1) \ldots (A-\lambda_{k-1})(A-\lambda_{k+1}) \ldots (A-\lambda_n)}{(\lambda_k-\lambda_1) \ldots (\lambda_k-\lambda_{k-1})(\lambda_k-\lambda_{k+1}) \ldots (\lambda_k-\lambda_n)} f(\lambda_k). \quad (1.5)$$

Under all other assumptions regarding the characteristic numbers $\lambda_1, \ldots, \lambda_n$, we can also construct a polynomial of degree not exceeding $n-1$ for $f(A)$; for example, we obtain such a polynomial by taking the limit in (1.5). However, it is always possible* to construct this polynomial in such a way that its degree will be less by 1 than the sum of the highest orders of the elementary divisors belonging to the different characteristic numbers of the matrix A.

---

*See also Section 6 in Chapter IV and Sections 1 and 2 in Chapter V of the book by F. R. Gantmakher [3].

Thus, if the matrix A has, for example, only one characteristic number and the highest order of the elementary divisor is equal to 2, then it is possible to construct for $f(A)$ a first-degree polynomial in A.

We obtain such minimum polynomials $P(A)$ as follows. Suppose that we have a matrix of order n

$$A = SJS^{-1}, \tag{1.6}$$

where J is a quasi-diagonal canonical matrix:

$$J = [J_{\rho_1}(\lambda_1), J_{\rho_2}(\lambda_2), \ldots, J_{\rho_m}(\lambda_m)], \quad \rho_1 + \ldots + \rho_m = n$$

and $J_\rho(\lambda)$ is a ρth-order Jordan matrix the elements* $\{J_\rho(\lambda)\}_{kl}$ of which are determined by the equations

$$\{J_\rho(\lambda)\}_{kk} = \lambda, \quad \{J_\rho(\lambda)\}_{k+1,\,k} = 1$$

and

$$\{J_\rho(\lambda)\}_{kl} = 0, \quad \text{if} \quad (k-l)(k-l-1) \neq 0.$$

If we have a matrix

$$f(A) = \sum_{k=0}^{n-1} A^k \varphi_k(\lambda_1, \ldots, \lambda_m) = P(A), \tag{1.7}$$

where the φ_k are numerical symmetric functions and $P(A)$ is the minimum polynomial for $f(A)$, then, on the basis of (1.3),

$$f(J) = \sum_{k=0}^{n-1} J^k \varphi_k(\lambda_1, \ldots, \lambda_m) = P(J). \tag{1.8}$$

But for the analytic function $f(J)$ we have the Lappo-Danilevskiy formula [1, p. 43]

$$f(J) = [G_{\rho_1}(f(\lambda_1)), \ldots, G_{\rho_m}(f(\lambda_m))], \tag{1.9}$$

where the ρth-order matrix $G_\rho(f(\lambda))$ is defined by

---

*By $\{B\}_{kl}$, we mean that element of the matrix B in the kth row and lth column.

$$G_\rho(f(\lambda)) = \left\| \begin{matrix} f(\lambda) & 0 & 0 \dots & 0 \\ \frac{f'(\lambda)}{1!} & f(\lambda) & 0 \dots & 0 \\ \frac{f''(\lambda)}{2!} & \frac{f'(\lambda)}{1!} & f(\lambda) \dots & 0 \\ \cdot & \cdot & \cdot & \cdot \\ \frac{f^{(\rho-1)}(\lambda)}{(\rho-1)!} & & \dots \frac{f'(\lambda)}{1!} & f(\lambda) \end{matrix} \right\|$$

In particular,

$$P(J) = [G_{\rho_1}(P(\lambda_1)), \dots, G_{\rho_m}(P(\lambda_m))]. \qquad (1.10)$$

Since, on the basis of (1.8), $f(J) = P(J)$, we have

$$G_{\rho_k}(f(\lambda_k)) = G_{\rho_k}(P(\lambda_k)) \quad (k = 1, 2, \dots, m). \qquad (1.11)$$

Remark 1.1. If $\lambda_1 = \lambda_2$ and $\rho_1 \geqslant \rho_2$, then the equality

$$G_{\rho_1}(f(\lambda_1)) = G_{\rho_1}(P(\lambda_1))$$

implies

$$G_{\rho_2}(f(\lambda_2)) = G_{\rho_2}(P(\lambda_2)),$$

which is obvious from the structure of these matrices.

Suppose now that we have an nth-order matrix

$$J = [J_{\rho_1}(\lambda_1), \dots, J_{\rho_m}(\lambda_m)], \ \rho_1 + \dots + \rho_m = n$$

with distinct $\lambda_1, \dots, \lambda_m$. From Eqs. (1.11) we obtain a system of linear equations for finding the coefficients $\varphi_k(\lambda_1, \dots, \lambda_m)$ of Lagrange's polynomial that appear in the formula (1.7):

$$f^{(k)}(\lambda_\nu) = P^{(k)}(\lambda_\nu) \qquad (1.11_1)$$

$$(k = 0, 1, 2, \dots, \rho_\nu - 1; \ \nu = 1, 2, \dots, m).$$

The determinant $\Delta(\lambda_1, \dots, \lambda_m)$ of the coefficients for unknown $\varphi_{n-1}, \varphi_{n-2}, \dots, \varphi_1, \varphi_0$ is constructed as follows. The first row is of the form $1, \lambda_1, \lambda_1^2, \dots, \lambda_1^{n-1}$. Below it are $\rho_1 - 1$ rows which are obtained successively by differentiating the first row $(\rho_1 - 1)$ times. The remaining characteristic numbers $\lambda_2, \dots, \lambda_m$ also form, respectively, $\rho_2, \dots, \rho_m$ rows. Thus,

$$\Delta(\lambda_1, \ldots, \lambda_m) = \begin{vmatrix} 1 & \lambda_1 & \lambda_1^2 \ldots & & \lambda_1^{n-1} \\ 0 & 1 & 2\lambda_1 \ldots & & (n-1)\lambda_1^{n-2} \\ \cdot & \cdot & \cdot & \cdot & \cdot \\ 0 & 0 & \ldots & & (n-1)\ldots(n-\rho_m+1)\lambda_m^{n-\rho_m} \end{vmatrix}$$

It can be shown that

$$\Delta(\lambda_1, \ldots, \lambda_m) = a(\lambda_1 - \lambda_2)^{\rho_1\rho_2}(\lambda_1 - \lambda_3)^{\rho_1\rho_3} \ldots (\lambda_{m-1} - \lambda_m)^{\rho_{m-1}\rho_m}, \qquad (1.11_2)$$

where a is a constant independent of $\lambda_1, \ldots, \lambda_m$.

Consequently, $\Delta(\lambda_1, \ldots, \lambda_m) \neq 0$, and all the coefficients* $\varphi_k(\lambda_1, \ldots, \lambda_m)$ of Lagrange's polynomial can be found in terms of

$$\lambda_1, \ldots, \lambda_m \text{ and } f^{(k)}(\lambda_\nu) \quad (\nu = 1, \ldots, m;\ k = 0, 1, \ldots, \rho_\nu - 1).$$

On the basis of Remark 1.1, the Lagrange polynomial that we have constructed is valid also for the case in which the matrix A in the expression $f(A)$ is of any order whatever greater than n, but it will have only the characteristic numbers $\lambda_1, \ldots, \lambda_m$ that correspond to the sets of elementary divisors whose orders do not exceed $\rho_1, \ldots, \rho_m$, respectively.

Thus, we have constructed Lagrange's polynomial of lowest degree for the matrix function $f(A)$.

This construction of Lagrange's formula is also possible for a function of a matrix A that is of the form

$$f(A) = \sum_{k=0}^{\infty} \alpha_k(A) A^k, \qquad (1.12)$$

where the $\alpha_k(A)$ are functions of the invariants** of the matrix A, that is, the $\alpha_k(A)$ are symmetric functions of the characteristic numbers of the matrix A. This follows from the fact that such a function $f(A)$ possesses the property (1.3).

A consequence of Remark 1.1. It follows from Remark 1.1 that Lagrange's polynomial of degree $n-1$ for an arbitrary matrix A of order n can be constructed as follows. Let $\lambda_1, \ldots, \lambda_m$ denote

---

*If $\rho_1 = \rho_2$, then $\varphi_k(\lambda_1, \ldots, \lambda_m)$ is a symmetric function with respect to λ_1, and λ_2, which is obvious from Eqs. (1.11_1). Therefore, if $\rho_1 = \ldots = \rho_\nu$, then $\varphi_k(\lambda_1, \ldots, \lambda_m)$ will also be a symmetric function with respect to $\lambda_1, \ldots, \lambda_\nu$. (If $\rho_1 = \rho_2$ is odd, then, by exchanging λ_1 and λ_2, we change the sign both in $\Delta(\lambda_1, \ldots, \lambda_m)$ and in the numerator of $\varphi_k(\lambda_1, \ldots, \lambda_m)$.)

**Here, by "invariants" is meant an arbitrary symmetric function.

the distinct characteristic numbers of the matrix A corresponding to the set of elementary divisors of orders $\rho_1^{(1)}, \ldots, \rho_{k_1}^{(1)}, \ldots, \rho_1^{(m)}, \ldots, \rho_{k_m}^{(m)}$, respectively. Consider the canonical matrix J with distinct characteristic numbers $\lambda_1, \ldots, \lambda_m$, to each of which corresponds a single elementary divisor of order $\rho_1^{(1)} + \ldots + \rho_{k_1}^{(1)}; \ldots; \rho_1^{(m)} + \ldots + \rho_{k_m}^{(m)}$, respectively. In accordance with Remark 1.1, the Lagrange polynomial of degree $n-1$ constructed for the matrix J according to formula (1.7), in which the denominators of the coefficients $\varphi_k(\lambda_1, \ldots, \lambda_m)$ are given by formula (1.11$_2$), will also be suitable for the matrix A.

We call the reader's attention to the following fact. In the case in which all the characteristic numbers $\lambda_1, \ldots, \lambda_n$ of the matrix A are distinct, if we write Lagrange's polynomial for $f(A)$ in the form

$$f(A) = \sum_{k=1}^{n-1} A^k \varphi_k(\lambda_1, \ldots, \lambda_n), \tag{1.13}$$

we see that the coefficients $\varphi_k(\lambda_1, \ldots, \lambda_n)$ are symmetric* functions of $\lambda_1, \ldots, \lambda_n$. In many cases, this enables us to express the coefficients φ_k directly in terms of the invariants of the matrix A, that is, directly in terms of the elements of the matrix A. When we write $f(A)$ in this form, we avoid the necessity of evaluating the roots of the nth polynomial, which is important in many cases. We shall later use this phenomenon, in particular, when seeking a solution of a system of linear differential equations with constant coefficients.

We denote the elements of the matrix A by a_{kl}, where k is the number of the row and l the number of the column containing the element a_{kl}. Sometimes, we shall denote the matrix A by $\|a_{kl}\|$. In this notation, all the elements of the matrix $\|r\|$ are equal to r. $|A|$ is the matrix whose elements are equal to the absolute values of the elements of the matrix A. The inequality $|A| \leqslant B$, where B is a matrix with positive elements, means that the absolute values of the elements of the matrix A do not exceed the corresponding elements of the matrix B.

We know [1] that if a complex power series $f(z) = \sum_{k=0}^{\infty} \alpha_k z^k$ has a radius of convergence ρ, then the series $f(A) = \sum_{k=0}^{\infty} \alpha_k A^k$, where

---

*We see this from the footnote on page 5, when the $\varphi_k(\lambda_1, \ldots, \lambda_n)$ are symmetric functions of $\lambda_1, \ldots, \lambda_n$ for multiple characteristic numbers also.

A is a matrix, converges absolutely for $|A| < \left\| \frac{1}{n} \rho \right\|$, where n is the order of the matrix A. In general, this series converges for matrices A whose characteristic numbers $\lambda_1, \ldots, \lambda_n$ lie in the circle of convergence of $f(z)$. If a function of a matrix A is given by the series (1.1) in a neighborhood of the matrix aI (or in a neighborhood of the zero matrix if $a=0$), then the values of $f(A)$ are obtained for other values of the matrix A by analytic continuation of the n^2 series of the elements of the matrix A.

Lagrange's formula also enables us to carry out this analytic continuation with the aid of the analytic continuation of only n functions of a single variable $f(\lambda_1), \ldots, f(\lambda_n)$.

For a second-order matrix A, Lagrange's formula takes the form

$$f(A) = \frac{\lambda_2 f(\lambda_1) - \lambda_1 f(\lambda_2)}{\lambda_2 - \lambda_1} + \frac{f(\lambda_2) - f(\lambda_1)}{\lambda_2 - \lambda_1} A. \tag{1.14}$$

If $f(A) = \exp At$, then

$$\exp At = \frac{\exp \lambda_1 t - \exp \lambda_2 t}{\lambda_1 - \lambda_2} A + \\ + \frac{\lambda_1 \exp \lambda_2 t - \lambda_2 \exp \lambda_1 t}{\lambda_1 - \lambda_2}. \tag{1.14$_1$}$$

If λ_1 and λ_2 approach the same value λ which is nonsingular for $f(\lambda)$, while remaining on a single Riemann plane of the function $f(\lambda)$, then (1.14) becomes

$$f(A) = f(\lambda)\cdot I - \lambda f'(\lambda)\cdot I + f'(\lambda) A. \tag{1.15}$$

Let us now write Lagrange's formula in the form (1.13) for a third-order matrix A:

$$f(A) = \varphi_2 A^2 + \varphi_1 A + \varphi_0, \tag{1.16}$$

where

$$\varphi_2 \Delta = (\lambda_1 - \lambda_2) f(\lambda_3) + (\lambda_2 - \lambda_3) f(\lambda_1) + (\lambda_3 - \lambda_1) f(\lambda_2),$$

$$\varphi_1 \Delta = -[(\lambda_1^2 - \lambda_2^2) f(\lambda_3) + (\lambda_2^2 - \lambda_3^2) f(\lambda_1) + (\lambda_3^2 - \lambda_1^2) f(\lambda_2)],$$

$$\varphi_0 \Delta = \lambda_1 \lambda_2 (\lambda_1 - \lambda_2) f(\lambda_3) + \lambda_2 \lambda_3 (\lambda_2 - \lambda_3) f(\lambda_1) + \lambda_3 \lambda_1 (\lambda_3 - \lambda_1) f(\lambda_2),$$

$$\Delta = (\lambda_1 - \lambda_2)(\lambda_2 - \lambda_3)(\lambda_1 - \lambda_3).$$

In accordance with what was said above, the coefficients of all powers of the matrix A both in formula (1.14) and in formula (1.16) are symmetric functions of the characteristic numbers of the matrix A. Let us suppose that the function $f(z)$ is multiple-valued. Then, as we shall immediately show, the limiting value of $f(A)$ as $A \to A_0$ is determined not only by the value A_0 but also by the path along which $A \to A_0$ in the space of elements of the matrix A.

Suppose that $\lambda_1^0, \ldots, \lambda_n^0$ are the characteristic numbers of the matrix A_0. If $\lambda_1^0, \ldots, \lambda_n^0$ are all distinct and if the $f(\lambda_k^0)$ are finite for $k = 1, \ldots, n$, then the limiting value of $f(A_0)$ will be finite, as can be seen from Lagrange's formula. If some of the numbers $\lambda_1^0, \ldots, \lambda_n^0$ are equal but situated on a single Riemann plane of the function $f(z)$ and if the derivatives of the appropriate order of $f(z)$ are finite, then $f(A_0)$ will also be finite and will be given by the corresponding form of Lagrange's formula. For example, in the case of second-order matrices, we obtain (1.15).

Let us suppose that some of the characteristic numbers $\lambda_1^0, \ldots, \lambda_n^0$ are equal and situated on different sheets of the Riemann surfaces* of the function $f(z)$. Then, some (or even all) of the elements $f_{kl}(A)$ of the limit matrix

$$f(A_0) = \| f_{kl}(A_0) \|$$

may be infinite. However, if $f(A_0)$ is a finite matrix, the limiting value, as Lappo-Danilevskiy has shown, will depend not only on the matrix A_0 and the values $f(\lambda_1^0), \ldots, f(\lambda_n^0)$, but also on the choice of the matrix S, which reduces the matrix A_0 to the canonical form (1.6). This limiting value can be obtained by taking the limit in Lagrange's formula.

Suppose that a matrix A is of the form

$$A = S[\lambda_1, \ldots, \lambda_n] S^{-1}.$$

Then, in accordance with formulas (1.3), (1.5) and (1.9), we have

$$f(A) = S[f(\lambda_1), \ldots, f(\lambda_n)] S^{-1} = P(A, f(\lambda_1), \ldots, f(\lambda_n)), \tag{1.17}$$

where $P(A, f(\lambda_1), \ldots, f(\lambda_n))$ is Lagrange's polynomial.

Let us suppose that the matrix A approaches A_0 in such a way that, close to the matrix A_0, we have

$$f(A) = S[f(\lambda_1) + \alpha_1, \ldots, f(\lambda_n) + \alpha_n] S^{-1} =$$
$$= S[f(\lambda_1), \ldots, f(\lambda_n)] S^{-1} + S[\alpha_1, \ldots, \alpha_n] S^{-1}$$

---

*That is, there exist $\lambda_k^0 = \lambda_l^0$ such that, for example, $f(\lambda_k^0) \neq f(\lambda_l^0)$.

or

$$f(A)=P(A,\ f(\lambda_1),\ \dots,\ f(\lambda_n))+P(A,\ \alpha_1,\ \dots,\ \alpha_n), \qquad (1.18)$$

where $f(\lambda_1), \dots, f(\lambda_n)$ are the values of $f(z)$ on the original sheets of the Riemann surface close to the points $\lambda_1^0, \dots, \lambda_n^0$. When some of the characteristic numbers $\lambda_1^0, \dots, \lambda_n^0$ coincide, the polynomial $P(A, f(\lambda_1), \dots, f(\lambda_n))$ approaches a limiting form of Lagrange's polynomial as $A \to A_0$; however, $P(A, \alpha_1, \dots, \alpha_n)$ may approach a matrix whose value depends on the choice of the matrix S. Following Lappo-Danilevskiy, we shall call these values of $f(A)$ *irregular*.

In general, suppose that

$$A=S\,[J_{\rho_1}(\lambda_1),\ \dots,\ J_{\rho_m}(\lambda_m)]\,S^{-1}.$$

Then, we have

$$f(A)=S\,[f(J_{\rho_1}(\lambda_1)),\ \dots,\ f(J_{\rho_m}(\lambda_m))]\,S^{-1}=$$
$$=S\,[G_{\rho_1}(f(\lambda_1)),\ \dots,\ G_{\rho_m}(f(\lambda_m))\,]\,S^{-1}.$$

Here, if $f(\lambda_k)=f(\lambda_l)$ for $\lambda_k=\lambda_l$, then $f(A)$ is a *regular* value. If $f(\bar{z})=f(z)+\alpha$, where α is a constant, is the value of $f(z)$ on an arbitrary Riemann sheet, then $f^{(k)}(\bar{z})=f^{(k)}(z)$, where $\bar{z}$ is the z-coordinate on the Riemann sheet. Then, the common value

$$f(A)=S\,[f(J_{\rho_1}(\lambda_1)),\ \dots,\ f(J_{\rho_m}(\lambda_m))]\,S^{-1}+ \\ +S\,[\alpha_1 I_{\rho_1},\ \dots,\ \alpha_m I_{\rho_m}]\,S^{-1}, \qquad (1.18_1)$$

where I_ρ is the unit ρth-order matrix. If $\alpha_k \neq \alpha_l$ for $\lambda_k=\lambda_l$, then $f(A)$ is, by definition, *an irregular value that depends on the choice of S*.

Let A be a second-order matrix. Then, on the basis of (1.14) and (1.18), we have

$$f(A)=P(A,\ f(\lambda_1),\ f(\lambda_2))+P(A,\ \alpha_1,\ \alpha_2), \qquad (1.19)$$

where

$$P(A,\ f(\lambda_1),\ f(\lambda_2))=\frac{\lambda_2 f(\lambda_1)-\lambda_1 f(\lambda_2)}{\lambda_2-\lambda_1}+\frac{f(\lambda_2)-f(\lambda_1)}{\lambda_2-\lambda_1}A$$

and

$$P(A,\ \alpha_1,\ \alpha_2)=\frac{\lambda_2\alpha_1-\lambda_1\alpha_2}{\lambda_2-\lambda_1}+\frac{\alpha_2-\alpha_1}{\lambda_2-\lambda_1}A.$$

If we set

$$A = \begin{Vmatrix} a & b \\ c & d \end{Vmatrix}, \tag{1.20}$$

we obtain

$$P(A,\ f(\lambda_1),\ f(\lambda_2)) =$$

$$= \begin{Vmatrix} \dfrac{(a-\lambda_1)f(\lambda_2)-(a-\lambda_2)f(\lambda_1)}{\lambda_2-\lambda_1}, & b\dfrac{f(\lambda_2)-f(\lambda_1)}{\lambda_2-\lambda_1} \\ c\dfrac{f(\lambda_2)-f(\lambda_1)}{\lambda_2-\lambda_1}, & \dfrac{(d-\lambda_1)f(\lambda_2)-(d-\lambda_2)f(\lambda_1)}{\lambda_2-\lambda_1} \end{Vmatrix}. \tag{1.21}$$

If we now make the substitution $f(\lambda_1) = \alpha_1$ and $f(\lambda_2) = \alpha_2$, we obtain $P(A,\ \alpha_1,\ \alpha_2)$.

Let us take the particular case of the matrix (1.20)

$$A = S\begin{Vmatrix} a+b & b \\ 2b & a \end{Vmatrix}S^{-1}.$$

Then, $\lambda_1 = a - b,\ \lambda_2 = a + 2b$, and the matrix $P(A,\ \alpha_1,\ \alpha_2)$ is of the form

$$P(A,\ \alpha_1,\ \alpha_2) = S\begin{Vmatrix} \dfrac{2\alpha_2+\alpha_1}{3} & \dfrac{\alpha_2-\alpha_1}{3} \\ 2\dfrac{\alpha_2-\alpha_1}{3} & \dfrac{\alpha_2+2\alpha_1}{3} \end{Vmatrix}S^{-1}.$$

We have

$$\lambda_1 \to a,\ \lambda_2 \to a \text{ and } A \to A_0 = a\mathrm{I}$$

as $b \to 0$. Here, suppose that $\alpha_1 \to m_1$ and $\alpha_2 \to m_2 \neq m_1$ and the matrix S is fixed. Then, in accordance with (1.15), we obtain the limiting value of $f(A_0)$ in the form

$$f(A_0) = f(a)\mathrm{I} - af'(a)\mathrm{I} + f'(a)a\mathrm{I} +$$

$$+ S\begin{Vmatrix} \dfrac{2m_2+m_1}{3} & \dfrac{m_2-m_1}{3} \\ 2\dfrac{m_2-m_1}{3} & \dfrac{m_2+2m_1}{3} \end{Vmatrix}S^{-1}$$

or

$$f(A_0) = f(a)\mathrm{I} + S \left\| \begin{matrix} \frac{2m_2 + m_1}{3} & \frac{m_2 - m_1}{3} \\ 2\frac{m_2 - m_1}{3} & \frac{m_2 + 2m_1}{3} \end{matrix} \right\| S^{-1}. \quad (1.22)$$

The second term is a matrix R that depends on the choice of the matrix S which reduces the matrix $A_0 = a\mathrm{I} = Sa\mathrm{I}S^{-1}$ to canonical form.

The characteristic numbers of the matrix R are m_1 and m_2. Therefore, by changing the value of the matrix S, the matrix R can also be written $R = S[m_1, m_2]S^{-1}$.

Consequently, formula (1.22) can be written in the form

$$f(A_0) = f(a)\mathrm{I} + S[m_1, m_2]S^{-1}, \quad (1.23)$$

where S is an arbitrary matrix with nonzero determinant.

In the case in which λ_1 and λ_2 approach a value a while remaining on a single sheet of the Riemann surface of the function $f(z)$, we have $m_1 = m_2 = m$ and $R = m\mathrm{I}$; that is, $f(A_0)$ no longer depends on the matrix S.

Formula (1.23) can also be obtained from (1.17) with

$$f(\lambda_1) = f(a) + m_1, \; f(\lambda_2) = f(a) + m_2.$$

Here, a different path $A \to a\mathrm{I}$ is taken since, in this case,

$$A = S \left\| \begin{matrix} \lambda_1 & 0 \\ 0 & \lambda_2 \end{matrix} \right\| S^{-1}$$

and S is fixed, whereas, in deriving (1.22), we have

$$A = S \left\| \begin{matrix} a+b & b \\ 2b & a \end{matrix} \right\| S^{-1} \to S \left\| \begin{matrix} a & 0 \\ 0 & a \end{matrix} \right\| S^{-1}$$

as $b \to 0$. Consequently, the matrix that transforms the matrix A to canonical form is changed (along with b).

However, it should be noted that, in the space of elements of the matrix A, there is also a path $A \to A_0$ such that the matrix of $f(A)$ has certain values approaching infinity.

If λ_1 and λ_2 approach a single value λ in such a way that they remain on different sheets of the Riemann surface of the function

$f(z)$ (for example, if the inequality $f(\lambda_1) \neq f(\lambda_2)$ remains valid even when $\lambda_1 = \lambda_2 = \lambda$) and if the limit matrix A is of the form

$$A_0 = \begin{Vmatrix} \lambda & 0 \\ p & \lambda \end{Vmatrix},$$

for some nonzero p, that is, if the characteristic number λ corresponds to a nonprime elementary divisor, then some of the elements of the matrix $f(A)$ always approach infinity.* It follows from this that the limiting form of Lagrange's polynomial (1.15) assumes all finite values of the matrix $f(A_0)$ or $f(SA_0S^{-1})$. These last two assertions follow from formula (1.21). On the basis of (1.19) and (1.21), it is easy to see that, for the multiple-valued function $f(z)$, the formula (1.23) assumes all possible finite values of the matrix $f(\lambda \mathrm{I})$. This is true because the general finite value of the matrix $f(\lambda \mathrm{I})$ can, according to (1.19), be written in the form

$$f(\lambda \mathrm{I}) = f(\lambda)\mathrm{I} + P(\lambda \mathrm{I},\ m_1,\ m_2),$$

where $P(\lambda \mathrm{I},\ m_1,\ m_2)$ is obtained from the matrix

$$P(A,\ \alpha_1,\ \alpha_2) = \begin{Vmatrix} \dfrac{(a-\lambda_1)\alpha_2 - (a-\lambda_2)\alpha_1}{\lambda_2-\lambda_1} & b\,\dfrac{\alpha_2-\alpha_1}{\lambda_2-\lambda_1} \\ c\,\dfrac{\alpha_2-\alpha_1}{\lambda_2-\lambda_1} & \dfrac{(d-\lambda_1)\alpha_2 - (d-\lambda_2)\alpha_1}{\lambda_2-\lambda_1} \end{Vmatrix},$$

with characteristic numbers α_1 and α_2 as $\alpha_1 \to m_1$ and $\alpha_2 \to m_2$.

If the matrix A is of order n, then, obviously,

$$f(A) \to f(\lambda)\mathrm{I} + S[m_1,\ \ldots,\ m_n]S^{-1} \quad \text{as} \quad A \to \lambda \mathrm{I}. \qquad (1.23_1)$$

With regard to the exponential function, we note also that

$$\left.\begin{aligned} e^A &= \begin{Vmatrix} e^{a_1} & 0 \\ 0 & e^{a_2} \end{Vmatrix}, & A &= \begin{Vmatrix} a_1 & 0 \\ 0 & a_2 \end{Vmatrix} \\ e^A &= \begin{Vmatrix} 1 & 0 \\ a & 1 \end{Vmatrix}, & A &= \begin{Vmatrix} 0 & 0 \\ a & 0 \end{Vmatrix} \\ e^A &= \begin{Vmatrix} e^a & 0 \\ e^a & e^a \end{Vmatrix}, & A &= \begin{Vmatrix} a & 0 \\ 1 & a \end{Vmatrix} \end{aligned}\right\} \qquad (1.24)$$

*Even in the general case of an nth-order matrix, this will always be true when the characteristic numbers λ_1 and λ_2 coincide with respect to the coordinates, forming a nonprime elementary divisor though remaining on different sheets of the Riemann surface of the function $f(z)$ [4]. We shall also call these values of $f(A)$ irregular.

If the matrices A and B commute, that is, if

$$AB = BA, \tag{1.25}$$

then, $e^{A+B} = e^A e^B$.

If the determinant of the matrix A is nonzero, then

$$\ln A = B \tag{1.26}$$

is defined as a solution of the equation

$$e^B = A. \tag{1.27}$$

The principle value of $\ln A$ *vanishes at* $A = I$.

Under condition (1.25), we have

$$\ln AB = \ln A + \ln B \tag{1.28}$$

(on the basis of (1.30), $\ln A$ and $\ln B$ commute). Therefore,

$$\ln Y^{-1} = -\ln Y + S[m_1, \ldots, m_n] S^{-1} 2\pi i$$

and, in particular, $\ln Y^{-1} = -\ln Y$ for suitable values of the logarithm on the right and on the left. Here, the m_k are integers.

In a neighborhood of $A = I$, the expansion

$$\ln A = \sum_{\nu=1}^{\infty} (-1)^{\nu-1} \frac{(A-I)^\nu}{\nu} \tag{1.29}$$

is valid, giving the principle value of $\ln A$. If the characteristic numbers $\lambda_1, \ldots, \lambda_n$ of the matrix A are distinct, then, from Lagrange's formula,

$$\ln A = \sum \frac{(A-\lambda_1) \ldots (A-\lambda_{k-1})(A-\lambda_{k+1}) \ldots (A-\lambda_n)}{(\lambda_k-\lambda_1) \ldots (\lambda_k-\lambda_{k-1})(\lambda_k-\lambda_{k+1}) \ldots (\lambda_k-\lambda_n)} \ln \lambda_k. \tag{1.30}$$

We obtain all values of $\ln A$ by means of analytic continuation and a limiting process on the basis of this formula.

It is shown in article [5] that it is possible to construct Lagrange's polynomial for $\ln A$ in which the coefficients are expressed directly in terms of the invariants of the matrix A. Thus, when we seek to find $\ln A$, we do not need to find the roots of the characteristic polynomial of the matrix A.

Let us find this polynomial for $\ln A$, following the reasoning used in Section 1 of article [5].

We denote by $x_1, \ldots, x_n$ the characteristic numbers of the matrix X. Then, in accordance with Lagrange's formula, we have

$$Y = \ln X = \alpha_{n-1} X^{n-1} + \alpha_{n-2} X^{n-2} + \ldots + \alpha_0, \tag{1.31}$$

where the α_i are rational functions of x_i and $\ln x_i$. Let us express explicitly the α_i in terms of the invariants of the matrix X. On the basis of formulas (1.6) and (1.9), we see that the $\ln x_i$ are the characteristic numbers of Y.

We introduce the notations

$$\sigma(Z) = \sum_{i=1}^{n} z_i = \sum_{k=1}^{n} z_{kk},$$

where the z_i and the z_{kk} are, respectively, the characteristic numbers and the diagonal elements* of the matrix Z;

$$\sigma(X^k) = \sigma_k = \sum_{i=1}^{n} x_i^k \; (k = 0, \ldots, n-1), \; x_1 \ldots x_n = D(X),$$

where $D(X)$ is the determinant of the matrix X.

We see from (1.31) that the matrices X and Y can be reduced to triangular form with the aid of the same matrix S. Therefore, we have

$$\left.\begin{aligned} \sigma(Y) &= \ln x_1 \ldots x_n = \alpha_{n-1}\sigma_{n-1} + \alpha_{n-2}\sigma_{n-2} + \ldots + \alpha_0 n \\ \sigma(XY) &= \sum_{i=1}^{n} x_i \ln x_i = \alpha_{n-1}\sigma_n + \alpha_{n-2}\sigma_{n-1} + \ldots + \alpha_0\sigma_1 \\ &\ldots\ldots\ldots\ldots\ldots\ldots\ldots\ldots \\ \sigma(X^{n-1}Y) &= \sum_{i=1}^{n} x_i^{n-1} \ln x_i = \alpha_{n-1}\sigma_{2n-2} + \\ &+ \alpha_{n-2}\sigma_{2n-3} + \ldots + \alpha_0\sigma_{n-1}. \end{aligned}\right\} \tag{1.32}$$

Let us find an explicit expression for the left members in terms of the invariants of the matrix X. With this in mind, we take $\ln x_i$ in the form

$$\ln x_i = \int_0^1 \frac{(x_i - 1)\,dt}{1 + t(x_i - 1)} \quad 0 \leq t \leq 1. \tag{1.33}$$

---

*Here, the equation written down follows from (1.4).

If we substitute this value into the left-hand members of Eqs. (1.32), we obtain

$$\left.\begin{aligned}
&\sigma(Y) = \ln x_1 \ldots x_n = \ln D(X)\\
&\sum_{i=1}^{n} x_i \ln x_i = \int_0^1 \sum_{i=1}^{n} \frac{x_i(x_i-1)\,dt}{1+t(x_i-1)} = \\
&\qquad = \int_0^1 \sum_{i=1}^{n} \frac{(x_i-1)^2+(x_i-1)}{1+t(x_i-1)}\,dt\\
&\ldots\ldots\ldots\ldots\ldots\ldots\ldots\ldots\\
&\sum_{i=1}^{n} x_i^l \ln x_i = \int_0^1 \sum_{i=1}^{n} \frac{x_i^l(x_i-1)}{1+t(x_i-1)}\,dt = \\
&\qquad = \int_0^1 \sum_{i=1}^{n} \Big[(x_i-1)^{l+1} + \frac{l}{1!}(x_i-1)^l + \\
&\qquad + \frac{l(l-1)(x_i-1)^{l-1}}{2!} + \ldots + (x_i-1)\Big] \times\\
&\qquad \times [1+t(x_i-1)]^{-1}\,dt\\
&\ldots\ldots\ldots\ldots\ldots\ldots\ldots\ldots\\
&\sum_{i=1}^{n} x_i^{n-1} \ln x_i = \int_0^1 \sum_{i=1}^{n} \frac{x_i^{n-1}(x_i-1)}{1+t(x_i-1)}\,dt = \\
&\int_0^1 \sum_{i=1}^{n} \frac{(x_i-1)^n + \frac{n-1}{1!}(x_i-1)^{n-1} + \ldots + (x_i-1)}{1+t(x_i-1)}\,dt.
\end{aligned}\right\} \quad (1.34)$$

Consider

$$M_k = \sum_{i=1}^{n} \frac{(x_i-1)^k}{1+t(x_i-1)} = \frac{\sum_{i=1}^{n} (x_i-1)^k \prod_{j\neq i} (1+t(x_j-1))}{\sum_{p=0}^{n} t^p S_p}, \quad (1.35)$$

where the S_p are the basic symmetric functions of $(x_1 - 1), \ldots, (x_n - 1)$,

$$S_n = \prod_{i=1}^{n} (x_i - 1),\ S_{n-1} = \sum_{i=1}^{n} \prod_{j \neq i} (x_j - 1), \ldots, S_1 = \sum_{i=1}^{n} (x_i - 1), S_0 = 1.$$

Furthermore, we have

$$N_k = \sum_{i=1}^{n} (x_i - 1)^k \prod_{j \neq i} (1 + t(x_j - 1)) =$$

$$= \sum_{i=1}^{n} (x_i - 1)^k \sum_{\nu=0}^{n-1} t^\nu S_{\nu,i} = \sum_{p=0}^{n-1} t^p A_p^k,\ S_{0i} = 1.$$

Here, $S_{l,i}$ is obtained from S_l by omitting terms containing $(x_i - 1)$ and

$$A_l^k = \sum_{i=1}^{n} (x_i - 1)^k S_{l,i},\ A_0^k = \sum_{i=1}^{n} (x_i - 1)^k.$$

It is easy to see that

$$(x_i - 1) S_{n-1,i} = S_n,\ (x_i - 1) S_{l,i} = S_{l+1} - S_{l+1,i},$$

$$\sum_{i=1}^{n} S_{l,i} = S_l (n - l).$$

By using this result, we obtain

$$A_{n-1}^k = \sum_{i=1}^{n} (x_i - 1)^k S_{n-1,i} = \sum_{i=1}^{n} (x_i - 1)^{k-1} S_n = S_n \sum_{i=1}^{n} (x_i - 1)^{k-1} = S_n \delta_{k-1},$$

$$A_l^k = \sum_{i=1}^{n} (x_i - 1)^k S_{l,i} = \sum_{i=1}^{n} (x_i - 1)^{k-1} [S_{l+1} - S_{l+1,i}] =$$

$$= S_{l+1} \delta_{k-1} - \sum_{i=1}^{n} (x_i - 1)^{k-2} [S_{l+2} - S_{l+2,i}] =$$

$$= S_{l+1} \delta_{k-1} - S_{l+2} \delta_{k-2} + \sum_{i=1}^{n} (x_i - 1)^{k-2} S_{l+2,i} = \ldots = \tag{1.36}$$

$$= \begin{cases} \sum_{m=1}^{n-l} (-1)^{m+1} S_{l+m} \delta_{k-m} & \text{for } n - l < k, \\ \sum_{m=1}^{k} (-1)^{m+1} S_{l+m} \delta_{k-m} & \text{for } n - l \geqslant k, \end{cases}$$

Here, $\delta_k = \sum_{i=1}^{n} (x_i - 1)^k$ and by δ_0, we mean $\delta_0 = l + k$ since

$$A_l^1 = \sum_{i=1}^{n} (x_i - 1) S_{l,\, i} = \sum_{i=1}^{n} [S_{l+1} - S_{l+1,\, i}] = S_{l+1}(l + 1).$$

The quantitites δ_k are rational functions of S_m (for $m = 1, \ldots, n$). The quantities S_m in the characteristic equation of the matrix $(X - I)$ are found to be rational functions of the elements of the matrix $(X - I)$.

Thus, the left-hand members of Eqs. (1.32) are found in the form [(on the basis of (1.34), (1.35), and (1.36)]

$$\sigma(X^l Y) = \int_0^1 \frac{\sum_{k=1}^{l+1} \sum_{p=0}^{n-1} \frac{l(l-1)\ldots k}{(l-k+1)!} t^p A_p^k}{\sum_{p=0}^{n} t^p S_p} dt \quad (l = 1, \ldots, n-1), \qquad (1.37)$$

where the A_p^k are rational functions of the elements of the matrix $(X - I)$ and hence of the matrix X.

If we now determine the quantitites α_i (for $i = 0, \ldots, n-1$) from the linear system (1.32), we find them directly in terms of the invariants of the matrix X.

Let us denote the determinant of the coefficients of the system (1.32) for unknown $\alpha_0, \alpha_1, \ldots, \alpha_{n-1}$ in terms of $\Delta(X) = \Delta$. If $x_1, \ldots, x_n$ are all distinct, then $\Delta(X) \neq 0$. Let us denote by $\bar{\Delta}_i$ the determinant obtained from $\Delta(X)$ by replacing the ith column with the left-hand members and let us denote by Δ_i the determinant $\bar{\Delta}_i$ in which the quantities $\sigma(X^l Y)$ are replaced with the expressions given by (1.37). Then, we obtain

$$\alpha_i = \frac{\bar{\Delta}_i}{\Delta} = \frac{\Delta_i}{\Delta} \quad (i = 0, 1, \ldots, n-1). \qquad (1.38)$$

Finally, we have*

$$Y = \ln X = \frac{1}{\Delta} \sum_{i=0}^{n-1} \Delta_i X^i. \qquad (1.39)$$

We note that the denominator of the fraction constituting the integrand in (1.37) is

$$\prod_{i=1}^{n} (1 + t(x_i - 1)) = \sum_{p=0}^{n} t^p S^p.$$

*This formula, in accordance with the consequence of Remark 1.1 becomes a finite limit formula for multiples of $x_1, \ldots, x_n$.

Therefore, this denominator has roots $t_k = (1 - x_k)^{-1}$ (for $k = 1, \ldots, n$). Since $0 \leqslant t \leqslant 1$, the integral (1.37) is real and finite if the characteristic number x_k (for $k = 1, \ldots, n$) of the matrix X is nonnegative. This leads to the following remark.

Remark 1.2. $\ln X$ given by formula (1.39) is real if none of the characteristic numbers $x_1, \ldots, x_n$ are negative. If any of these numbers are negative, then the path of integration [0,1] in (1.37) [or (1.33)] should be taken in the complex plane. But then, as can be shown, $\ln X$ would have to be complex also. We shall not prove this here since we shall soon prove it by using other considerations.

For a second-order matrix X, formula (1.39) takes the form

$$\ln X = \frac{(S_1 + 2)\ln D - 2M}{4S_2 - S_1^2} X + \frac{(S_1 + 2) M - S_1^2 - 2S_1 + 2S_2 - 2}{4S_2 - S_1^2}, \tag{1.40}$$

where

$$S_1 = \sigma - 2, \; S_2 = D - \sigma + 1, \; \sigma = x_1 + x_2, \; D = x_1 x_2$$

and

$$M = \int_0^1 \frac{(S_1 S_2 + 2S_2)t + S_1^2 - 2S_2 + S_1}{S_2 t^2 + S_1 t + 1} dt.$$

For a third-order matrix X, we have

$$\ln X = \alpha_2 X^2 + \alpha_1 X + \alpha_0, \tag{1.41}$$

where α_2, α_1, and α_0 are determined from the equations

$$P_0 = \alpha_2 k_2 + \alpha_1 \sigma_1 + 3\alpha_0, \quad k_2 = \sigma_1^2 - 2\sigma_2,$$
$$P_1 = \alpha_2 k_3 + \alpha_1 k_2 + \alpha_0 \sigma_1, \quad k_3 = \sigma_1^3 - 3\sigma_1\sigma_2 + 3\sigma_3,$$
$$P_2 = \alpha_2 k_4 + \alpha_1 k_3 + \alpha_0 k_2, \quad k_4 = \sigma_1^4 - 4\sigma_1^2\sigma_2 + 4\sigma_1\sigma_3 + 2\sigma_2^2$$

and the free terms P_0, P_1, and P_2 are determined by the equations

$$P_0 = \ln \sigma_3,$$
$$P_1 = \int_0^1 \frac{b_3(b_1 + 3)t^2 + (b_1 b_2 - 3b_3 + 2b_2)t + b_1 + b_1^2 - 2b_2}{1 + b_1 t + b_2 t^2 + b_3 t^3} dt,$$
$$P_2 = \int_0^1 \frac{M_2 t^2 + M_1 t + M_0}{1 + b_1 t + b_2 t^2 + b_3 t^3} dt.$$

$$M_0 = b_1^3 - 3b_1b_2 + 2b_1^2 + 3b_3 - 4b_2 + b_1,$$

$$M_1 = b_1^2b_2 + 2b_1b_2 - b_1b_3 - 2b_2^2 + 2b_2 - 6b_3,$$

$$M_2 = b_3(b_1^2 + 2b_1 - 2b_2 + 3),$$

$$b_1 = \sigma_1 - 3, \quad b_2 = \sigma_2 - 2\sigma_1 + 3, \quad b_3 = \sigma_3 + \sigma_1 - \sigma_2 - 1.$$

Here, σ_1, σ_2, and σ_3 are polynomials in the elements of the matrix X that are defined as the coefficients of the characteristic equation of the matrix X

$$D(X - \lambda I) = \lambda^3 - \sigma_1\lambda^2 + \sigma_2\lambda - \sigma_3 = 0,$$

and, at the same time, $\sigma_1 = x_1 + x_2 + x_3$, $\sigma_2 = x_1x_2 + x_1x_3 + x_2x_3$, $\sigma_3 = x_1x_2x_3$, where x_1, x_2, and x_3 are the characteristic numbers of the matrix X, that is, the roots of the equation $-D(X - \lambda I) = 0$.

Let us examine in greater detail the form of ln A when the real matrix A has negative characteristic numbers.

Suppose that $A = SBS^{-1}$, where B is a quasi-diagonal real matrix; $B = [B_1, \ldots, B_k]$ and B_ν (for $\nu = 1, \ldots, k$) are real square matrices either with a single elementary divisor corresponding to the real characteristic number λ_ν or with two elementary divisors corresponding to the two complex conjugate characteristic numbers λ_k and λ_{k+1}. Here, the matrices S may also be assumed real.

On the basis of (1.3), we have

$$\ln A = S[\ln B_1, \ldots, \ln B_k] S^{-1}. \tag{1.42}$$

We take* as real the values of ln B_ν for those B_ν that have characteristic numbers λ_ν not equal to negative numbers. Suppose now that B_ν corresponds to a negative characteristic number λ_ν of the matrix A. Then, the matrix B_ν has only one elementary divisor and $B_\nu = S_\nu J(\lambda_\nu) S^{-1}$,

$$\ln B_\nu = S_\nu \ln J(\lambda_\nu) S_\nu^{-1} = S_\nu \ln[-J(\lambda_\nu)\cdot(-1)] S_\nu^{-1} =$$

$$= S_\nu[\ln(-J(\lambda_\nu)) + \pi i I] S_\nu^{-1}. \tag{1.43}$$

Here, S_ν is a real matrix with nonzero determinant and $\ln(-J(\lambda_\nu))$ is a real matrix since the characteristic number of the matrix $-J(\lambda_\nu)$ is equal to $-\lambda_\nu > 0$. If we substitute the value of (1.43) into (1.42), we obtain

$$\ln A = A_1 + \pi i SL(0, 1) S^{-1}, \tag{1.44}$$

where A_1 is a real matrix having characteristic numbers equal to ln λ_ν if λ_ν is not equal to a negative number and $\ln(-\lambda_\nu)$ if $\lambda_\nu < 0$.

---

*According to formula (1.39).

$L(0, 1)$ is a real diagonal matrix of order n in which we have **1** at positions corresponding to the roots $\lambda_\nu < 0$ and 0 at all other positions. We note also that the matrix A_1 obviously commutes with the matrix $\pi iSL(0, 1)S^{-1} = i\pi A_2$.

Let us write (1.44) in the form

$$\ln A = A_1 + \pi i A_2. \tag{1.45}$$

Here, the matrix A_2 has characteristic numbers equal only to zero and unity. We call this value of ln A the ***principal value.***

Remark 1.3. We might have set

$$\ln B_\nu = S_\nu [\ln(-J(\lambda_\nu)) - \pi i I] S_\nu^{-1}$$

for some (or even all) of the negative characteristic numbers λ_ν. Then, at the corresponding positions in the matrix $L(0, 1)$, we would have had -1 instead of 1. Of course, when $\lambda_\nu < 0$, we could also have set

$$\ln B_\nu = S_\nu [\ln(-J(\lambda_\nu)) + (2n+1)\pi i] S_\nu^{-1} \tag{1.45$_1$}$$

or

$$\ln B_\nu = S_\nu [\ln(-J(\lambda_\nu)) + (2n-1)\pi i] S_\nu^{-1}, \tag{1.45$_2$}$$

where n is an integer (positive or negative). The matrix A_2 can also be taken as follows:

$$A_2 = SL[0, 2m, (2n+1), (2n_1-1)] S^{-1}, \tag{1.46}$$

where L is a diagonal matrix the elements in which are equal to 0 or $2m$ if they correspond to nonnegative characteristic numbers and to $(2n+1)$ or $(2n_1-1)$ if they correspond to negative numbers; the numbers m, n, and n_1 are integers. Obviously, formulas (1.45$_1$), (1.45$_2$), and (1.46) yield a value of ln A other than the principal value. We note also that ln A is a multiple-valued function and that, in accordance with (1.18) or (1.23$_1$), all the values of $\ln aI$ are obtained in the form

$$\ln aI = I \ln a + 2\pi i S [m_1, \ldots, m_n] S^{-1}, \tag{1.47}$$

where S^{-1} is an arbitrary matrix such that $D(S) \neq 0$ and $m_1, \ldots, m_n$ are arbitrary integers. Lappo-Danilevskiy termed such values of ln aI "irregular" when the numbers $m_1, \ldots, m_n$ are not all equal, as was noted earlier. For a second-order matrix $A = aI$ with $a = 1$, by setting $\ln a = \ln 1 = 0$, we obtain

$$\ln \mathrm{I} = 2\pi i S [m_1, m_2] S^{-1}. \tag{1.48}$$

In particular,

$$\ln \mathrm{I} = 2\pi S \begin{Vmatrix} 0 & -n \\ n & 0 \end{Vmatrix} S^{-1}. \tag{1.49}$$

These values of ln I are real for an arbitrary real matrix S.

For $a = -\mathrm{I}$, we have $\ln a = \pi i$ and

$$\ln [-\mathrm{I}] = i\pi S [2m_1 + 1, 2m_2 + 1] S^{-1}. \tag{1.50}$$

If S is an arbitrary real matrix, then

$$\begin{aligned} \ln [-\mathrm{I}] &= \pi S \begin{Vmatrix} 0 & -(2n+1) \\ 2n+1 & 0 \end{Vmatrix} S^{-1} = \\ &= \pi i S_1 \begin{Vmatrix} 2n+1 & 0 \\ 0 & -2n-1 \end{Vmatrix} S_1^{-1} \end{aligned} \tag{1.51}$$

has a real value.

Remark 1.4. If the matrix A has an even number of negative characteristic numbers, then, for example,* on the basis of (1.51), we can set the imaginary part of $\ln A$ equal to 0 in (1.43), (1.44), and (1.45). But, when we do this, we will obtain a nonprincipal (and irregular) value of ln A.

In conclusion, we note that the function $f(A)$ of a matrix A can be defined by using, for example, Lagrange's formula

$$f(A) = \sum_{k=1}^{n-1} A^k \varphi_k(\lambda_1, \ldots, \lambda_n). \tag{1.52}$$

Here, the scalar functions $\varphi_k(\lambda_1, \ldots, \lambda_n)$ are defined in terms of $f(z)$ and its derivatives in a neighborhood of the characteristic numbers $\lambda_1, \ldots, \lambda_n$ of the matrix A. It is in just this way that Gantmakher [3] defines $f(A)$. Thus, we have the values of $f(A)$ when $f(z)$, together with the relevant derivatives (that is, those that appear in the construction of Lagrange's formula), is determined in a neighborhood of the characteristic numbers $\lambda_1, \ldots, \lambda_n$ or, as Gantmakher says, $f(A)$ is defined on the spectrum of the matrix A. We note that in this case,

*Since $\ln J(\lambda_\nu) = \ln(-J(\lambda_\nu)) + \ln(-1 \cdot \mathrm{I}_{2m}) = \ln(-J(\lambda_\nu)) + [\ln(-1 \cdot \mathrm{I}_2), \ldots, \ln(-1 \cdot \mathrm{I}_2)]$. Here, $\ln(-1 \cdot \mathrm{I}_2)$ is given by formula (1.51) and the matrix $[\ln(-1 \cdot \mathrm{I}_2), \ldots, \ln(-1 \cdot \mathrm{I}_2)]$ is a quasi-diagonal mth-order matrix.

in a neighborhood of each characteristic number λ_k, one may take a different $f_k(z)$; that is, $f_1(z),\dots, f_n(z)$ are not necessarily elements of the same analytic function $f(z)$.

2. Auxiliary Theorems

Let $f(z)$ denote an analytic, possibly multiple-valued function that is holomorphic in a neighborhood of points a_k (where $k = 1,\dots, n$). Suppose that the series

$$X = \sum_{k=0}^{\infty} X_k \varepsilon^k \tag{2.1}$$

converges for $|\varepsilon| < \varepsilon_1$, where the X_k are nth-order matrices that do not depend on ε and the characteristic numbers $x_i = x_i(\varepsilon)$ of the matrix X are such that $x_i(0) = a_k$.

Let us define a function $Y = f(X)$ in a neighborhood of $\varepsilon = 0$ on the spectrum of the matrix X in such a way that $f(x_k(0)) = f(x_l(0))$ if $x_k(0) = x_l(0)$.*

Theorem 2.1. *The matrix Y can be represented in the form of a convergent series*

$$Y = \sum_{k=0}^{\infty} Y_k \varepsilon^k, \quad Y_0 = f(X_0), \quad |\varepsilon| < \rho. \tag{2.2}$$

Proof: We have

$$Y = \sum_{k=0}^{n-1} \varphi_k X^k, \tag{2.3}$$

where the scalar quantitites φ_k are defined** by the equations

$$\sum_{k=1}^{n} x_k^s f(x_k) = \sum_{k=0}^{n-1} \varphi_k \sigma(X^{k+s}) \quad (s = 0, 1,\dots, n-1). \tag{2.4}$$

The determinant of the coefficients of the unknowns φ_k is nonzero for distinct characteristic numbers $x_1,\dots, x_n$.

---

*In other words, $Y_0 = f(X_0)$ is a regular value (see p. 9).

**See formulas (1.32).

Because of the hypotheses made, both $\sigma(X^k)$ and the left-hand members of these equations are single-valued* functions of ε in a neighborhood of $\varepsilon=0$. Since the Lagrange polynomial $f(X)$ takes on a finite limiting form** when the characteristic numbers of the matrix X coincide [1, 2, 3], it follows that the φ_k and $f(X)$ are holomorphic functions in a neighborhood of $\varepsilon = 0$.

We note that, when there are multiple characteristic numbers

$$x_{j+1}(\varepsilon) = x_{j+2}(\varepsilon) = \ldots = x_{j+p}(\varepsilon)$$

we can first define $x_k = x_k(\varepsilon, \tau)$ by setting, for example,

$$x_{j+1} = x_{j+1}(\varepsilon) + b_1\tau, \ldots, \; x_{j+p} = x_{j+p}(\varepsilon) + b_p\tau.$$

Here, if the given root belongs to a circular system of q elements, then each element $x_j^{(k)}$ (for $k = 1, \ldots, q$) of this circular system will also be a root of multiplicity p; that is, we shall have***

$$x_{j+1}^{(k)} = x_{j+2}^{(k)} = \ldots = x_{j+p}^{(k)} \; (k = 1, \ldots, q).$$

Then, we need to consider the characteristic numbers

$$x_{j+1}^{(k)} = x_{j+1}^{(k)}(\varepsilon) + b_1\tau, \ldots, \; x_{j+p}^{(k)} = x_{j+p}^{(k)}(\varepsilon) + b_p\tau \; (k = 1, \ldots, q).$$

We shall have n distinct characteristic numbers. The left-hand members of Eqs. (2.4) and the $\sigma(X^k)$ will be single-valued functions of ε for all $|\tau| \leqslant \tau_0$. For $\tau = 0$, we obtain $\varphi_k = \varphi_k(\varepsilon, 0)$ as single-valued functions of ε in a neighborhood of $\varepsilon = 0$.

The existence of a limiting finite form of Lagrange's formula can, obviously, be used in a different manner. For $Y = \ln X$, the theorem**** is also obvious on the basis of (1.39). For second- and third-order matrices X, it is obvious on the basis of formulas (1.40) and (1.41).

---

*Here, as we can see, every circular system [6] of characteristic numbers $x_k(\varepsilon)$ (for $k = p, p+1, \ldots, p+m$) is symmetric.

**These limiting values of φ_k can be found, for example, by using the corollary to Remark 1.1.

***Therefore, $\varphi_k(\lambda_1, \ldots, \lambda_m)$ in (1.8) will also be a symmetric function of $\lambda_1, \ldots, \lambda_q$, (which belong to a single circular system) and $\varphi_k(x_1(\varepsilon), \ldots, x_m(\varepsilon))$ will be a single-valued function of ε in a neighborhood of $\varepsilon = 0$. It is easy to see that $\varphi_k(\varepsilon)$ will also be finite for $\varepsilon = 0$ if any of the $x_1(0), \ldots, x_m(0)$ coincide. Theorem (2.1) follows from this.

****For the case in which $Y = \ln X$, this theorem is studied in [14] for $X_0 = I$. It is basically proven for arbitrary X_0 in [7] and [4] by different methods. However, Artem'yev initiated essentially this type of investigating procedure in his works [8, 9], as did Shtokalo in [10]. In [7] the question of the expansion of the function $\ln(\Sigma X_k \varepsilon^k)$ in a series in terms of the parameter ε and of the characteristic numbers of that function is studied for the first time in complete detail. Unfortunately, this work was unknown to me prior to the end of 1956. Therefore, it is not mentioned in [4], which was completed in 1954 (cf. footnotes on p. 211 in [11] and on p. 5 in [4]. In [12] the results of other authors [13] are repeated.

For the principal value of $Y = \ln X$, these formulas enable us also to find the expansion (2.2). We can find a nonprincipal value by use of (1.18) or by making the substitution $f(x_k) = \ln x_k + 2m\pi i$ with suitable constants m in (2.4).

Remark 2.1. Theorem 2.1 remains valid in the case in which different holomorphic functions $f_k(z)$ are taken in the definition of $f(X)$ in a neighborhood of the limiting values of $x_k(0) = a_k$ since the values of $f(z)$ at the points $x_{j+1}(\varepsilon), \ldots, x_{j+p}(\varepsilon)$ belonging to a single circular system of roots of the characteristic equation

$$x^n + a_{n-1}(\varepsilon)x^{n-1} + \ldots + a_1(\varepsilon)x + a_0(\varepsilon) = 0 \qquad (2.5)$$

of the matrix (2.1) are calculated with the aid of the function $f(z) = f_j(z)$, which is given by its element in a neighborhood of the point a_j. This remark follows from the fact that the left-hand members of Eq. (2.4) and the $\sigma(X^n)$ are symmetric functions of $x_{j+1}, \ldots, x_{j+p}$.

Remark 2.2. The series (2.2) converges at least in the circle $|\varepsilon| \leqslant r < \varepsilon_1$ in which there is no more than one branch point of the roots of the characteristic equation (2.5) if the roots $x_1(\varepsilon), \ldots, x_n(\varepsilon)$ do not assume singular values of the function $f(z)$ at these values of ε.

Consequently, the series (2.2) converges at least in the circle $|\varepsilon| \leqslant r < \varepsilon_1$ in which the discriminant $\Delta(\varepsilon)$ of Eq. (2.5) does not vanish for $\varepsilon \neq 0$.

On the other hand, if $x_1(0), \ldots, x_n(0)$ are distinct, the series (2.2) will also converge in the circle $|\varepsilon| \leqslant r < \varepsilon_1$ in which there is no more than one zero of the discriminant $\Delta(\varepsilon)$. (However, in a neighborhood of $\varepsilon = 0$, the functions $f(x_k(\varepsilon))$ must be such that the value of $f(X(\varepsilon))$ will be regular in a neighborhood of a branch point of ε_1.) However, the radius of convergence of the series (2.2) may be greater than this, as will be shown at the end of this section.

Theorem 2.2. *Suppose that the function $Y = f(X)$ referred to in Theorem 2.1 is defined in a neighborhood of $\varepsilon = 0$ on the spectrum $x_1(\varepsilon), \ldots, x_n(\varepsilon)$ in such a way that $f(x_k(0)) = f(x_l(0))$ if $x_k(0) = x_l(0)$. (In the case $Y = \ln X$, the principal values of $\ln x_1(\varepsilon), \ldots, \ln x_k(\varepsilon))$ are taken, for example.) If the characteristic numbers $x_k(\varepsilon)$ (for $k = 1, \ldots, n$) of the matrix (2.1) do not assume singular values of the function $f(z)$ in the region $|\varepsilon| < \varepsilon_1$ (in the case of $Y = \ln X$, we must have $x_k(\varepsilon) \neq 0$ in the region $|\varepsilon| < \varepsilon_1$), then the invariants of the matrix $Y = f(X)$ can be represented in the form of series $\sum_{k=0}^{\infty} \beta_k \varepsilon^k$ in the circle $|\varepsilon| \leqslant r < \varepsilon_1$ in which there is no more than one* branch point ε_0 of the roots of the characteristic equation (2.5).*

---

*If $\varepsilon = 0$ is a branch point, then $\varepsilon_0 = 0$. If the point $\varepsilon_0 \neq 0$ is a branch point in the circle $|\varepsilon| \leqslant r$, then $x_1(0), \ldots, x_n(0)$ are distinct and we need to take $f(x_k(\varepsilon_0)) = f(x_l(\varepsilon_0))$ if $x_k(\varepsilon_0) = x_l(\varepsilon_0)$.

Library
I.U.P.
Indiana, Pa.
517.382 Er91
c. 1

This theorem follows from Remark 2.2, but we shall prove it anew.

Proof: The characteristic numbers $x_k(\varepsilon)$ (for $k = 1,\dots, n$) of the matrix (2.1) are determined from Eq. (2.5), where the $a_k(\varepsilon)$ (for $k = 1,\dots, n$) are holomorphic functions of ε in the region $|\varepsilon| < \varepsilon_1$. It follows from this that the characteristic numbers in the region $|\varepsilon| < \varepsilon_1$ have only algebraic singular points and, for every ε_0 in the region $|\varepsilon| < \varepsilon_1$, are representable in the form of series of integral powers of $(\varepsilon - \varepsilon_0)$ or $(\varepsilon-\varepsilon_0)^{1/k}$, where k is a positive integer less than n. The characteristic numbers of the matrix Y are equal to $f(x_1(\varepsilon)),\dots, f(x_n(\varepsilon))$. The invariants σ_k (for $k = 1,\dots, n$) of the matrix Y are known symmetric kth-degree polynomials in $f_1(x_1(\varepsilon)),\dots, f_n(x_n(\varepsilon))$:

$$\sigma_k(\varepsilon) = \sigma_k[f(x_1(\varepsilon)),\dots, f(x_n(\varepsilon))].$$

The algebraic singular point ε_0 (closest to $\varepsilon = 0$) of the functions $x_1(\varepsilon),\dots, x_n(\varepsilon)$ is not a singular point of $\sigma_k(\varepsilon)$ since the functions $\sigma_k(\varepsilon)$ are single-valued in a neighborhood of the point ε_0 (because they are symmetric functions of $f(x_1),\dots, f(x_n)$, and the $x_k(\varepsilon)$ do not assume singular values of $f(z)$ in the region $|\varepsilon| < \varepsilon$). The assertion follows from this.

For example, suppose that there are two branch points ε_1 and ε_2 of the roots of Eq. (2.5). If, in a neighborhood of the point ε_1, we take values of $f(x_k(\varepsilon))$ in such a way that the left-hand members of Eqs. (2.4) are single-valued (that is, $f(X(\varepsilon))$ is a regular value in a neighborhood of the point ε_1), then these values of $f(x_k(\varepsilon))$ in a neighborhood of ε_2 may be such that $f(X(\varepsilon))$ will be a nonregular value in a neighborhood of the point ε_2. But then, in a neighborhood of this point, the coefficients $\varphi_k(\varepsilon)$ may be nonsingle-valued. On the other hand, if there is no more than one branch point in the region $|\varepsilon| < r$, then $f(X(\varepsilon))$ will be a regular value when the function $f(X(\varepsilon))$ is continued analytically.

Example:

$$\ln V = \ln \begin{Vmatrix} \lambda & \lambda^2 - 1 \\ 1 & \lambda \end{Vmatrix},$$

$$v_1 = \lambda + \sqrt{\lambda^2 - 1},\ v_2 = \lambda - \sqrt{\lambda^2 - 1},\ \ln v_1 = \ln(\lambda + \sqrt{\lambda^2 - 1}),$$

$$\ln v_2 = \ln(\lambda - \sqrt{\lambda^2 - 1}),\ -1 < \lambda < 1,\ D(\lambda) = \ln v_1 \cdot \ln v_2.$$

Suppose that $\ln v_1(1) = \ln v_2(1) = 0$. Then, $D(\lambda)$ is a single-valued function in a neighborhood of $\lambda = 1$. But, if we extend $D(\lambda)$ into a neighborhood of $\lambda = -1$, we obtain

$$D(\lambda) = \ln(\lambda + \sqrt{\lambda^2 - 1})\,[\ln(\lambda - \sqrt{\lambda^2 - 1}) - 2\pi i],\quad \ln(-1) = \pi i$$

since

$$\ln v_1 = \ln e^{i\varphi} \to \pi i, \ \ln v_2 = \ln e^{-i\varphi} \to -\pi i$$

as $\lambda \to -1$. If λ now moves around the point $\lambda = -1$ at a close distance, then $D(\lambda)$ becomes

$$D(\lambda) = \ln(\lambda - \sqrt{\lambda^2 - 1})\,[\ln(\lambda + \sqrt{\lambda^2 - 1}) - 2\pi i],$$

that is, $D(\lambda)$ is a nonsingle-valued function in a neighborhood of $\lambda = -1$. On the other hand, if we assume $D(\lambda)$ single-valued in a neighborhood of $\lambda = -1$, then $D(\lambda)$ is nonsingle-valued in a neighborhood of $\lambda = 1$. If $D(\lambda)$ is expanded in a neighborhood of $\lambda = 0$, then the radius of convergence is $|\lambda| < 1$. But if we take $D(\lambda)$ in a neighborhood of $\lambda = 2$ in such a way that $\ln V$ is regular in a neighborhood of $\lambda = 1$, then the expansion in powers of $(\lambda - 2)$ will converge for $|\lambda - 2| < 3$.

If we take

$$V = \begin{Vmatrix} e^{\lambda} & e^{2\lambda} - 1 \\ 1 & e^{\lambda} \end{Vmatrix},$$

then

$$D(\lambda) = \ln(e^{\lambda} + \sqrt{e^{2\lambda} - 1}) \cdot \ln(e^{\lambda} - \sqrt{e^{2\lambda} - 1})$$

and $D(\lambda)$ can be expanded in powers of λ: $D(\lambda) = \sum_{k=1}^{\infty} \sigma_k \lambda^k$, and this series will converge for $|\lambda| < \pi$ since there is only one branch point $\lambda = 0$ in this region. However, we need to remember that the radius of convergence of the series $\sum_{k=0}^{\infty} \beta_k \varepsilon^k$ in Theorem 2.2 may be larger than this. This will be shown at the end of this section.

Let us now consider the question of expanding an irregular value of a function of a matrix in a series in terms of a parameter. Consider the nth-order matrix

$$X = \sum_{k=0}^{\infty} X_k \varepsilon^k, \ |\varepsilon| < r, \tag{2.6}$$

where the matrices X_k are independent of ε. Let us denote by x_{kl} the elements of the matrix X. Suppose that the elementary divisors of the matrix (2.6) are primes and that the characteristic numbers

$x_1(\varepsilon),\ldots, x_n(\varepsilon)$ are holomorphic functions in a neighborhood of $\varepsilon = 0$. Suppose that a function $f(z)$ (in general, multiple-valued) is holomorphic in a neighborhood of the characteristic numbers $z = a_k = x_k(0)$ (for $k = 1,\ldots, n$) of the matrix X_0. Then, we have

Theorem 2.3. *The function*

$$Y = f(X) \tag{2.7}$$

can be represented by a convergent series

$$Y = \sum_{k=0}^{\infty} Y_k \varepsilon^k, \quad Y_0 = f(X_0), \tag{2.8}$$

where $f(X_0)$ is any, possibly irregular, value (if $a_k = a_l$).

Proof: We have

$$\left.\begin{aligned} X_0 &= S_0 [a_1,\ldots, a_n] S_0^{-1} \\ X &= S(\varepsilon) [x_1(\varepsilon),\ldots, x_n(\varepsilon)] S^{-1}(\varepsilon) \\ x_k(\varepsilon) &\to x_k(0) = a_k, \; S(\varepsilon) \to S_0 \quad \text{as} \quad \varepsilon \to 0 \end{aligned}\right\} \tag{2.9}$$

and the elements of the matrix $S(\varepsilon)$ are holomorphic functions in a neighborhood of $\varepsilon = 0$. On the basis of (1.3) and (1.9),

$$Y = S(\varepsilon) [f(x_1(\varepsilon)),\ldots, f(x_n(\varepsilon))] S^{-1}(\varepsilon). \tag{2.10}$$

We note that here we can set $S_0 = I$. Specifically, we may write

$$X = S_0 \overline{X} S_0^{-1} = S_0 \sum_{k=0}^{\infty} \overline{X}_k \varepsilon^k \cdot S_0^{-1}, \; \overline{X}_0 = [a_1,\ldots, a_n].$$

Since

$$f(X) = S_0 f\left[\sum_{k=0}^{\infty} \overline{X}_k \varepsilon^k\right] \cdot S_0^{-1},$$

the problem amounts to examining the function $f\left(\sum_{k=0}^{\infty} \overline{X}_k \varepsilon^k\right)$. Here, $\overline{X}_0 = [a_1,\ldots, a_n]$; that is, here we have $S_0 = I$. This enables us to assume that the elements x_{kl} of the matrix (2.6) approach 0 as $\varepsilon \to 0$ when $k \neq l$.

The theorem follows from (2.9) and (2.10). If $f(X_0)$ in (2.8) is irregular, it depends on $S_0 = S(0)$.

Remark 2.3. Instead of requiring that the elementary divisors of the matrix X be prime, we may require that the characteristic numbers $x_k(\varepsilon)$ be holomorphic in a neighborhood of $\varepsilon = 0$ and that the canonical structure of the matrix*

$$X = S(\varepsilon)\,[J_1(x_1(\varepsilon)),\ldots,\ J_m(x_m(\varepsilon))]\,S^{-1}(\varepsilon)$$

remain the same for all $|\varepsilon| < R$.

Example: $Y = \ln X,\ X = \sum_{k=0}^{\infty} X_k \varepsilon^k,\ X_0 = \exp A$. Suppose that the canonical structure of the matrix

$$X = S(\varepsilon)\,[J_{\rho_1}(x(\varepsilon)),\ldots,\ J_{\rho_\nu}(x_\nu(\varepsilon))]\,S^{-1}(\varepsilon)$$

remains invariant for all $|\varepsilon| < R$ and that among the characteristic numbers $a_k = x_k(0)$ (for $k = 1,\ldots,\nu$) of the matrix A there are some such that

$$a_k - a_l = 2m\pi i \quad (m \text{ — an integer}).$$

$$A = S_0\,[J_{\rho_1}(a_1),\ldots,\ J_{\rho_\nu}(a_\nu)]\,S_0^{-1},\quad S(\varepsilon) \to S_0$$

as $\varepsilon \to 0$ and $a_k = b_k + 2m_k\pi i$ (for $k = 1,\ldots,\nu$), where the m_k are integers and $b_k - b_l \neq 2m\pi i$ for nonzero integral m. Then,

$$Y = \sum_{k=0}^{\infty} Y_k \varepsilon^k, \tag{2.11}$$

$$Y_0 = \ln\exp A + S_0\,[2m_1\pi i\, I_{\rho_1},\ldots,\ 2m_\nu \pi i\, I_{\rho_\nu}]\,S_0^{-1},$$

where

$$\ln\exp A = S_0\,[J_{\rho_1}(b_1),\ldots,\ J_{\rho_\nu}(b_\nu)]\,S_0^{-1}$$

is the principal value of ln exp A.

Remark 2.4. We note that the point $\varepsilon = \varepsilon_1$ at which $\Delta(\varepsilon_1) = 0$ can be a singular point for the series (2.2) such that, in a neighborhood of $\varepsilon = \varepsilon_1$, the series (2.2) obtained by analytic continuation of the series (2.2) constructed in a neighborhood of the point $\varepsilon = 0$ will be an irregular value of $Y = f(X(\varepsilon))$. Here, the canonical structure of $f(X(\varepsilon))$ may be the same as for $X(\varepsilon)$ (that is, it may have the same set of elementary divisors) or it may be different in accordance with what was said between formulas (1.23) and (1.24). In the second case,

*The existence of holomorphic functions $S(\varepsilon)$ and $S^{-1}(\varepsilon)$ in a neighborhood of $\varepsilon = 0$ was first shown by Yu. S. Bogdanov in 1947, but his proof was not published (see [95]).

that is, if certain nonprime elementary divisors of the matrix $X(\varepsilon)$ correspond to certain elementary divisors of the matrix $Y = f(X(\varepsilon))$ then the limiting values of certain elements of the matrix $f(X(\varepsilon))$ will be infinite as $\varepsilon \to \varepsilon_0$. In the first case, on the other hand, the norm of the matrix $f(X(\varepsilon))$ may be either bounded or unbounded as $\varepsilon \to \varepsilon_0$. However, we need to keep in mind that the series (2.2) can converge in the circle $|\varepsilon| < |\varepsilon_1|$ (where $\Delta(\varepsilon_1) = 0$) even in the case in which the value of $f(X(\varepsilon_1))$ is irregular at the point $\varepsilon = \varepsilon_1$. This case is noted by Theorem 2.3 and Remark 2.3.

Following the reasoning on pp. 86-87 of [14], let us consider separately the case of second-order matrices and $Y = f(X) = \ln X$. Here, we have

$$Y = \frac{X(\varepsilon) - x_2(\varepsilon)}{x_1(\varepsilon) - x_2(\varepsilon)} \ln x_1(\varepsilon) + \frac{X(\varepsilon) - x_1(\varepsilon)}{x_2(\varepsilon) - x_1(\varepsilon)} \ln x_2(\varepsilon), \tag{2.12}$$

where x_1 and x_2 are roots of the equation

$$x^2 - \sigma(X)x + D(X) = 0, \ 2x = \sigma(X) \pm \sqrt{\Delta(\varepsilon)},$$
$$\Delta(\varepsilon) = \sigma^2(X) - 4D(X).$$

Suppose (as we shall always assume) that $X(\varepsilon)$ is real and that

$$D(X) = x_1 x_2 \neq 0 \tag{2.13}$$

for all values of ε in question.

According to what was said above, the only singular points $\varepsilon = \varepsilon_0$ of the series (2.2) can be points at which $x_1 = x_2$, that is, points at which

$$\Delta(\varepsilon_0) = \sigma^2(X(\varepsilon_0)) - 4D(X(\varepsilon_0)) = 0. \tag{2.14}$$

In view of (2.12), the singular points $\varepsilon = \varepsilon_0$ are the points at which $x_1 = x_2$ and the arguments of x_1 and x_2 differ only in sign. On the other hand, if Eq. (2.14) is not satisfied in the circle of convergence of the series (2.1), then the series (2.2) will converge in the same circle as does (2.1). Let us suppose that

$$D(X) = x_1(\varepsilon) x_2(\varepsilon) = 1. \tag{2.15}$$

Then,

$$2x = \sigma(X(\varepsilon)) \pm \sqrt{\sigma^2(X(\varepsilon)) - 4}$$

and the only singular values $\varepsilon = \varepsilon_0$ are the points at which

$$\Delta(\varepsilon) = \sigma^2(X(\varepsilon)) - 4 = 0. \tag{2.16}$$

We see from (2.15) that, in this case, the arguments of x_1 and x_2 are always of opposite sign. Therefore, in this case, the singular values of ε_0 are those points at which $x_1 = x_2$ and the arguments of x_1 and x_2 are nonzero. In particular, those points at which

$$\sigma(X(\varepsilon)) = -2, \tag{2.17}$$

may be singular values of ε since, at such points, $x_1 = x_2 = -1$ and their arguments are π and $-\pi$.

However, the roots $\varepsilon = \varepsilon_1$ of Eq. (2.17) are not necessarily singular points for the series (2.2) since, in a neighborhood of the point $\varepsilon = \varepsilon_1$, an arbitrary irregular value of ln $X(\varepsilon)$ can be expanded in a series of positive powers of $\varepsilon - \varepsilon_1$ if, for example, for $\varepsilon = \varepsilon_1$ (where ($\Delta^{(k)}(\varepsilon)$ is the kth derivative), we have

$$\Delta(\varepsilon_1) = 0 \text{ and } \Delta^{(k)}(\varepsilon_1) = 0 \ (k = 1, 2, \ldots, 2m-1), \ \Delta^{(2m)}(\varepsilon_1) \neq 0,$$

where m is a positive integer. In this case, $x_1(\varepsilon_1) = x_2(\varepsilon_1)$ but $x_1(\varepsilon)$ and $x_2(\varepsilon)$ are holomorphic in a neighborhood of the point $\varepsilon = \varepsilon_1$. Therefore, an arbitrary irregular value of ln $X(\varepsilon)$ can be represented in a neighborhood of the point $\varepsilon = \varepsilon_1$ in the form of a series of positive powers of $\varepsilon - \varepsilon_1$.

Suppose, for example, that we have $Y = \ln X(\varepsilon)$, where

$$X(\varepsilon) = \begin{Vmatrix} \varepsilon + (\varepsilon^2 - 1) & (\varepsilon^2 - 1) \\ \varepsilon + 1 & \varepsilon \end{Vmatrix}, \quad D(X(\varepsilon)) = 1.$$

Here, the characteristic numbers $x_1(\varepsilon)$ and $x_2(\varepsilon)$ are

$$x_1 = \varepsilon + \frac{(\varepsilon^2 - 1)}{2} + \frac{1}{2}\sqrt{(\varepsilon + 3)(\varepsilon - 1)(\varepsilon + 1)^2},$$

$$x_2 = \varepsilon + \frac{(\varepsilon^2 - 1)}{2} - \frac{1}{2}\sqrt{(\varepsilon + 3)(\varepsilon - 1)(\varepsilon + 1)^2}.$$

We have $x_1 = x_2$ if $\varepsilon = -3, -1$, or 1. In a neighborhood of the point $\varepsilon = -1$, the functions $x_1(\varepsilon)$ and $x_2(\varepsilon)$ are holomorphic. Here, if we take a regular value of ln $X(\varepsilon)$ in a neighborhood of the point $\varepsilon = 1$, we obtain the series

$$Y = \ln X(\varepsilon) = \sum_{k=0}^{\infty} X_k \varepsilon^k. \tag{2.18}$$

which converges in the region $|\varepsilon| < 3$ although this value of $\ln X(\varepsilon)$ is irregular in a neighborhood of the point $\varepsilon = -1$ because, as we go from the point $\varepsilon = 1$ along the real ε-axis to the point $\varepsilon = -1$, we obtain $x_1 = x_2 = -1$ with the distinct arguments π and $-\pi$ since x_1 approaches the point $x_1 = -1$ while remaining in the upper half-plane and x_2 in the lower. We can see this by performing the calculation.

Consider

$$\ln x_1(\varepsilon) = \ln\left(\varepsilon + \frac{\varepsilon^2 - 1}{2} + \frac{1}{2}\sqrt{(\varepsilon+3)(\varepsilon-1)(\varepsilon+1)^2}\right),$$

$$\ln x_2(\varepsilon) = \ln\left(\varepsilon + \frac{\varepsilon^2 - 1}{2} - \frac{1}{2}\sqrt{(\varepsilon+3)(\varepsilon-1)(\varepsilon+1)^2}\right).$$

Here, if we take the principal values of the logarithm, we obtain

$$\ln x_1 - \ln x_2 = 2\ln x_1, \quad \ln x_1 = -\ln x_2.$$

Therefore, from (2.12), we have

$$Y = X(\varepsilon)\frac{2\ln x_1}{x_1 - x_2} - \frac{x_1 + x_2}{x_1 - x_2}\ln x_1.$$

If we denote the elements of the matrix Y by Y_{kl}, we obtain

$$x_1 - x_2 = \sqrt{(\varepsilon+3)(\varepsilon-1)(\varepsilon+1)^2}, \quad x_1 + x_2 = \varepsilon^2 + 2\varepsilon - 1,$$

$$Y_{11} = \frac{2(\varepsilon^2 + \varepsilon - 1)}{x_1 - x_2}\ln x_1 - \frac{x_1 + x_2}{x_1 - x_2}\ln x_1 =$$

$$= \frac{\varepsilon^2 - 1}{x_1 - x_2}\ln x_1,$$

$$Y_{22} = \frac{2\varepsilon \ln x_1}{x_1 - x_2} - \frac{x_1 + x_2}{x_1 - x_2}\ln x_1 = \frac{(1 - \varepsilon^2)}{x_1 - x_2}\ln x_1,$$

$$Y_{12} = \frac{2(\varepsilon^2 - 1)}{x_1 - x_2}\ln x_1, \qquad Y_{21} = \frac{2(\varepsilon + 1)}{x_1 - x_2}\ln x_1,$$

or

$$Y_{11} = \frac{\sqrt{\varepsilon - 1}}{\sqrt{\varepsilon + 3}}\ln x_1, \quad Y_{22} = -\frac{\sqrt{\varepsilon - 1}}{\sqrt{\varepsilon + 3}}\ln x_1,$$

$$Y_{12} = 2\frac{\sqrt{\varepsilon - 1}}{\sqrt{\varepsilon + 3}}\ln x_1, \quad Y_{21} = \frac{2}{\sqrt{(\varepsilon + 3)(\varepsilon - 1)}}\ln x_1,$$

from which we see that all the elements of the matrix Y are holomorphic functions in the region $|\varepsilon| < 3$.

On the other hand, if we take a regular value of $Y = \ln X(\varepsilon)$ in a neighborhood of the point $\varepsilon = -3$, then $Y = \ln X(\varepsilon)$ can be represented in the form of a series

$$Y = \sum_{k=0}^{\infty} \beta_k (\varepsilon + 3)^k,$$

which converges in the region $|\varepsilon + 3| < 4$ since the closest singular point is $\varepsilon = 1$ because, in accordance with Theorem 2.3, the matrix Y will again be holomorphic in a neighborhood of the point $\varepsilon = -1$.

Let us now consider that case of a second-order matrix in which, in the series (2.1), we have $X_0 = I$ and $D(X(\varepsilon)) = 1$. In this case, the characteristic numbers x_1 and x_2 of the matrix X can be found from the formula

$$2x = \sigma(X(\varepsilon)) \pm \sqrt{\sigma^2(X(\varepsilon)) - 4},$$

where $\sigma(X(0)) = 2$; that is, we have $x_2(0) = x_1(0) = 1$. If we take the principal value of $Y = \ln X(\varepsilon)$, we have the convergent series (2.2).

If the function $\sigma(X(\varepsilon))$ increases from 0 with increasing ε, there will be no singular points of the series (2.2) on the positive half of the ε-axis. If the function $\sigma(X(\varepsilon))$ does not vanish for real values of ε, there will be no singular points of the series (2.2) on the real ε-axis. This is true because the only possible singular points of $\varepsilon = \varepsilon_1$ are those points at which $\sigma(X(\varepsilon_1)) = 2$ or $\sigma(X(\varepsilon_1)) = -2$. If $\Delta(\varepsilon)$ remains nonnegative as ε varies along the real axis starting at $\varepsilon = 0$ when $\Delta(0) = 0$, $x_1(0) = x_2(0) = 1$, and the arguments of $x_1(0)$ and $x_2(0)$ are equal, then $x_1(\varepsilon)$ and $x_2(\varepsilon)$ remain on the real axis. Therefore, their arguments cannot differ. For $x_1(\varepsilon)$ to be equal to $x_2(\varepsilon)$ and for their arguments to become different, it is necessary that $x_1(\varepsilon) = x_2(\varepsilon) = -1$ when the arguments of $x_1(\varepsilon)$ and $x_2(\varepsilon)$ are equal to π and $-\pi$. This is possible only when $\sigma(X(\varepsilon)) = -2$.

Thus, the singular point $\varepsilon = \varepsilon_1$ of the series (2.2) that is closest to $\varepsilon = 0$ can only be a point at which $\sigma(X(\varepsilon_1)) = -2$. From this it follows that, if $\sigma(X(\varepsilon))$ does not vanish on the real ε-axis, the series (2.2) cannot have a singular point on it. For example, this will be the case if the elements x_{12} and x_{21} of the matrix $X(\varepsilon)$ are of the same sign. To see this, note that, if $\sigma(X(\varepsilon)) = x_{11} + x_{22} = 0$, we have (since $D(X(\varepsilon)) = 1$ and hence $x_{11}x_{22} = x_{12}x_{21} + 1$)

$$-x_{11}^2 = x_{21}x_{12} + 1$$

so that x_{11} is imaginary, which is impossible for real $X(\varepsilon)$.

Let us exhibit a region of convergence of a series (2.2) on the basis of bounds for the elements of the matrix $X(\varepsilon)$ in the case in which X_0 in the series (2.1) is I. Since $Y = \ln X(\varepsilon)$ (the principal value) can be represented in the form

$$Y = \sum_{k=0}^{\infty} \frac{(-1)^k}{k+1} (X(\varepsilon) - I)^k. \tag{2.19}$$

it is clear that the series (2.19) converges in the case in which the maximum absolute value of the characteristic number of the matrix $(X(\varepsilon)-I$ is less than $1/n$. If this inequality is satisfied, the series (2.2) converges. A bound for the maximum absolute value of the characteristic numbers of a matrix A with positive elements appears, for example, in [1, 3]. Sometimes, a bound for the maximum absolute value $x(\varepsilon)$ of the characteristic numbers of a matrix $X(\varepsilon)$ can be obtained by using a series of the form $I+\sum_{k=1}^{\infty} A_k \varepsilon^k$ that majorizes the series (2.1). We shall use this later (see Sect. 10).

In Section 34 we shall also exhibit cases in which $\Delta(\varepsilon) \neq 0$ in the entire region in question (except possibly at the point $\varepsilon = 0$). Consequently, the series (2.2) will converge in the same region* as does the series (2.1).

3. Functions of Several Matrices and of a Countable Set of Matrices

Lappo-Danilevskiy first [1] began to examine functions of m matrices $X_1, \ldots, X_m$ of order n and constructed a theory of such functions. Specifically, he studied functions of matrices $X_1, \ldots, X_m$

$$F(X_1, \ldots, X_m) = \alpha_0 + \sum_{\nu=1}^{\infty} \sum_{j_1 \ldots j_\nu}^{1 \ldots m} X_{j_1} \ldots X_{j_\nu} \alpha_{j_1 \ldots j_\nu}, \tag{3.1}$$

where the α are complex numbers and $j_1 \ldots j_\nu$ range independently of each other over all possible values from 1 to m. Lappo-Danilevskiy called the series (3.1) a "series of compositions." Following Lappo-Danilevskiy, let us write the series (3.1) in the form

$$F(X_1, \ldots, X_m) = \sum_{\nu=0}^{\infty} [X\alpha]_\nu, \tag{3.2}$$

where

$$[X\alpha]_\nu = \sum_{j_1 \ldots j_\nu}^{1, 2 \ldots m} X_{j_1} \ldots X_{j_\nu} \alpha_{j_1 \ldots j_\nu}, \quad [X\alpha]_0 = \alpha_0. \tag{3.3}$$

It is easy to see that the series (3.1) is a set of a particular form of n^2 series of mn^2 independent variable elements of the matrices $X_1, \ldots, X_m$.

*All cases in which ρ_1 and ρ_2 remain complex for Eq. (33.1).

Let $|X|$ denote the matrix whose elements are equal to the absolute value of the corresponding elements of the matrix X. We indicate that none of the elements of the matrix $|X|$ exceed $\rho > 0$, where $\|\rho\|$ is a matrix whose elements are all equal to ρ, by writing

$$|X| \leqslant \|\rho\|. \tag{3.4}$$

If the series (3.1) converges in the region

$$|X_j| < \|\rho_i\|, \tag{3.5}$$

then the function $F(X_1, \ldots, X_m)$ is said to be holomorphic in a neighborhood of zero matrices. If $|\alpha_{j_1 \ldots j_\nu}| < \alpha^{(\nu)}$ in the series (3.1) and if the series $\sum_{\nu=0}^{\infty} \alpha^{(\nu)} \xi^{\nu}$, where ξ is a complex number, converges in the region $|\xi| < n\rho$, then the series (3.1) converges in the region

$$|X_1| + \ldots + |X_m| < \|\rho\| \tag{3.6}$$

and is said to be uniformly holomorphic in the region (3.6).

If the series (3.1) converges for arbitrary finite matrices $X_1, \ldots, X_m$, it is called an *entire series*. As Lappo-Danilevskiy showed, the usual theorem on the uniqueness of the expansion of a function in a power series does not hold for functions of several matrices. We do, however, have the following valid assertion. *If a function of several matrices $F(X_1, \ldots, X_m)$ can be represented in the form (3.1) for arbitrary arrangement of the matrices $X_1, \ldots, X_m$, then the coefficients $\alpha_{j_1 \ldots j_\nu}$ are uniquely determined.* In other words, *if*

$$\sum_{\nu=0}^{\infty} [X\alpha]_\nu = \sum_{\nu=0}^{\infty} [X\beta]_\nu$$

for arbitrary arrangement of the matrices $X_1, \ldots, X_m$, then $\alpha_{j_1 \ldots j_\nu} = \beta_{j_1 \ldots j_\nu}$. Let us denote the infinite sequence of matrices $X_1, X_2, \ldots$, by X. If the series $\sum_{p=1}^{\infty} |X_p|$ converges, then the sequence of matrices X is said to be *regular*.

Let us denote by α_0, $\alpha_{p_1 \ldots p_\nu}$ (for $\nu = 1, 2, \ldots$) certain complex numbers. If the series

$$\sum_{p_1=1}^{\infty} \cdots \sum_{p_\nu=1}^{\infty} |X_{p_1} \ldots X_{p_\nu}| \, |\alpha_{p_1 \ldots p_\nu}|$$

converges, let us consider the series

$$\sum_{p_1=1}^{\infty}\cdots\sum_{p_\nu=1}^{\infty} X_{p_1}\ldots X_{p_\nu}\alpha_{p_1\ldots p_\nu} = [X\alpha]_\nu\,,\quad [X\alpha]_0 = \alpha_0\,. \tag{3.7}$$

If $|\alpha_{p_1\ldots p_\nu}| < \alpha^{(\nu)}$, then the series (3.7) converges for an arbitrary regular sequence of matrices since, obviously,

$$\sum_{p_1=1}^{\infty}\cdots\sum_{p_\nu=1}^{\infty} X_{p_1}\ldots X_{p_\nu} = \left[\sum_{p=1}^{\infty} X_p\right]^\nu$$

and

$$\sum_{p_1=1}^{\infty}\cdots\sum_{p_\nu=1}^{\infty} |X_{p_1}\ldots X_{p_\nu}|\,|\alpha_{p_1\ldots p_\nu}| \leqslant \sum_{p_1=1}^{\infty}\cdots\sum_{p_\nu=1}^{\infty} |X_{p_1}|\ldots|X_{p_\nu}|\,\alpha^{(\nu)} =$$

$$= \alpha^{(\nu)}\left[\sum_{p=1}^{\infty}|X_p|\right]^\nu .$$

Let us now consider a series for a regular sequence of matrices

$$F(X) = \sum_{\nu=0}^{\infty}[X\alpha]_\nu = \sum_{\nu=0}^{\infty}\left(\sum_{p_1=1}^{\infty}\cdots\sum_{p_\nu=1}^{\infty} X_{p_1}\ldots X_{p_\nu}\alpha_{p_1\ldots p_\nu}\right), \tag{3.8}$$

assuming that $|\alpha_{p_1\ldots p_\nu}| < \alpha^{(\nu)}$. If this series converges for every set of matrices $X_1, X_2, \ldots$ satisfying the condition

$$\sum_{p=1}^{\infty}|X_p| < \|\rho\|, \tag{3.9}$$

we shall say that the series (3.8) converges in a neighborhood of zero matrices X. On the other hand, if the series (3.8) converges for every positive ρ when condition (3.9) is satisfied, then the series (3.8) is said to be an *entire series*. We note that if the series

$$f(\xi) = \sum_{\nu=1}^{\infty}\alpha^{(\nu)}\xi^\nu$$

has radius of convergence $n\rho$, then the series (3.8) converges in the region (3.9). If the equation

$$\sum_{\nu=0}^{\infty}[X\alpha]_{\nu}=\sum_{\nu=0}^{\infty}[X\beta]_{\nu}$$

holds for a regular sequence of matrices X of arbitrary order, then $\alpha_{p_1 \ldots p_\nu}=\beta_{p_1 \ldots p_\nu}$.

4. Classes of Systems of Linear Differential Equations That Can Be Integrated in Closed Form

Suppose that the elements $x_{kl}(t)$ of a matrix X are functions of t. Let us write this matrix in the form

$$X=\|x_{kl}(t)\|.$$

Then, we define the derivative of the matrix X with respect to t as that matrix whose elements are the derivatives of the corresponding elements of the matrix X:

$$\frac{dX}{dt}=\left\|\frac{dx_{kl}(t)}{dt}\right\|.$$

If we have matrices X and Y that are functions of t, then

$$\frac{d(XY)}{dt}=\frac{dX}{dt}Y+X\frac{dY}{dt}.$$

If we have m matrices $X_1(t), \ldots, X_m(t)$, then

$$\frac{d(X_1(t)\ldots X_m(t))}{dt}=\sum_{k=1}^{m}X_1X_2\ldots X_{k-1}\frac{dX_k}{dt}X_{k+1}\ldots X_m.$$

Suppose that the matrices

$$\frac{dX_k}{dt}\quad(k=1, \ldots, m)$$

commute with the matrices

$$X_1, X_2, \ldots, X_{k-1}, X_{k+1}, \ldots, X_m.$$

Then,

$$\frac{d(X_1\ldots X_m)}{dt}=\sum_{k=1}^{m}X_1X_2\ldots X_{k-1}X_{k+1}\ldots X_m\frac{dX_k}{dt}.$$

Consequently, if the matrix $X(t)$ commutes with its derivative $\frac{dX}{dt}$, then

$$\frac{de^X}{dt} = e^X \frac{dX}{dt} = \frac{dX}{dt} e^X.$$

This follows immediately from the definition of the function e^X on the basis of (1.2).

By definition, we also have

$$\int X dt = \| \int x_{kl}(t)\, dt \|.$$

Consider the system of linear differential equations

$$\begin{aligned} \frac{dx_1}{dt} &= x_1 P_{11}(t) + \ldots + x_n P_{n1}(t), \\ &\cdots\cdots\cdots\cdots \\ \frac{dx_n}{dt} &= x_1 P_{1n}(t) + \ldots + x_n P_{nn}(t). \end{aligned} \tag{4.1}$$

This system has n linearly independent solutions

$$x_{k1}, \ldots, x_{kn} \ (k = 1, \ldots, n), \tag{4.2}$$

which can be written in the form of a matrix

$$X = \left\| \begin{matrix} x_{11}, \ldots, x_{1n} \\ \cdots \\ x_{n1}, \ldots, x_{nn} \end{matrix} \right\| \tag{4.3}$$

in which each element x_{kl} is the lth function of the kth solution of the system (4.1).

Consider also the coefficient matrix of the system (4.1)

$$P(t) = \left\| \begin{matrix} P_{11}(t), \ldots, P_{1n}(t) \\ \cdots\cdots \\ P_{n1}(t), \ldots, P_{nn}(t) \end{matrix} \right\|. \tag{4.4}$$

If we substitute successively the solutions of (4.2) into Eq. (4.1), we obtain n^2 equations, which may be written in matrix form as follows:

$$\frac{dX}{dt} = XP. \tag{4.5}$$

The matrix X is called an *integral matrix*. Since the matrix $X(t)$ is composed of linearly independent solutions of the system (4.1), it follows that $D(X(t)) \neq 0$ in the region of continuity of the matrix $P(t)$. We shall say that an integral matrix $X(t)$ that is equal to the unit matrix I at $t=0$ (that is, $X(0)=I$)is normalized at the point $t=0$. If $X(t)$ is a normalized integral matrix at the point $t=0$, then every other integral matrix $X_1(t)$ can be expressed in the form $X_1(t) = AX(t)$, where A is a constant matrix.

Let us note certain cases in which the integral matrix X can be found in closed form.

Let us suppose that the matrix $P(t)$ in the matrix equation (4.5) possesses the property that

$$P(t) \int P(t)\,dt = \int P(t)\,dt \cdot P(t), \tag{4.6}$$

that is, let us suppose that the matrix $P(t)$ commutes* with its integral. Then the integral matrix X that is normed at the point $t=0$ can be obtained in the form [1]

$$X = \exp \int_0^t P dt, \tag{4.7}$$

since, on the basis of (4.6),

$$\frac{dX}{dt} = \exp \int_0^t P dt \cdot P = XP.$$

In particular, if

$$P = A\varphi(t), \tag{4.8}$$

where A is a constant matrix and $\varphi(t)$ is a numerical function of t, then, in accordance with (4.7), we obtain

$$X = \exp A \int_0^t \varphi(t)\,dt. \tag{4.9}$$

Suppose now that $\varphi(t) = 1$ and that the characteristic numbers $\lambda_1, \ldots, \lambda_n$ of the matrix A are distinct. Then, in accordance with Lagrange's formula, we obtain from (4.9)

$$X = \sum_{k=1}^{n} \frac{(A-\lambda_1)\ldots(A-\lambda_{k-1})(A-\lambda_{k+1})\ldots(A-\lambda_n)}{(\lambda_k-\lambda_1)\ldots(\lambda_k-\lambda_{k-1})(\lambda_k-\lambda_{k+1})\ldots(\lambda_k-\lambda_n)} e^{\lambda_k t}. \tag{4.10}$$

*A thorough study of the structure of the matrices $P(t)$ possessing the property (4.6) is made in the article by Bogdanov and Chebotarev [15]. This study is closely connected with the work of V. V. Morozov, in which a study is made of matrices possessing the property that $P(t_1)P(t_2) = P(t_2)P(t_1)$. Reference [15] includes a bibliography on matrices possessing the property (4.6). A special case of (4.6) is studied by V. Amato [16]. Linear systems that can be integrated in finite form were also studied in [17-19].

If we write X in the form

$$X = \varphi_{n-1} A^{n-1} + \varphi_{n-2} A^{n-2} + \ldots + \varphi_1 A + \varphi_0,$$

then the φ_k (for $k=0, 1, \ldots, n-1$) will be symmetric functions* of $\lambda_1, \ldots, \lambda_n$. This enables us to obtain the integral matrix X without finding the characteristic numbers of the matrix A.

We note that the second-order matrices $P(t)$ possessing the property (4.6) are of the form

$$P = \left\| \begin{matrix} \varphi_1(t) + b_1 \varphi_2(t) & \varphi_2(t) \\ b_2 \varphi_2(t) & \varphi_1(t) \end{matrix} \right\|, \tag{4.11}$$

where $\varphi_1(t)$ and $\varphi_2(t)$ are numerical functions of t and where b_1 and b_2 are constants.**

Thus, when $P(t)$ in the matrix equation (4.5) is of the form (4.11), we have X in the form

$$X = \exp \left\| \begin{matrix} \bar{\varphi}_1 + b_1 \bar{\varphi}_2 & \bar{\varphi}_2 \\ b_1 \bar{\varphi}_2 & \bar{\varphi}_1 \end{matrix} \right\|, \tag{4.12}$$

where $\bar{\varphi}_k = \int\limits_0^t \varphi_k(t)\, dt$. If

$$P = \sum_{k=1}^{m} A_k \varphi_k(t), \tag{4.13}$$

where A_k (for $k=1, \ldots, m$) are constant commutative matrices and the $\varphi_k(t)$ are numerical functions, then condition (4.6) is obviously satisfied.

Fedorov [20] obtained the following interesting generalization of Lappo-Danilevskiy's system, for which we have a solution analogous to (4.7). Suppose that the matrix $P(t)$ in Eq. (4.5) possesses the property

$$L \cdot [P(t) B^n] = 0 \quad (n = 1, 2, \ldots), \tag{4.14}$$

where

$$\frac{dB}{dt} = P(t), \quad MN - NM = [MN]$$

and L is a constant vector, that is, a matrix all of the elements of which are zero except those in one row and the elements in that row are independent of t. Then,

*This is obvious from (2.4). We note that Shtokalo [10] obtained a solution to (4.10) in the form $X = \frac{1}{2\pi i} \int\limits_{(c)} (pE - A)^{-1} e^{pt}\, dp$, where c is a closed contour encircling all the characteristic numbers of the matrix A.

**Here, we do not include the case of $P_{12} = P_{21} = 0$ and $P_{11} \neq P_{22}$. The elements of the matrix (4.11) satisfy the equations $P_{11} - P_{22} = b_1 P_{12}$, $P_{21} = b_2 P_{12}$.

$$X = L \exp B \tag{4.15}$$

is a solution of Eq. (4.5).

To see this, note that, on the basis of (4.14), we have

$$LPB^n = LB^nP \tag{4.16}$$

and

$$L\underbrace{B \dots B}_{m} P \underbrace{B \dots B}_{n} = LPB^{m+n} = LB^{m+n} P.$$

Therefore, since

$$\frac{d(\exp B)}{dt} = \sum_{n=0}^{\infty} \frac{1}{n!} \sum_{k=1}^{n} B^{n-k} P B^{k-1}$$

it follows that

$$\frac{d(L \cdot \exp B)}{dt} = L \cdot \exp B \cdot P \quad \text{or} \quad \frac{dX}{dt} = XP,$$

where X is given by Eq. (4.15).

From (4.16), we have $LPB^n = LB^{n-1} PB$. Therefore,

$$L[PB^n] = LB^{n-1}[PB]. \tag{4.17}$$

Since

$$LB^k[PB] = 0 \quad (k = 1, \dots, m), \tag{4.18}$$

where m is the degree of the minimum polynomial*

$$B^m + \sigma_1 B^{m-1} + \sigma_2 B^{m-2} + \dots + \sigma_{m-1} B + \sigma_m = 0, \tag{4.19}$$

satisfied by the matrix B (see [21] and also Sect. 1 of the present book), it follows that Eq. (4.18) holds for $k > m$. Thus, we have obtained the

Theorem (Fedorov). *If the matrix $P(t)$ in (4.5) is such that there exists a constant vector L satisfying Eqs. (4.18), then Eq. (4.5) has a solution of the form (4.15).*

If the vector L has ν arbitrary parameters, we obtain from (4.5) ν linearly independent solutions. From this it follows that the order of the system (4.5) is depressed by ν units.

*The σ_k in (4.19) are scalar functions of the characteristic numbers of the matrix B.

If the matrix $P(t)$ is of second order and if there exists a constant vector L satisfying the equation $L[PB]=0$, then the system (4.5) can be integrated.

5. Other Systems of Linear Differential Equations That Are Integrable in Closed Form

We note another case in which the solution of the system (4.5) can be obtained in closed form [22].

Suppose that we have a system of linear differential equations

$$\frac{dX}{dt} = X[U_1\varphi_1(t) + U_2\varphi_2(t)], \tag{5.1}$$

where $\varphi_1(t)$ and $\varphi_2(t)$ are continuous functions of t and where U_1 and U_2 are constant matrices possessing the property that

$$U_1(U_2U_1 - U_1U_2) - (U_2U_1 - U_1U_2)U_1 = 0. \tag{5.2}$$

We note that if the matrices U_1 and U_2 commute, then condition (5.2) is satisfied. But then condition (4.6) is also satisfied, so that this case reduces to that already examined.

Now, let us suppose that the matrix U_1, in addition to satisfying condition (5.2), possesses the property that

$$U_2U_1 - U_1U_2 = P(U_1), \tag{5.3}$$

where $P(U_1)$ is a polynomial in U_1 with numerical coefficients. If to every characteristic number of the matrix U_1 there corresponds only one elementary divisor, then condition (5.3) is satisfied. Under conditions (5.2) and (5.3), the integral matrix $X(t)$, normalized for $t=0$, is obtained in the form*

---

*Fedorov presented a more general case than the system (5.1), in which $X(t)$ is obtained in closed form [23]. Morozov [24] has found necessary and sufficient conditions for U_1 and U_2 under which we have (5.4). Salakhova and Chebotarev [25] have found necessary and sufficient conditions for the system

$$\frac{dY}{dt} = Y\{A(t) + B(t)\},\ A = \sum_{i=1}^{p} A_i\varphi_i(t),\ B(t) = \sum_{j=1}^{q} B_j\psi_j(t),$$

where A_i and B_j are constant matrices and

$$[A_i, A_k] = 0\ (i, k = 1, \dots, p),\ [B_j, B_k] = 0,\ (j, k = 1, \dots, q),$$

to have a solution of the form

$$Y = e^{M(t)}e^{D(t)},\ D(t) = \int_0^t B(t)\,dt \quad\text{and}\quad \left[M(t), \frac{dM}{dt}\right] = 0.$$

This condition reduces to satisfaction of the equation $[A(t), [B(t), A(t)]] = 0$ for arbitrary $\varphi_j(t)$ and $\psi_i(t)$.

$$X(t)=e^{\int\limits_0^t e^{U_2L_2(t)}U_1e^{-U_2L_2(t)}\varphi_1(t)\,dt}\,e^{U_2L_2(t)} \tag{5.4}$$

where

$$L_k(t)=\int\limits_0^t \varphi_k(t)\,dt \quad (k=1,\ 2). \tag{5.5}$$

Let U_1 and U_2 be two second-order matrices of the forms

$$U_1=\begin{Vmatrix} a & 0 \\ c & a \end{Vmatrix},\quad U_2=\begin{Vmatrix} b_1 & 0 \\ 0 & b_2 \end{Vmatrix}. \tag{5.6}$$

Then, conditions (5.2) and (5.3) are satisfied since to the characteristic number of the matrix U_1 there corresponds one elementary divisor. In this case, on the basis of (1.24), we have

$$e^{\pm U_2L_2(t)}=\begin{Vmatrix} e^{\pm b_1L_2(t)} & 0 \\ 0 & e^{\pm b_2L_2(t)} \end{Vmatrix}$$

and
$$e^{U_2L_2(t)}U_1e^{-U_2L_2(t)}=e^{U_2L_2(t)}\left(\begin{Vmatrix} 0 & 0 \\ c & 0 \end{Vmatrix}+a\mathrm{I}\right)e^{-U_2L_2(t)}=$$

$$=\begin{Vmatrix} 0 & 0 \\ ce^{(b_2-b_1)L_2(t)} & 0 \end{Vmatrix}+a\mathrm{I}.$$

Consequently, Eq. (5.4) can be written in the form

$$X(t)=e^{\begin{Vmatrix} 0 & 0 \\ c\int\limits_0^t e^{(b_2-b_1)L_2(t)}\varphi_1(t)\,dt & 0 \end{Vmatrix}}\,e^{aL_1(t)}\,e^{U_2L_3(t)}$$

so that, on the basis of formulas (1.24), we finally have

$$X(t)=e^{aL_1(t)}\begin{Vmatrix} e^{b_1L_2(t)} & 0 \\ e^{b_1L_2(t)}c\int\limits_0^t e^{(b_2-b_1)L_2(t)}\varphi_1(t)\,dt & e^{b_2L_2(t)} \end{Vmatrix}. \tag{5.7}$$

From this we obtain the sum of the diagonal elements and the determinant of the matrix $X(t)$ in the form

$$\sigma(X(t)) = e^{aL_1(t)}\left[e^{b_1L_2(t)} + e^{b_2L_2(t)}\right], \tag{5.8}$$

$$D(X(t)) = e^{2aL_1(t)}\, e^{(b_1+b_2)L_2(t)}. \tag{5.9}$$

We shall have occasion to use these formulas in what follows. We have considered the case of the system (5.1) in which the elements of the second-order matrices U_1 and U_2 in the upper right-hand corner are equal to 0.

We have already mentioned the special case of condition (5.2) in which the matrices U_1 and U_2 commute. In this case, the integral matrix of the system (5.1) can be written in the form

$$X(t) = e^{U_1\int_0^t \varphi_1(t)\,dt + U_2\int_0^t \varphi_2(t)\,dt}$$

The general case, in which condition (5.2) is satisfied but the second-order matrices U_1 and U_2 do not commute and do not simultaneously have a zero element on the diagonal, can be written in the form

$$U_1 = \begin{Vmatrix} a_1 & b_1 \\ c_1 & d_1 \end{Vmatrix}, \quad U_2 = \begin{Vmatrix} a_2 & b_2 \\ c_2 & a_2 \end{Vmatrix} \tag{5.10}$$

where the elements a, b, c, and d are related by

$$c_1b_2 + b_1c_2 = 0, \quad 4c_1^2b_2 - c_2(a_1 - d_1)^2 = 0.$$

Consequently, the general form of such matrices can be written

$$U_1 = \begin{Vmatrix} a+2cm & -cm^2 \\ c & a \end{Vmatrix}, \quad U_2 = \begin{Vmatrix} b & m^2n \\ n & b \end{Vmatrix} \tag{5.11}$$

The characteristic numbers of the matrix U_2 are of the form

$$\lambda_1 = b + mn, \quad \lambda_2 = b - mn \tag{5.12}$$

and those of the matrix U_1 are of the form

$$\xi_1 = a + cm, \quad \xi_2 = a + cm. \tag{5.13}$$

We may write

$$U_2 = A^{-1}\begin{Vmatrix} b+mn & 0 \\ 0 & b-mn \end{Vmatrix}A, \quad A = \begin{Vmatrix} 1 & m \\ 1 & -m \end{Vmatrix}. \tag{5.14}$$

From formula (1.3) we have

Therefore,

$$e^{U_2L_2(t)}U_1e^{-U_2L_2(t)} =$$

$$= A^{-1}e^{\begin{Vmatrix} b+mn & 0 \\ 0 & b-mn \end{Vmatrix} L_2(t)} AU_1A^{-1}e^{-\begin{Vmatrix} b+mn & 0 \\ 0 & b-mn \end{Vmatrix} L_2(t)} A =$$

$$= A^{-1}\begin{Vmatrix} a+cm & 2cme^{2mnL_2(t)} \\ 0 & a+cm \end{Vmatrix} A.$$

This formula enables us to write the solution of (5.4) in the form

$$X(t) = e^{(a+cm)L_1(t)+bL_2(t)} A^{-1}e^{\begin{Vmatrix} 0 & 2cm\int\limits_0^t e^{2mnL_2(t)}\varphi_1(t)dt \\ 0 & 0 \end{Vmatrix}} \times e^{\begin{Vmatrix} mn & 0 \\ 0 & -mn \end{Vmatrix} L_2(t)} A.$$

On the basis of formulas (1.24), we can obtain

$$X(t) = e^{(a+cm)L_1(t)+bL_2(t)} \times$$

$$\times A^{-1}\begin{Vmatrix} e^{mnL_2(t)} & 2cme^{-mnL_2(t)}\int\limits_0^t e^{2mnL_2(t)}\varphi_1(t)\,dt \\ 0 & e^{-mnL_2(t)} \end{Vmatrix} A. \tag{5.15}$$

From this formula, we obtain

$$\sigma(X(t)) = e^{(a+cm)L_1(t)+(b+mn)L_2(t)} + e^{(a+cm)L_1(t)+(b-mn)L_2(t)} \tag{5.16}$$

and

$$D(X(t)) = e^{2(a+cm)L_1(t)+2bL_2(t)} \tag{5.17}$$

6. The Construction of Solutions of Certain Linear Systems of Differential Equations in the Form of a Series of Several Matrices (of a Series of Compositions)

Linear systems of differential equations possess the distinctive property that their general solution can be expressed in the form of certain series that converge uniformly in every closed interval in which the coefficients of the system are continuous.

Suppose that the matrix $P(t)$ in Eq. (4.5) is continuous in the interval $0 \leqslant t \leqslant p$. Then, we obtain the matrix $X(t)$ that is normalized at the point $t=0$ in the form

$$X = \sum_{k=0}^{\infty} X_k(t), \quad X_0(t) = \mathrm{I}, \tag{6.1}$$

where

$$X_k(t) = \int_0^t X_{k-1}(t)\,P(t)\,dt, \tag{6.2}$$

and the series (6.1) converges uniformly in the interval $0 \leqslant t \leqslant p$ since it is majorized by the series

$$Y = e^{Mt}, \tag{6.3}$$

where M is a constant matrix the elements of which are positive numbers equal to the maxima of the absolute values of the corresponding elements of the matrix $P(t)$ (that is, $|P(t)| \leqslant M$). Thus, we have a bound for the speed of convergence of the series (6.1).

To prove this assertion, we need to satisfy the equation

$$\frac{dX}{dt} = XP\lambda \tag{6.4}$$

(where λ is a parameter) formally with the series

$$X = \sum_{k=0}^{\infty} X_k(t)\,\lambda^k, \quad X_0(t) = \mathrm{I}. \tag{6.5}$$

To determine the coefficients $X_k(t)$, we obtain the recursion formula

$$X_k(t) = \int_0^t X_{k-1}(t)\,P(t)\,dt. \tag{6.6}$$

From this, we obtain the inequalities

$$|X_k(t)| \leqslant \int_0^t |X_{k-1}(t)|\,M dt, \quad |X_k(t)| \leqslant M^k t^k \frac{1}{k!} \quad (t > 0). \tag{6.7}$$

Consequently, the series (6.5) is majorized by the series

$$J = \sum_{k=0}^{\infty} M^k \lambda^k t^k \frac{1}{k!},$$

that is,

$$\left|\sum_{k=0}^{\infty} X_k(t)\,\lambda^k\right| \leqslant \sum_{k=0}^{\infty} \frac{1}{k!} M^k \lambda^k t^k = e^{M\lambda t}.$$

It follows from this that the series (6.5) converges uniformly in the interval $0 \leqslant t \leqslant p$ for every value of λ including the value $\lambda = 1$. This proves the assertion.*

Let us suppose that

$$P(t) = \sum_{k=1}^{m} A_k \varphi_k(t), \tag{6.8}$$

where the A_k are constant matrices and the $\varphi_k(t)$ are numerical functions that are continuous in the interval $0 \leqslant t \leqslant p$. Then, in the series (6.1), we have obviously

$$X_k(t) = \sum_{j_1 \ldots j_k}^{1 \ldots m} A_{j_1} \ldots A_{j_k} \varphi_{j_1 \ldots j_k}(t). \tag{6.9}$$

Here,

$$\varphi_{j_1 \ldots j_k}(t) = \int_0^t \varphi_{j_1 \ldots j_{k-1}}(t) \varphi_{j_k}(t)\, dt. \tag{6.10}$$

This is obtained from formula (6.2).

Thus, in the case of (6.8), we have the integral matrix $X(t)$ normalized at the point $t = 0$ in the form of a series of compositions

$$X(t) = I + \sum_{k=1}^{\infty} \sum_{j_1 \ldots j_k}^{1 \ldots m} A_{j_1} \ldots A_{j_k} \varphi_{j_1 \ldots j_k}(t), \tag{6.11}$$

which converges for arbitrary finite values of the matrices $A_1, \ldots, A_m$ and of t in the interval $0 \leqslant t \leqslant p$.

We note now that the series (6.1) and (6.11) converge uniformly in the region D of the complex variable t if the matrix $P(t)$ is a continuous function of t in that (closed) region.

Consider now the system

$$\frac{dX}{dt} = X \sum_{k=0}^{\infty} P_k(t) \varepsilon^k, \tag{6.12}$$

where X and the $P_k(t)$ are nth-order matrices, where the series

$$P(t, \varepsilon) = \sum_{k=0}^{\infty} P_k(t) \varepsilon^k \tag{6.13}$$

converges for all $0 \leqslant t \leqslant b$ in the region $|\varepsilon| < r$, where the $P_k(t)$ are continuous in the interval $0 \leqslant t \leqslant b$, where $|P(t, \varepsilon)| \leqslant M$ (where in

*This assertion remains in force if we assume that $\int_0^t |P(t)|\, dt < \infty$. Here, the meaning of the constant M in (6.3) is modified.

turn M is a constant matrix with positive elements), and where $0 \leqslant \varepsilon \leqslant \varepsilon_1 < r$.

Theorem 6.1.* (Lyapunov). *An integral matrix X normalized at the point $t = 0$ can be represented in the form of a series*

$$X = \sum_{k=0}^{\infty} X_k(t)\varepsilon^k, \quad X_0(0) = I, \; X_k(0) = 0, \quad k \geqslant 1 \tag{6.14}$$

that converges for $|\varepsilon| < r$ for all values of t in the interval $0 \leqslant t \leqslant b$, where the $X_k(t)$ are continuous matrix functions of t in the interval $0 \leqslant t \leqslant b$ that are defined inductively by

$$\frac{dX_0(t)}{dt} = X_0(t)P_0(t), \quad \frac{dX_k}{dt} = X_kP_0 + + X_{k-1}P_1 + \ldots + X_0P_k, \tag{6.15}$$

or

$$X_k(t) = \int_0^t (X_{k-1}P_1 + \ldots + XP_k)_\tau X_0^{-1}(\tau)\, d\tau\, X_0(t). \tag{6.16}$$

Proof: Consider the auxiliary system**

$$\frac{dY}{dt} = YP(t, \varepsilon)\lambda, \tag{6.17}$$

where λ is a numerical parameter. We have

$$Y = \sum_{k=0}^{\infty} Y_k(t, \varepsilon)\lambda^k, \tag{6.18}$$

$$Y_k(t, \varepsilon) = \int_0^t Y_{k-1}(t, \varepsilon)P(t, \varepsilon)\, dt, \quad k \geqslant 1, \quad Y_0(t, \varepsilon) = I, \tag{6.19}$$

and the series (6.18) converges uniformly in the region $0 \leqslant t \leqslant b$, $|\varepsilon| \leqslant \varepsilon_1 < r$, $|\lambda| \leqslant R$, where ε_1 is an arbitrary positive number less than r.

To see that this is true, note that, since $|P(t, \varepsilon)| \leqslant M$, we have the series

$$Y = \exp(Mt\lambda) = \sum_{k=0}^{\infty} \frac{M^k t^k \lambda^k}{k!}$$

which majorizes the series (6.18). This Y is a solution of the equation

$$\frac{dY}{dt} = YM\lambda. \tag{6.20}$$

---

*See also [9], in which this theorem is formulated in a different way.

**Here, we follow Lyapunov [26].

If we set $\lambda = 1$ in (6.18), we obtain a solution of Eq. (6.12):

$$X = \sum_{k=0}^{\infty} Y_k(t, \varepsilon). \tag{6.21}$$

This series converges uniformly in the region $0 \leqslant t \leqslant b$, $|\varepsilon| \leqslant \varepsilon_1 < r$, and the matrices $Y_k(t, \varepsilon)$ are holomorphic in the region $|\varepsilon| < r$. From this it follows that (6.14) holds.

Remark 6.1. The series

$$\sum_{k=0}^{\infty} |P_k(t)| \varepsilon_1^k = \bar{P}_1(t) \quad 0 \leqslant t \leqslant b \tag{6.22}$$

converges for $0 < \varepsilon_1 < r$.

Let us suppose* that $|\bar{P}_1(t)| \leqslant \|1\| \varphi(t)$, where $\|1\|$ denotes a matrix every element of which is unity and $\varphi(t)$ is a scalar positive function** such that $\int_0^b \varphi(t)\,dt < \infty$. *Then, the series (6.14) converges uniformly in the interval* $0 \leqslant t \leqslant b$ *for* $|\varepsilon| < \varepsilon_1$. This is true because the series

$$\frac{\|1\| \varphi(t)}{1 - \dfrac{\varepsilon}{\varepsilon_1}} = \|1\| \varphi(t) \sum_{k=0}^{\infty} \left(\frac{\varepsilon}{\varepsilon_1}\right)^k$$

majorizes the series (6.13), that is,

$$|P_k(t)| \leqslant \frac{\|1\| \varphi(t)}{\varepsilon_1^k}.$$

The matrix

$$Y = \exp \frac{\|1\|}{1 - \dfrac{\varepsilon}{\varepsilon_1}} \int_0^t \varphi(t)\,dt = \sum_{k=0}^{\infty} Y_k(t) \varepsilon^k$$

is a solution of the equation

$$\frac{dY}{dt} = Y \frac{\|1\| \varphi(t)}{1 - \dfrac{\varepsilon}{\varepsilon_1}} \tag{6.23}$$

*Here we depart slightly from Lyapunov's line of reasoning [26].

**If $\int_0^b |\bar{P}_1(t)|\,dt < \infty$, then $|\bar{P}_1(t)| = \|1\| \varphi(t)$, where, for example, $\varphi(t) = \Sigma |p_{kl}(t)|$.

and also a majorant for the series (6.14). This last assertion follows from the fact that

$$|X_0(t)| \leqslant \exp \|1\| \int_0^t \varphi(t)\,dt,$$

since $|P_0(t)| \leqslant \|1\| \varphi(t)$ and, in accordance with (6.16), $|X_k(t)| \leqslant Y_k(t)$, because

$$|X_0^{-1}(\tau) X_0(t)| \leqslant \exp \|1\| \int_\tau^t \varphi(t)\,dt.$$

Here, the matrices

$$X_0^{-1}(\tau) \cdot X_0(t) \text{ and } \exp \|1\| \int_\tau^1 \varphi(t)\,dt$$

are solutions (normalized at the point $t = \tau$) of the first of Eqs. (6.15) and Eq. (6.23) for $\varepsilon = 0$, respectively. Therefore, the reasoning followed with regard to Eqs. (6.17) and (6.20) is applicable to them.

A somewhat different approach to these problems and other cases of the matrix $P(t, \varepsilon)$ are examined in [9] and [26, Chapter III].

7. Solution of the Poincaré–Lappo–Danilevskiy Problem

Now, we shall solve the Poincaré–Lappo–Danilevskiy problem in the analytic theory of linear systems of differential equations.

Afterwards, we shall show that the solution of this problem is closely connected with the theory of linear systems of differential equations with periodic coefficients.

Let us suppose that P in Eq. (4.5) is an analytic function of a complex variable z that is single-valued in a neighborhood of the point $z = a$. If $P(z)$ is a regular function at the point $z = a$ (that is, if all elements of the matrix $P(z)$ are regular functions at the point $z = a$)

$$P(z) = \sum_{k=0}^{\infty} P_k (z-a)^k, \tag{7.1}$$

where the P_k are matrices that are constant with respect to z, then, as we know, the integral matrix $X(z)$ with initial value B_0 at the point $z = a$ will also be holomorphic in a neighborhood of the point $z = a$; that is, we have

$$X(z) = \sum_{k=0}^{\infty} B_k (z - a)^k, \tag{7.2}$$

where the B_k are constant matrices and the series (7.2) converges for $|z - a| < r$. Here, r is the distance from the point a to the closest singular point of the matrix $P(z)$ [in other words, r is the distance from a to the closest singular point of the elements of the matrix $P(z)$]. This also follows directly from the reasoning followed above with regard to the uniform convergence of the series (6.1) in the region of continuity of the matrix $P(z)$. Here, the functions $X_k(z)$ will obviously be regular functions in the region of regularity of the function $P(z)$.

Now, let us assume that $P(z)$ has a single-valued isolated singularity at the point $z = a$; that is, at the point $z = a$, the matrix $P(z)$ has either a pole or an essential singularity, so that the matrix $P(z)$ can be expanded in a Laurent series in a neighborhood of the point $z = a$.

Suppose that $X(z)$ is an integral matrix of Eq. (4.5) with initial value X_0 at a point $z = z_0$ in a neighborhood of the point $z = a$. Let us assume that $D(X_0) \neq 0$. Then in a region of regularity of the matrix $P(z)$, we also have $D(X(z)) \neq 0$ according to a familiar property of a fundamental system of solutions of a linear system of differential equations. Let us continue $X(z)$ analytically along a curve L encircling the point $z = a$ and passing through $z = z_0$. The curve L does not pass through a singular point of the matrix $P(z)$ and does not encircle any singular points of $P(z)$ other than the point $z = a$. In general, when we complete a circuit around the singular point $z = a$, we obtain at the point z_0 a value $X(z_0) = \overline{X}$ different from X_0. Thus, when we make the circuit around $z = a$ remaining in a neighborhood of the point $z = z_0$, we obtain an integral matrix $\overline{X}(z)$ different from $X(z)$. But since $X(z)$ is made up of a fundamental system of solutions, the new integral matrix $\overline{X}(z)$ can be expressed in terms of $X(z)$ by means of the equation

$$\overline{X}(z) = V(a) X(z), \tag{7.3}$$

where $V(a)$ is a constant matrix defined by the equation

$$\overline{X}_0 = V(a) X_0, \quad V(a) = \overline{X}_0 X_0^{-1}. \tag{7.4}$$

Since $D(X(z)) \neq 0$ and since a fundamental system of solutions remains a fundamental system under arbitrary analytic continuations along a curve that does not pass through a singular point of the matrix $P(z)$, it follows that $D(\overline{X}(z)) \neq 0$.

The matrix $V(a)$ is called an integral transformation around the point $z = a$.

If $X_0 = I$, that is, if the integral matrix $X(z)$ is normalized at the point $z = z_0$, we shall denote the integral substitution by $V(a, z_0) = \overline{X}(z_0)$. Here, $\overline{X}(z)$ is the value of the integral matrix $X(z)$ at the point $z = z_0$ after encirclement of the point $z = a$.

We shall also assume that the matrix $X(z)$ is normalized at the point $z = z_0$.

Let us define W by

$$2\pi i W(a, z_0) = \ln V(a, z_0), \tag{7.5}$$

so that

$$\exp 2\pi i W(a, z_0) = V(a, z_0). \tag{7.6}$$

We introduce the function

$$N(z) = (z - a)^{-W} X(z) = e^{-W \ln(z-a)} X(z).$$

On the basis of (7.3), after we go around the point $z = a$ this function assumes the value

$$\overline{N}(z) = e^{-W \ln(z-a) - 2\pi i W} V(a, z_0) X(z) = N(z).$$

Thus, the function $N(z)$ is single-valued in a neighborhood of $z = a$. It follows from this that

$$X(z) = (z - a)^W N(z - a), \tag{7.7}$$

where $N(z - a)$ is a single-valued (matrix-valued) function in a neighborhood of $z = a$. The factor $(z - a)^W$ characterizes every multiple-valued singularity of the matrix $X(z)$ in a neighborhood of the point $z = a$ and $N(z - a)$ is a matrix that can be represented in a neighborhood of the point $z = a$ a in the form of a Laurent series. Following Lappo-Danilevskiy, we shall call W the exponential transformation in a neighborhood of the point $z = a$.

If the point $z = a$ is a first-order pole of the matrix $P(z)$, then $z = a$ is called a *regular singular point* of the systems (4.1) and (4.5).

From the analytic theory of linear differential equations, we know that, in this case, $N(z - a)$ may be assumed regular at the point $z = a$, that is,

$$N(z - a) = \sum_{k=0}^{\infty} N_k (z - a)^k,$$

where the N_k are constant matrices. If the characteristic numbers of the matrix $P_{-1} = (z - a) P(z)|_{z=a}$ do not differ from each other by integers, the representation of the solution in the form (7.7) is given in Lappo-Danilevskiy's book [1]. In the case in which some of the characteristic numbers of the matrix P_{-1} differ by an integer, the question of the construction of an integral matrix of the form (7.7) is studied in the works of Donskaya [27, 28].

Suppose that we have a system of differential equations of the form

$$\frac{dY}{dz} = Y \sum_{j=1}^{n} \frac{U_j}{z - a_j}, \tag{7.8}$$

where the U_j are constant matrices (with respect to z) and the a_j are simple poles of the coefficient matrix.

Lappo-Danilevskiy first gave a general representation for matrices W_j characterizing the multiple-valuedness of the integral matrix $Y(z)$ in a neighborhood of the corresponding points $z = a_j$. Specifically, he showed that, for the case of $Y(z_0) = I$, the matrices W_j can be represented in the form

$$\Delta(U_j) W_j = \sum_{\nu=1}^{\infty} \sum_{\varkappa=1}^{\nu} \sum_{j_1 \ldots j_\varkappa}^{1 \ldots m} U_{j_1} \ldots U_{j_\varkappa} \delta_{\nu-\varkappa}(U_j) Q_j(a_j \ldots a_{j_\varkappa} \mid z_0).$$

Here, the $\delta_k(U_j)$ are polynomials of the elements of the matrix U_j; $\Delta(U_j)$ is an entire function of the elements of the matrix U_j; the series of compositions of $U_1, \ldots, U_m$ converges for all finite values of the matrices $U_1, \ldots, U_m$; the quantities $Q_j(a_{j_1} \ldots a_{j_\varkappa} \mid z_0)$ are functions of $a_1, \ldots, a_m$, and z_0 as calculated from the recursion formulas. From this it is clear that the W_j are meromorphic functions of the matrices $U_1, \ldots, U_m$. Lappo-Danilevskiy not only gave an explicit and general representation for the functions W_j (the Poincaré problem*) but also characterized the W_j in an exhaustive way as functions of the matrices $U_1, \ldots, U_m$. We shall later be interested in constructing the exponential transformations also in the case in which the singular point $z = a$ of the matrix $P(z)$ is a pole of arbitrary order and hence the function $N(z - a)$, although single-valued in a neighborhood of $z = a$, is not regular at the point $z = a$. We note that, for the system (7.8), the matrices W_j are similar to the matrices U_j, (which, following Lappo-Danilevskiy, we shall call differential transformations); that is, $W_j = S_j U_j S_j^{-1}$, where S_j is a matrix such that $D(S_j) \neq 0$. In the case of a system

$$\frac{dX}{dt} = X \sum_{k=-1}^{\infty} U_k (z - a)^k \tag{7.9}$$

*H. Poincaré posed the problem of factoring out a multiple-valued factor of the matrix $X(z)$. Lappo-Danilevskiy solved the problem of the general representation of the matrix W in terms of the parameters of the matrix $P(t)$ and made a study of the nature of W as a function of these parameters.

(where the U_k are constant matrices), we also have $W = SU_{-1}S^{-1}$ (see [29]) in the representation $X(z)=(z-a)^W\overline{X}(z)$ (where $\overline{X}(z)$ is a single-valued matrix in a neighborhood of $z=a$ and W is a matrix that is constant with respect to z) if the characteristic numbers of the matrix U_{-1} do not differ by integral values. Donskaya [27, 28] has shown when this formula remains valid without satisfaction of the condition stated regarding the characteristic numbers of the matrix P_{-1}. The fact that we do not always have $W = SU_{-1}S^{-1}$ is pointed out in the book by Gantmakher [3], who proved Donskaya's result by a different procedure.

Consider a system of differential equations of the form

$$\frac{dY}{dz} = Y\sum_{\nu=-s}^{l} T_\nu z^\nu, \tag{7.10}$$

where the T_ν are constant matrices with respect to z and Y is an integral matrix which we assume to be normalized at the point $z=b$, that is,

$$Y(z/b)|_{z=b} = I.$$

In accordance with the above,

$$Y(z/b) = z^W\overline{Y}(z), \tag{7.11}$$

where W is a constant matrix with respect to z (though it is a function of the matrices $T_{-s}, \ldots, T_l$) and $\overline{Y}(z)$ is a single-valued matrix. We denote by V the integral transformation of the matrix (7.10) around the point $z=0$, so that $V = e^{2\pi iW}$.

From Lappo-Danilevskiy's theorem, we have

$$V = e^{2\pi iW} = I + \sum_{\nu=1}^{\infty}\ \sum_{p_1\ldots p_\nu=-s}^{l} T_{p_1}\ldots T_{p_\nu}\, b^{p_1+\ldots+p_\nu+\nu}\times$$

$$\times\sum_{\mu=0}^{\nu}\alpha^{*(0)}_{p_1\ldots p_\mu}\sum_{\varkappa=0}^{\nu-\mu}\alpha^{(\varkappa)}_{p_{\mu+1}\ldots p_\nu}(2\pi i)^\varkappa. \tag{7.12}$$

Here, under the second summation sign are all possible products of the ν matrices $T_{-s}, \ldots, T_l$, and the α are rational numbers defined by the recursion formulas

$$\alpha_{p_1}^{(0)} = \begin{cases} \dfrac{1}{p_1+1} & p_1+1 \neq 0 \\ \text{arbitrary} & p_1+1=0. \end{cases}$$

For example, we may set

$$\alpha_{p_1}^{(1)} = \begin{cases} 0 & p_1+1 \neq 0 \\ 1 & p_1+1=0, \end{cases}$$

$$(p_1 + \ldots + p_\nu + \nu)\, \alpha_{p_1 \ldots p_\nu}^{(\nu)} = 0,$$

$$(p_1 + \ldots + p_\nu + \nu)\, \alpha_{p_1 \ldots p_\nu}^{(\mu)} + (\mu+1)\, \alpha_{p_1 \ldots p_\nu}^{(\mu+1)} = \alpha_{p_1 \ldots p_{\nu-1}}^{(\mu)}$$

$$(\mu = \nu-1,\ \nu-2,\ \ldots,\ 1,\ 0).$$

In the case in which $p_1 + \ldots + p_\nu + \nu \neq 0$, we have

$$\alpha_{p_1 \ldots p_\nu}^{(\nu)} = 0, \quad \alpha_{p_1 \ldots p_\nu}^{(\mu)} = \frac{1}{p_1 + \ldots + p_\nu + \nu} \times$$

$$\times \left[\alpha_{p_1 \ldots p_{\nu-1}}^{(\mu)} - (\mu+1)\, \alpha_{p_1 \ldots p_\nu}^{(\mu+1)} \right].$$

If we now set successively $\mu = \nu - 1,\ \nu - 2,\ \ldots,\ 1,\ 0$, we obtain

$$\alpha_{p_1 \ldots p_\nu}^{(\nu-1)} = \frac{1}{p_1 + \ldots + p_\nu + \nu}\, \alpha_{p_1 \ldots p_{\nu-1}}^{(\nu-1)},$$

$$\alpha_{p_1 \ldots p_\nu}^{(\nu-2)} = \frac{1}{p_1 + \ldots + p_\nu + \nu} \times$$

$$\times \left[\alpha_{p_1 \ldots p_{\nu-1}}^{(\nu-2)} - \frac{\nu-1}{p_1 + \ldots + p_\nu + \nu}\, \alpha_{p_1 \ldots p_{\nu-1}}^{(\nu-1)} \right].$$

$$\alpha_{p_1 \ldots p_\nu}^{(\nu-3)} = \frac{1}{p_1 + \ldots + p_\nu + \nu} \left[\alpha_{p_1 \ldots p_{\nu-1}}^{(\nu-3)} \right.$$

$$\left. - \frac{\nu-2}{p_1 + \ldots + p_\nu + \nu}\, \alpha_{p_1 \ldots p_{\nu-1}}^{(\nu-2)} + \frac{(\nu-2)(\nu-1)}{(p_1 + \ldots + p_\nu + \nu)^2}\, \alpha_{p_1 \ldots p_{\nu-1}}^{(\nu-1)} \right]$$

and, in general,

$$\alpha^{(\mu)}_{p_1\ldots p_\nu}=\frac{1}{p_1+\ldots+p_\nu+\nu}\left[\alpha^{(\mu)}_{p_1\ldots p_{\nu-1}}-\right.$$

$$-\frac{\mu+1}{p_1+\ldots+p_\nu+\nu}\alpha^{(\mu+1)}_{p_1\ldots p_{\nu-1}}+\frac{(\mu+1)(\mu+2)}{(p_1+\ldots+p_\nu+\nu)^2}\times$$

$$\times\alpha^{(\mu+2)}_{p_1\ldots p_{\nu-1}}+\ldots+(-1)^{\nu-\mu-1}\times$$

$$\left.\times\frac{(\mu+1)(\mu+2)\ldots(\nu-1)}{(p_1+\ldots+p_\nu+\nu)^{\nu-\mu-1}}\alpha^{(\nu-1)}_{p_1\ldots p_{\nu-1}}\right].$$

In the case in which $p_1+\ldots+p_\nu+\nu=0$, we have

$$\alpha^{(\mu+1)}_{p_1\ldots p_\nu}=\frac{1}{\mu+1}\alpha^{(\mu)}_{p_1\ldots p_{\nu-1}}\quad(\mu=\nu-1,\ \nu-2,\ldots,\ 1,0)$$

and the $\alpha^{(0)}_{p_1\ldots p_\nu}$ are arbitrary. For the complete formulas see [1, p. 188].

The series* (7.12) for V is entire, that is, it converges for all finite values of the matrices $T_{-s},\ldots,T_l$ and its coefficients do not depend on the order of these matrices. Lappo-Danilevskiy [1] also expressed W in the form of a series of compositions of the matrices $T_{-s},\ldots,T_l$ that converge in a neighborhood of the zero values of $T_{-s},\ldots,T_l$. Thus, he solved Poincaré's problem of the representation of W as a function of $T_{-s},\ldots,T_l$ in the case of an irregular singular point $z=0$. The simplest expression for W is given in [5]. Specifically, W is represented in the form

$$W=\sum_{\nu=1}^{\infty}\sum_{p_1\ldots p_\nu=-s}^{\infty}T_{p_1}\ldots T_{p_\nu}\,b^{p_1+\ldots+p_\nu+\nu}\times$$

$$\times\sum_{\mu=0}^{\nu}\overset{*}{\alpha}{}^{(0)}_{p_1\ldots p_\mu}\alpha^{(1)}_{p_{\mu+1}\ldots p_\nu}. \qquad (7.13)$$

The general representation of W (that is, a representation that holds for all values of the matrices $T_{-s},\ldots,T_l$) and a study of the analytic properties of the functions $W=W(T_{-s},\ T_{-s+1},\ldots,\ T_0,T_1,\ldots)$ for the case in which $l=\infty$ appear in works by the author [29] and [5]. These investigations remain valid in general for a system of the form

*Lappo-Danilevskiy also constructed the corresponding expression for V in the case in which $l=\infty$ in Eqs. (7.10). This can be extended to the case in which $s=\infty$.

$$\frac{dY}{dz} = Y \sum_{\nu=-\infty}^{\infty} T_\nu z^\nu. \tag{7.14}$$

In the case of the system (7.8), the function W is, as we have seen, a meromorphic function of the matrices $U_1, \ldots, U_m$.

In the case of an irregular singular point $z=0$, W is an infinite-valued function of the parameters $(T_{-s}, \ldots, T_0, T_1, \ldots)$ of the system (7.14) [5]. For the case in which $T_{-s}, \ldots, T_l$ are second-order matrices, the general representation W is of the form [29]

$$W = \frac{\ln(t + \sqrt{t^2 - 1})}{2\pi i \sqrt{t^2 - 1}} [Ve^{-\pi i \sigma(T_{-1})} - t] + \frac{\sigma(T_{-1})}{2}, \tag{7.15}$$

where

$$t = \frac{\sigma(V)}{2} e^{-\pi i \sigma(T_{-1})}.$$

For V we have the general representation (7.12) in the form of a power series. Lappo-Danilevskiy constructed a single-valued factor $\overline{Y}(z)$ in (7.11) of the form

$$\overline{Y}(z) = I + \sum_{\nu=1}^{\infty} \sum_{p_1 \ldots p_\nu = -s}^{\infty} T_{p_1} \ldots T_{p_\nu} \times$$

$$\times \sum_{\mu=0}^{\nu} b^{p_1 + \ldots + p_\mu + \mu} z^{p_{\mu+1} + \ldots + p_\nu + \nu - \mu} \, a^{*(0)}_{p_1 \ldots p_\mu} \, a^{(0)}_{p_{\mu+1} \ldots p_\nu}. \tag{7.15$_1$}$$

8. Formulation of Certain Problems of Linear Systems of Differential Equations with Real Periodic Coefficients

In this section we shall consider a system of linear homogeneous differential equations with periodic coefficients

$$\frac{dX}{dt} = XP(t). \tag{8.1}$$

Here, $P(t)$ is a continuous periodic matrix with period 2π:

$$P(t + 2\pi) = P(t). \tag{8.2}$$

We have already noted that an integral matrix (let us say, normalized at the point $t=0$) can be represented by the series (6.1), which converges uniformly in an arbitrary finite interval $0 \leqslant t \leqslant p$. Because of the periodicity of the matrix $P(t)$, the matrix $X(t+2\pi)$ will also be an integral matrix. To see this, note that, for $t=\tau+2\pi$, we obtain from (8.1)

$$\frac{dX(\tau+2\pi)}{d\tau} = X(\tau+2\pi)P(\tau+2\pi) = X(\tau+2\pi)P(\tau),$$

from which the assertion follows.

From a familiar property of fundamental systems of solutions of linear differential equations, $X(t+2\pi)$ can be expressed in terms of $X(t)$ by the equation

$$X(t+2\pi) = VX(t), \tag{8.3}$$

where V is a constant matrix with nonzero determinant for $t=0$. From this, we obtain

$$X(2\pi) = V. \tag{8.4}$$

Thus, as we increase t by the period 2π, the integral matrix $X(t)$ is multiplied on the left by a constant matrix V, which is equal to the value of $X(t)$ at $t=2\pi$. In accordance with (6.1), we have

$$V = \sum_{k=0}^{\infty} X_k(2\pi), \quad X_0(t) = \mathrm{I}, \tag{8.5}$$

where $X_k(t)$ is given by Eq. (6.2).

Let us define a matrix W by

$$2\pi W = \ln V, \quad V = e^{2\pi W} \tag{8.6}$$

and a function N by the equation

$$N(t) = e^{-Wt}X(t). \tag{8.7}$$

The function $N(t)$ is periodic with period 2π. This is true because

$$N(t+2\pi) = e^{-Wt-2\pi W}X(t+2\pi) = e^{-Wt}e^{-2\pi W}VX(t) = N(t).$$

From this we see that the integral matrix of the system (8.1) normalized at the point $t=0$ can be represented in the form

$$X(t) = e^{Wt}N(t), \tag{8.8}$$

where the matrix W is defined by (8.6) and $N(t)$ is a periodic matrix with period 2π.

Let us now pose the following question: When will W and $N(t)$ in Eq. (8.8) be real matrices, assuming that $P(t)$ in the system (8.1) is real? Since the integral transformation is real, it follows, as was shown in Sect. 1, that $\ln V$ must be real (we recall that we are dealing here with the principle value of $\ln V$) if none of the characteristic numbers $\lambda_1, \ldots, \lambda_n$ of the matrix V are negative.*

In the case in which there are negative characteristic numbers (none of them can be zero since $D(V) \neq 0$), in accordance with (1.45) we have

$$\ln V = V_1 + \pi i V_2, \tag{8.9}$$

where V_1 and V_2 are real commutative matrices. Here, V_2 is of the form

$$V_2 = SL(0, 1) S^{-1}.$$

Here, $L(0,1)$ is a diagonal matrix the elements of which are equal to zero and unity. From this we see that if the matrix V has any negative characteristic numbers, then, in accordance with (8.6) and (8.8),

$$X(t) = e^{\frac{1}{2\pi} V_1 t} e^{\frac{i}{2} SL(0,1)S^{-1}t} N(t)$$

or

$$X(t) = e^{W_1 t} N_1(t). \tag{8.10}$$

Here, $W_1 = \frac{1}{2\pi} V_1$ is a real matrix. Therefore,

$$N_1(t) = e^{\frac{i}{2} SL(0,1)S^{-1}t} N(t)$$

is also a real matrix since the matrix $X(t)$ is real. Let us show that the matrix $N_1(t)$ possesses the properties that $N_1(t + 2\pi) \neq N_1(t)$ but $N_1(t + 4\pi) = N_1(t)$. We have

$$N_1(t + 2\pi) = e^{\frac{i}{2} SL(0,1)S^{-1}t} e^{\pi i SL(0,1)S^{-1}} N(t) \neq N_1(t),$$

$$e^{\frac{i}{2} SL(0,1)S^{-1}t} N(t) = N_1(t);$$

*We see from the equation $D(V) = \exp \int_0^{2\pi} \sigma(P(t))dt$ that the number of negative characteristic numbers of the matrix V is always even (Lyapunov). Therefore, we can always take $\ln V$ real. But this real value of $\ln V$ will not be the principle value (cf. Remark 1.4), nor will it be a regular value.

because $D(N(t)) \neq 0$ we would otherwise have

$$e^{\pi i SL(0,1)S^{-1}} = Se^{\pi i L(0,1)}S^{-1} = SL(e^{2\pi i 0}, e^{\pi i})S^{-1} =$$
$$= SL(1, -1)S^{-1} = I,$$

which is not the case.

Furthermore, we have

$$N_1(t + 4\pi) = N_1(t)\, e^{2\pi i SL(0,1)S^{-1}} = N_1(t)\, SL(e^{\pi i 0}, e^{2\pi i})S^{-1} =$$
$$= N_1(t)\, SL(1, 1)S^{-1} = N_1(t),$$

since $SL(1, 1)S^{-1} = I$.

Thus, if any of the characteristic numbers of the matrix V are negative, the integral matrix $X(t)$, which is normalized at the point $t = 0$, can be represented in the form (8.10), where W_1 is a constant real matrix and the matrix $N_1(t)$ is a real periodic matrix with period 4π.

This assertion was proven in essence by Lyapunov in his remarkable dissertation. Here, we have only given it in a somewhat different form and have proven it in a different way. We note also that W_1 is not equal to $\frac{1}{2\pi}$ ln V, whereas we had $W\frac{1}{2\pi}\ln V$ in (8.8).

We note, however, that*

$$W_1 = \frac{1}{4\pi}\ln X(4\pi) = \frac{1}{4\pi}\ln V^2. \tag{8.11}$$

Here, if we used formula (1.46), our reasoning would remain the same and the value obtained for $N_1(t)$ would be the same (though $N(t)$ would be different). We note also that the general value (cf. formula (1.46)) is

$$\ln X(4\pi) = V_1 + \pi i V_2, \tag{8.12}$$

where $V_2 = SL(2m)S^{-1}$ and $L(2m)$ is a diagonal matrix with elements equal to even numbers (possibly 0) and where V_1 is the principal (and regular) value of $\ln X(4\pi)$ if the matrix $X(4\pi)$ has no negative characteristic numbers. In formula (8.11), W_1 is a real matrix. However, the matrix $X(4\pi)$ can have negative characteristic numbers (if the matrix $X(2\pi)$ had purely imaginary characteristic numbers) since $X(4\pi) = X^2(2\pi)$. Therefore, $\ln X(4\pi)$ may be an irregular value (cf. Remark 1.4). Taking the principle value of $\ln X(4\pi)$ in this case, we again obtain

---

* From (8.10) since $N_1(0) = N_1(4\pi) = I$.

$$\ln X(4\pi) = V_1(4\pi) + \pi i V_2(4\pi),$$

where $V_2(4\pi)$ is a matrix that commutes with $V_1(4\pi)$ and has a purely diagonal canonical form with characteristic numbers equal to zero and unity. Then, we may write

$$X(t) = \exp W_2 t \cdot N_2(t),$$

where

$$W_2 = \frac{1}{4\pi} V_1(4\pi), \quad N_2(t) = \exp \frac{\pi i}{4\pi} V_2(4\pi) \cdot N_1(t).$$

We also have

$$W_2 = \frac{1}{8\pi} \ln X(8\pi), \quad N_2(t + 8\pi) = N_2(t).$$

It may happen that we finally end up with

$$W = \frac{1}{2^k \pi} \ln X(2^k \pi), \tag{8.13}$$

where $\ln X(2^k \pi)$ is a *real* and *principal* value* and $N_k(t)$ is a real periodic function with period $2^k \pi$:

$$X(t) = \exp\left[\left(\frac{1}{2^k \pi} \ln(2^k \pi)\right) t\right] N_k(t). \tag{8.14}$$

9. Solution of the Problems Posed in Section 8 on the Basis of Real Functions

Let us look at the problem of finding an expression for W in formula (8.8) or W_1 in formula (8.10).

First of all, we obtain W in the form (8.6) in terms of V, which is a convergent series (8.5). By using the form of Lagrange's polynomial that we derived earlier, we can give a representation of W. Suppose, for example, that $P(t)$ is a second-order matrix. Then, as we saw in (1.40), we can write

$$2\pi W = \ln V = \frac{\sigma \ln D - 2M}{4D - \sigma^2} V + \frac{\sigma M + 2D - \sigma^2}{4D - \sigma^2} \tag{9.1}$$

$$M = \int_0^1 \frac{\sigma(D - \sigma + 1)t + \sigma^2 - 2D - \sigma}{(D - \sigma + 1)t^2 + (\sigma - 2)t + 1} dt,$$

$$\sigma = \sigma(V), \quad D = D(V).$$

---

*Also regular. Obviously, such a k always exists.

In accordance with (8.5), we have

$$\sigma(V)=\sum_{k=0}^{\infty}\sigma(X_k(2\pi)). \tag{9.2}$$

If the matrix $P(t)$ is second-order and the characteristic numbers of the matrix V are negative,* then, in formula (8.10), we have

$$N_1(t)=e^{\frac{i}{2}t}N(t). \tag{9.3}$$

For a system of n equations, we obtain W from formula (1.31) (or, more precisely, from (1.39)).

On the other hand, if the matrix V does have negative characteristic numbers, then, in accordance with (8.11), we have

$$4\pi W_1=\ln X(4\pi)=\sum_{k=0}^{n-1}\alpha_k X^k(4\pi) \tag{9.4}$$

or possibly (see (8.13))

$$2^k\pi W=\ln X(2^k\pi)\ \text{(principal value)}.$$

Example. Suppose that we have the system

$$\frac{dX}{dt}=XP(t), \tag{9.5}$$

where $P(t)$ is a second-order matrix:

$$P(t)=\begin{Vmatrix}p_{11}(t) & p_{12}(t)\\ p_{21}(t) & p_{22}(t)\end{Vmatrix};$$

the elements of which are

$$p_{11}(t)=a_{11}\cos^2\frac{t}{2}+a_{22}\sin^2\frac{t}{2}-(a_{12}+a_{21})\sin\frac{t}{2}\cos\frac{t}{2},$$

$$p_{12}(t)=\frac{1}{2}+a_{12}\cos^2\frac{t}{2}-a_{21}\sin^2\frac{t}{2}+(a_{11}-a_{22})\sin\frac{t}{2}\cos\frac{t}{2}$$

$$p_{21}(t)=-\frac{1}{2}+a_{21}\cos^2\frac{t}{2}-a_{12}\sin^2\frac{t}{2}+(a_{11}-a_{22})\times$$
$$\times\sin\frac{t}{2}\cos\frac{t}{2},$$

$$p_{22}(t)=a_{11}\sin^2\frac{t}{2}+a_{22}\cos^2\frac{t}{2}+(a_{21}+a_{12})\sin\frac{t}{2}\cos\frac{t}{2}.$$

---

*If there is one negative characteristic number, the second will also be negative.

The integral matrix X normalized at the point $t = 0$ is of the form

$$X(t) = e^{\left\|\begin{matrix} a_{11} & a_{12} \\ a_{21} & a_{22} \end{matrix}\right\| t} \left\|\begin{matrix} \cos\frac{t}{2} & \sin\frac{t}{2} \\ -\sin\frac{t}{2} & \cos\frac{t}{2} \end{matrix}\right\|.$$

Here,

$$X(2\pi) = -e^{\left\|\begin{matrix} a_{11} & a_{12} \\ a_{21} & a_{22} \end{matrix}\right\| 2\pi} = V.$$

Let us find the characteristic numbers of the matrix V. Suppose that

$$A = \left\|\begin{matrix} a_{11} & a_{12} \\ a_{21} & a_{22} \end{matrix}\right\| = S \left\|\begin{matrix} \lambda_1 & 0 \\ 0 & \lambda_2 \end{matrix}\right\| S^{-1},$$

where S is a matrix and λ_1 and λ_2 are real numbers. Then,

$$V = S \left\|\begin{matrix} -e^{2\pi\lambda_1} & 0 \\ 0 & -e^{2\pi\lambda_2} \end{matrix}\right\| S^{-1}$$

and, consequently, the characteristic numbers μ_1 and μ_2 of the matrix V are equal:

$$\mu_1 = -\exp 2\pi\lambda_1, \quad \mu_2 = -\exp 2\pi\lambda_2 .$$

If

$$\left\|\begin{matrix} a_{11} & a_{12} \\ a_{21} & a_{22} \end{matrix}\right\| = S \left\|\begin{matrix} \lambda & 0 \\ 1 & \lambda \end{matrix}\right\| S^{-1},$$

we have

$$V = S \left\|\begin{matrix} -\exp 2\pi\lambda & 0 \\ -\exp 2\pi\lambda & -\exp 2\pi\lambda \end{matrix}\right\| S^{-1}$$

and

$$\mu_1 = \mu_2 = -\exp 2\pi\lambda.$$

Thus, the period of the matrix $P(t)$ is in this case equal to 2π and, in the representation of the matrix

$$X = \exp At \cdot N(t),$$

the matrix

$$N(t) = \begin{Vmatrix} \cos\frac{t}{2} & \sin\frac{t}{2} \\ -\sin\frac{t}{2} & \cos\frac{t}{2} \end{Vmatrix}$$

is of period 4π and the characteristic numbers of the integral substitution V are negative.

Consider now the system

$$\frac{dX}{dt} = XP(t), \tag{9.6}$$

where $P(t)$ is a periodic real nth-order matrix with period 2π. In connection with it, consider the system

$$\frac{dX}{dt} = XP(t)\lambda, \tag{9.7}$$

where λ is a real parameter. Let us seek a solution of the system (9.7) in the form

$$X = \exp At \cdot Z(t), \tag{9.8}$$

where A is a real constant matrix and $Z(t)$ is a real periodic matrix. We shall use the method expounded in [14].

In accordance with (6.5), we have, for the system (9.7),

$$X(t) = \sum_{k=0}^{\infty} X_k(t)\lambda^k, \quad X_0 = I. \tag{9.9}$$

This series converges for all finite values of λ. For the matrix V, we have, in accordance with (8.5),

$$V = \sum_{k=0}^{\infty} X_k(2\pi)\lambda^k, \quad X_0 = I. \tag{9.10}$$

This series also converges for all finite λ. In accordance with formula (8.6),

$$A = \frac{1}{2\pi} \ln V = \sum_{k=1}^{\infty} A_k \lambda^k. \tag{9.11}$$

This series converges for sufficiently small values of λ in accordance with a theorem of Lappo-Danilevskiy [1] or Theorem 2.1 of the present book. From the relations

$$Z(t) = \exp\left(-\sum_{k=1}^{\infty} A_k \lambda^k t\right) \cdot \sum_{k=0}^{\infty} X_k(t) \lambda^k, \quad X_0 = I$$

we see that $Z(t)$ can be represented in the form of a series

$$Z(t) = I + \sum_{k=1}^{\infty} Z_k(t) \lambda^k \tag{9.12}$$

If we substitute (9.8) into (9.7) and multiply on the left by exp $(-At)$, we obtain

$$\frac{dZ}{dt} = ZP\lambda - AZ. \tag{9.13}$$

If we substitute (9.11) and (9.12) into this equation and equate coefficients of like powers of λ, we obtain

$$\frac{dZ_k}{dt} = Z_{k-1} P - A_k - \sum_{l=1}^{k-1} A_l Z_{k-l}, \tag{9.14}$$

$$\frac{dZ_1}{dt} = P - A_1. \tag{9.15}$$

Since $P(t)$ and $Z_1(t)$ are periodic matrices, we have

$$Z_1 = \int_0^t (P(t) - A_1)\, dt, \tag{9.16}$$

$$A_1 = \frac{1}{2\pi} \int_0^{2\pi} P(t)\, dt, \tag{9.17}$$

$$Z_1 = \int_0^t P(t)\, dt - \frac{t}{2\pi} \int_0^{2\pi} P(t)\, dt. \tag{9.18}$$

From this, we see that the matrix Z_1 is of period 2π. The matrix Z_2 can be found from the equation

$$\frac{dZ_2}{dt} = Z_1 P - A_2 - A_1 Z_1. \tag{9.19}$$

Since the matrix $Z_1 P - AZ_1$ is periodic, we have

$$A_2 = \frac{1}{2\pi}\int_0^{2\pi} (Z_1P - A_1Z_1)\, dt \tag{9.20}$$

and

$$Z_2 = \int_0^t (Z_1P - A_1Z_1)\, dt - A_2t. \tag{9.21}$$

In general, we have

$$A_k = \frac{1}{2\pi}\int_0^{2\pi}\left[Z_{k-1}P - \sum_{l=1}^{k-1} A_lZ_{k-l}\right] dt, \tag{9.22}$$

$$Z_k = \int_0^t\left[Z_{k-1}P - \sum_{l=1}^{k-1} A_lZ_{k-l}\right] dt - A_kt\,. \tag{9.23}$$

Thus, the coefficients of the series (9.11) and (9.12) will be found and these series will converge for sufficiently small values of λ. If they converge (see Sect. 2) for $\lambda = 1$, we obtain the solution of the system (9.6) by setting $\lambda = 1$ in (9.11) and (9.12).

We call the reader's attention to the following fact. We saw above that, in formula (9.8), A and $Z(t)$ may at times be real only under the condition that $Z(t)$ is of period 4π and not 2π. Here, on the other hand, A and Z_1 in (9.11) and (9.12) are always real and $Z(t)$ is of period 2π. The apparent contradiction is explained by the fact that, for sufficiently small values of λ, the matrix V given by the series (9.11) is always close to the unit matrix. Consequently, its characteristic numbers are always close to unity. In other words, for small values of λ, the characteristic numbers of the matrix V will not be negative. Therefore, in accordance with what was said earlier, for small values of λ, the matrices A and $Z(t)$ in formula (9.8) will be real and $Z(t)$ will be of period 2π. These considerations show that the series (9.11) and (9.12) cannot converge for values of λ at which V has negative characteristic numbers. In the example of (9.5), the matrix P is such that, for the system (9.7), the series (9.11) and (9.12) diverge for $\lambda = 1$ since the integral substitution V for the system (9.5) has, as we have seen, negative characteristic numbers and A and $Z(t)$ will be real only when the period of $Z(t)$ is 4π.

This phenomenon restricts the applicability of the method described. For some systems, the series (9.11) and (9.12) can, of course, converge for $\lambda = 1$ and may even be entire (as was shown in Sect. 2).

In [14] it is shown that if a second-order matrix $P(t)$ is of period $\omega = 1$, if $|p_{21}(t)| \leqslant a_1$, and if $|p_{12}(t)| \leqslant a_2$, then the series (9.11) and (9.12) converge for $|\lambda| < \frac{\ln 2}{\sqrt{a_1 a_2}}$. Consequently, when $a_1 a_2 < \ln^2 2$, these series also converge for $\lambda = 1$ (see Sect. 11 of the present book).

In stability questions we often need only to have a representation of the magnitude of the characteristic number of the matrix A. It follows from Remark 2.2 and Theorem 2.2 that, if we find the invariants of the matrix A by using the series (9.11), that is, if we find $D(A)$ and $\sigma(A)$, then the series representing these quantities will converge in the region $|\lambda| < \lambda_1$, in which there is no more than one branch point* λ_0 of the roots of the characteristic equation of the matrix (9.10). It follows** from this that the series (7.13) and also the series of the invariants $\sigma(W)$ and $D(W)$ of the exponential substitution W (given by (7.13)) constructed by Lappo-Danilevskiy will converge at least in a region of the matrices $T_{-s}, \ldots, T_l$, where the discriminant of the characteristic equation of the matrix (7.12) does not vanish except when $T_{-s} = \ldots = T_l = 0$.

It should be noted that the invariants of the matrix W coincide with the invariants of the matrix H constructed by Lappo-Danilevskiy in the form

$$H = \sum_{\nu=1}^{\infty} \sum_{p_1 \ldots p_\nu = -s}^{l} T_{p_1} \ldots T_{p_\nu} \delta^{(0)}_{p_1+\ldots+p_\nu+\nu} \alpha^{(1)}_{p_1 \ldots p_\nu}, \tag{9.24}$$

where $\delta^{(0)}_p$ is the Kronecker delta and the $\alpha^{(1)}_{p_1 \ldots p_\nu}$ are given by the formulas of Sect. 7. Here, H is the exponential substitution of the so-called metacanonical integral matrix [1] of the system (7.14)

$$Z(z) = z^H \overline{Z}(z),$$

where

$$\overline{Z}(z) = I + \sum_{\nu=1}^{\infty} \sum_{p_1 \ldots p_\nu = -s}^{\infty} T_{p_1} \ldots T_{p_\nu} z^{p_1+\ldots+p_\nu+\nu} \alpha^{(0)}_{p_1 \ldots p_\nu}. \tag{9.24$_1$}$$

The matrix H is similar to the matrix W. This enables us to find approximative expressions for the characteristic numbers of the matrix A by use of the series (9.11), where the A_k are given by formulas (9.17), (9.20), and (9.22) for $\lambda = 1$; if $\sigma^2(V) - 4D(V) \neq 0$ for $|\lambda| \leqslant 1$, $\lambda \neq 0$, that is, if

---

*Here, we need to take that branch $D(A)$ that is single-valued in a neighborhood of the branch point λ_0 (see Remark 2.2).

**Since A and W are defined analogously. In this section we shall establish the exact equation showing the relationship between A and W.

$$\sigma^2(V) - 4\exp\lambda\int_0^{2\pi}\sigma(P)\,dt \neq 0$$

for $|\lambda| \leqslant 1$, $\lambda \neq 0$.

The characteristic equation for the second-order matrix A is of the form

$$\lambda^2 - \sigma(A)\lambda + D(A) = 0. \tag{9.25}$$

On the basis of Jacobi's formula,

$$D(X(2\pi)) = D(\exp 2\pi A)\,D(Z(2\pi)) =$$

$$= \exp\sigma(2\pi A)\cdot D(Z(2\pi)) = \exp\int_0^{2\pi}\sigma(P)\,dt\,.$$

Here, the matrix $Z(t)_{t=0}$, which is periodic with period 2π, is equal to I because $X(0) = \text{I}$ (see (9.9)). Therefore, $D(Z(2\pi)) = 1$. Consequently,

$$\exp\sigma(2\pi A) = \exp\int_0^{2\pi}\sigma(P)\,dt\,,$$

$$\sigma(A) = \frac{1}{2\pi}\int_0^{2\pi}\sigma(P)\,dt\,. \tag{9.26}$$

We note that the following cases may arise:

Case I.

$$\sigma(A) > 0,\quad D(A) > 0,\quad \sigma^2(A) - 4D(A) > 0 \tag{9.27}$$

Then, the characteristic numbers of the matrix A are positive.

Case II.

$$\sigma(A) \geqslant 0,\quad D(A) < 0 \quad \text{or} \quad \sigma(A) < 0,\ D(A) < 0,$$
$$\sigma^2(A) - 4D(A) > 0\,. \tag{9.28}$$

In this case only one characteristic number is positive, the other negative.

Case III.

$$\sigma(A) < 0,\quad D(A) > 0,\quad \sigma^2(A) - 4D(A) > 0. \tag{9.29}$$

Here, the characteristc numbers are negative.

Case IV.

$$\sigma(A) = 0, \quad D(A) > 0. \tag{9.30}$$

Here, the characteristic numbers are purely imaginary.

Case V.

$$\sigma^2(A) - 4D(A) = 0. \tag{9.31}$$

Here, the characteristic numbers coincide and they vanish for $\sigma(A) = 0$.

Case VI.

$$\sigma^2(A) - 4D(A) < 0. \tag{9.32}$$

Here, the characteristic numbers are complex with real part equal to $\frac{\sigma(A)}{2}$.

Later, we shall bring up certain cases in which the real nth-order matrix A and all its characteristic numbers are purely imaginary (see Sects. 16 and 44).

10. Expansion of an Exponential Matrix in a Series of Powers of a Parameter

Consider now a system of the form

$$\frac{dX}{dt} = X \sum_{k=0}^{\infty} P_k(t)\varepsilon^k \tag{10.1}$$

Here, the $P_k(t)$ are nth-order matrices that are continuous and periodic with period 2π. The series (10.1) converges for $|\varepsilon| < r$. In accordance with Theorem 6.1, the integral matrix of Eq. (10.1) normalized at the point $t = 0$ can be expressed as a series of the form

$$X(t) = \sum_{k=0}^{\infty} X_k(t)\varepsilon^k, \quad X_0(0) = I, \quad X_k(0) = 0, \quad k \geqslant 1, \tag{6.14}$$

that converges for $|\varepsilon| < r$. Consequently, we have the integral substitution in the form

$$V(\varepsilon) = X(2\pi) = \sum_{k=0} X_k(2\pi)\varepsilon^k, \quad |\varepsilon| < r. \tag{10.2}$$

It was shown in Sect. 8 that the integral matrix (6.14) can be represented in the form (8.8)

$$X(t, \varepsilon) = \exp(W(\varepsilon)t)\cdot Z(t, \varepsilon), \tag{10.3}$$

where W is the real constant matrix defined by Eq. (8.6), where

$$2\pi W(\varepsilon) = \ln V(\varepsilon) \tag{10.4}$$

(principal and regular value), and where $Z(t, \varepsilon)$ is a periodic real matrix with period 2π if the matrix $V(\varepsilon)$ has no negative characteristic numbers. On the other hand, if the matrix $V(\varepsilon)$ does have negative characteristic numbers, then $W(\varepsilon)$, as defined by Eq. (10.4), will not be real* (cf. (8.9)).

If we wish W to be real in (10.3), we need to take (see (8.11))

$$4\pi W(\varepsilon) = \ln X(4\pi). \tag{10.5}$$

Here, $N(t, \varepsilon)$ will be of period 4π. But here, $\ln X(4\pi)$ may be a nonprincipal (and nonregular) value if we wish this quantity to be real. However, we can always take (see (8.13))

$$W = \frac{1}{2^k\pi}\ln X(2^k\pi) \tag{10.6}$$

(where k is a positive integer), so that $\ln X(2^k\pi)$ will be a real, regular, and principal value. Here, $Z(t, \varepsilon)$ in the formula

$$X(t, \varepsilon) = \exp W(\varepsilon)t\cdot Z_k(t, \varepsilon) \tag{10.7}$$

will be periodic with period $2^k\pi$.

On the basis of the theorems in Sect. 2, $W(\varepsilon)$ and $Z(t, \varepsilon)$ can be represented in the form of series in positive powers of ε[if $\ln X(2^k\pi)$ in (10.6) is the principal (or a regular) value].**

Let us suppose that the integral matrix $X_0(t)$ of the limiting system

$$\frac{dX_0}{dt} = X_0(t)P_0(t), \quad X_0(0) = I \tag{10.8}$$

*If we take the principal or regular value of $\ln V(\varepsilon)$.

**However, we can sometimes choose an irregular value for $\ln X(2^k\pi)$ (see Remark 2.3).

has been obtained in the form

$$X_0(t) = \exp(A_0 t)\cdot Z_0(t),\quad Z_0(0) = I,\quad Z_0(t+2\pi) = Z_0(t). \tag{10.9}$$

If the matrix $V_0 = X_0(2\pi)$ has no negative characteristic numbers, this is possible. In this case, the characteristic numbers of the matrix $V(\varepsilon)$ obviously will not be negative for small values of ε and $W(\varepsilon)$ will be real in formula (10.3), but $Z(t, \varepsilon)$ will be of period 2π. The matrix A_0 in (10.9) is given by the equation (see (8.6))

$$2\pi A_0 = \ln X_0(2\pi), \tag{10.10}$$

and we may assume here that $\ln X_0(2\pi)$ is the principal value. Then, the characteristic numbers a_k (for $k = 1, \ldots, n$) of the matrix A_0 obviously satisfy the condition $a_k - a_l \neq im$ (where m is an integer), or $\ln X_0(2\pi)$ will be a regular value.

According to Theorem 2.1, we have $W(\varepsilon)$ in the form of a series

$$W(\varepsilon) = \sum_{k=0}^{\infty} W_k \varepsilon^k,\quad 2\pi W_0 = \ln X_0(2\pi) = 2\pi A_0, \tag{10.11}$$

which converges at least (see Remark 2.1) in a circle $|\varepsilon| \leqslant R < r$, in which there are no zeros of the discriminant $\Delta(\varepsilon)$ of the characteristic equation of the matrix (10.2)

$$\lambda^n + V_1(\varepsilon)\lambda^{n-1} + \ldots + V_{n-1}(\varepsilon)\lambda + V_n(\varepsilon) = 0 \tag{10.12}$$

for $\varepsilon \neq 0$. Here, the $V_k(\varepsilon)$ are series that converge in the same region as the series (10.2). If the characteristic numbers of the matrix $X_0(2\pi)$ are not only nonnegative but also distinct, the series (10.11) also converges in the circle $|\varepsilon| \leqslant R < r$, in which there is no more than one zero of the discriminant $\Delta(\varepsilon)$. Here, $\ln V(\varepsilon)$ must be taken in such a way that it will be single-valued in a neighborhood of the point $\varepsilon = \varepsilon_*$ at which the discriminant $\Delta(\varepsilon)$ vanishes. In the region of convergence of the series (10.11), the matrices $W(\varepsilon)$ and $Z(t, \varepsilon)$ remain real and $Z(t, \varepsilon)$ is of period 2π.

Let us suppose now that the matrix $X_0(2\pi)$ also has negative characteristic numbers. Then, we again find the series (10.11), but it will not yield a real function if we require that $Z(t+2\pi, \varepsilon) = Z(t, \varepsilon)$. On the other hand, if the matrix $X_0(4\pi) = X_0^2(2\pi)$ has no negative characteristic numbers and we assume that the function $Z(t, \varepsilon)$ is of period 4π, then we can again find $W(\varepsilon)$ in the form (10.11) and it will be real. However, in this last case, the function $Z_0(t)$ in (10.9) will also be of period 4π and $W(\varepsilon)$ can be found in accordance with (10.5), where $X(4\pi)$ has no negative characteristic numbers. Whenever the series (10.11) converges, so will the series

$$Z(t, \varepsilon) = \sum_{k=0}^{\infty} Z_k(t)\,\varepsilon^k, \tag{10.13}$$

which is obvious from (6.14) and (10.3).

A particular case of the system (10.1) is the one in which the matrix $P_0(t) = P_0$ is *constant*. Then, $X_0(t) = \exp P_0 t$. If the characteristic numbers P_k^0 (for $k = 1, \ldots, n$) of the matrix P_0 are such that $P_k^0 - P_l^0 \neq im$ (where m is an integer), we may, in accordance with (10.9), assume that $A_0 = P_0$ and $Z_0(t) = \mathrm{I}$.

Let us suppose now that* $P_k^0 - P_l^0 = im$, but that the matrix $\exp 2\pi P_0$ has no negative characteristic numbers. Then, $2\pi P_0 = \ln \exp 2\pi P_0$ is not a regular value. But we can write

$$X_0(t) = \exp A_0 t Z_0(t), \tag{10.14}$$

where $2\pi A_0 = \ln \exp 2\pi P_0$ is the principal (and regular) value and

$$Z_0(t) = \exp(-A_0 t) \exp P_0 t.$$

Here, A_0 is a real matrix (since the matrix $\exp 2\pi P_0$ has no negative characteristic numbers) and $Z_0(t)$ is real and periodic with period 2π. To see this, note that

$$Z_0(t + 2\pi) = \exp[-2\pi A_0] \cdot \exp 2\pi P_0 \cdot \exp[-A_0 t] \cdot \exp P_0 t = \\ = \exp[-A_0 t] \cdot \exp P_0 t,$$

since

$$\exp[-2\pi A_0] \cdot \exp[2\pi P_0] = \\ = \exp[-2\pi A_0] \cdot \exp[\ln \exp 2\pi P_0] = \mathrm{I},$$

because $2\pi A_0 = \ln \exp 2\pi P_0$ and the matrices $\exp[-A_0 t_1]$ and $\exp P_0 t_2$ commute.**

Thus, $2\pi A_0$ in (10.14) is the principal value of $\ln \exp 2\pi P_0$.

We could have proceeded in this case in a different manner. Specifically, since $2\pi P_0 = \ln \exp 2\pi P_0$ is not a regular value, we may write (see (1.46))

---

*For example, $P_0 = \begin{Vmatrix} 0 & -1 \\ 1 & 0 \end{Vmatrix}$, $P_1^0 - P_2^0 = 2i$ $\exp 2\pi P_0 = \mathrm{I}$.

**$2\pi A_0 = \ln \exp 2\pi P_0$ is the principal (and regular) value. Therefore, it is a polynomial (Lagrange's) in P_0.

$$P_0 = A_1 + iA_2 = \frac{1}{2\pi} \ln \exp 2\pi P_0 , \tag{10.15}$$

where the matrices A_1 and A_2 commute, where $2\pi A_1 = \ln \exp 2\pi A_1$ is the principal (and regular) value, where A_1 is a real matrix, and where the characteristic numbers of the matrix A_2 are equal to 0 and/or other integers. Then,

$$X_0(t) = \exp P_0 t = \exp A_1 t \cdot \exp i A_2 t = \exp A_1 t \cdot Z_0(t) ,$$

where the matrix

$$Z_0(t) = \exp i A_2 t \tag{10.15$_1$}$$

is periodic with period 2π and real since the matrices P_0 and A_1 are real. We have obtained **(10.14)**. If the matrix exp $2\pi P_0$ has negative* characteristic numbers, then the principal (and regular) value ln exp $2\pi P_0$ will, in accordance with **(1.45)**, be complex; also, A_2 in **(10.15)** has characteristic numbers equal to 1/2 if they correspond to negative characteristic numbers. Therefore, the function (10.15) is of period 4π. Consequently, we have exp $4\pi P_0$ = exp $4\pi A_1$ instead of exp $2\pi P_0$ = exp $2\pi A_1$.

But if the matrix exp $4\pi P_0$ does not have negative characteristic numbers, we may write

$$\exp P_0 t = \exp B_0 t \cdot Z_0(t), \tag{10.16}$$

where, for $4\pi B_0$, we must take the principal value of ln exp $4\pi P_0$ (it will be regular and real) or follow the second procedure, that is, use (10.15). Specifically, we need to write

$$X_0(t) = \exp P_0 t = \exp A_1 t \cdot \exp i A_2 t,$$

where the second factor is a periodic function with period 4π and $4\pi A_1 = \ln \exp 4\pi A_1$ (the principal value) is regular and real (if the matrix exp $4\pi P_0$ has no negative characteristic numbers). If we do not require W_0 (and along with it W) to be real in **(10.11)**, we can always (that is, even when the matrix exp $4\pi P_0$ has negative characteristic numbers) take for $4\pi A_0$ in **(10.14)** the principal and regular value of ln exp $4\pi P_0$. However, in many cases, it is necessary to take A_0 real. A_0 can always be chosen real on the basis of (8.13). Here, $Z_0(t)$ will be of period $2^k\pi$.

Thus, in all cases, we have **(10.3)**, where $W(\varepsilon)$ and $Z(t, \varepsilon)$ are real and representable in the form of the series **(10.11)** and **(10.13)**. Note the following facts: **(1)** if the matrix $X_0(2\pi)$ does not have negative characteristic numbers, then A_0 is given by equation

*For example, $P_0 = \begin{Vmatrix} 0 & -\frac{1}{2} \\ \frac{1}{2} & 0 \end{Vmatrix} = S \begin{Vmatrix} i/2 & 0 \\ 0 & -i/2 \end{Vmatrix} S^{-1}$, $\exp 2\pi P_0 = -I$.

(10.10) (where the principal value of ln $X_0(2\pi)$ is meant) and the matrix $Z_0(t)$ is real and periodic with period 2π; (2) on the other hand, if the matrix $X_0(2\pi)$ has negative characteristic numbers but the matrix $X_0(4\pi)$ does not, then the real matrix A_0 is determined by the principal value of

$$4\pi A_0 = \ln X_0(4\pi), \tag{10.17}$$

but the matrix $Z_0(t)$ will be real and periodic with period 4π.

Suppose that P_0 is a constant matrix such that $\exp 2\pi P_0$ has no negative characteristic numbers and suppose that $P_k^0 - P_l^0 = mi$. Then, we may proceed as follows:

If we introduce into (10.15)* a new unknown matrix** Y defined by $X = Y \exp iA_2 t$ and substitute it into (10.1), we obtain

$$YiA_2 \exp iA_2 t + \frac{dY}{dt} \exp iA_2 t = Y \exp iA_2 t \cdot (P_0 + P_1(t)\varepsilon + \ldots).$$

Since the matrices $P_0 = A_1 + iA_2$ and A_2 commute with A_1, we obtain by multiplying the above equation on the right by $\exp(-A_2 it)$

$$\frac{dY}{dt} = Y[A_1 + \exp iA_2 t\,(P_1(t)\varepsilon + \ldots)\cdot \exp(-iA_2 t)].$$

Since the matrix $\exp\ iA_2 t$ is periodic with period 2π, we have

$$\frac{dY}{dt} = Y[A_1 + \overline{P}_1(t)\varepsilon + \overline{P}_2(t)\varepsilon^2 + \ldots],$$

where the $\overline{P}_k(t)$ (for $k = 1, 2, \ldots$) are periodic with period 2π and $\ln \exp 2\pi A_1 = 2\pi A_1$ is the principal value. Instead of making the transformation $X = Y \exp iA_2 t$, we could have made the transformation

$$X = Y \exp(-A_0 t)\cdot \exp P_0 t,$$

where $2\pi A_0 = \ln \exp 2\pi P_0$ is the principal value. From what was said above, this amounts to the same thing.

An analogous transformation can be made in the case in which the matrix $\exp\ 2\pi P_0$ has negative characteristic numbers but the matrix $\exp\ 4\pi P_0$ does not. Specifically, we introduce Y defined by

$$X = Y \exp(-A_0 t)\cdot \exp P_0 t,$$

---

*We recall that, since the matrix $\exp\ 2\pi P_0$ has no negative characteristic numbers, it follows that the characteristic numbers of the matrix A_2 in (10.15) are integers.

**Such a transformation was first used in [7], where the question of series expansion of the characteristic numbers of the matrix (10.11) was studied. See also [30].

where the real matrix $4\pi A_0 = \ln \exp 4\pi P_0$ is the principal and regular value. Or, we may write in this case

$$X_0(t) = \exp A_0 t \cdot \exp(-A_0 t) \cdot \exp P_0 t = \exp A_0 t \cdot Z_0(t),$$

where

$$4\pi A_0 = \ln \exp 4\pi P_0$$

is the principal value and the matrix

$$Z_0(t) = \exp(-A_0 t) \cdot \exp P_0 t$$

is periodic with period 4π. Specifically,

$$Z_0(t + 4\pi) = \exp(-4A_0 \pi) \cdot \exp 4\pi P_0 \cdot \exp(-A_0 t) \cdot \exp P_0 t = \\ = \exp(-A_0 t) \cdot \exp P_0 t,$$

since

$$\exp(-4\pi A_0) \cdot \exp 4\pi P_0 = \\ = \exp(-4\pi A_0) \cdot \exp[\ln \exp 4\pi P_0] = I.$$

Now, in the expansions (10.11) and (10.13), we need to set respectively

$$4\pi W_0 = 4\pi A_0 = \ln \exp X_0(4\pi) = \ln \exp 4\pi P_0$$

and

$$Z_0(t) = \exp(-A_0 t) \cdot \exp P_0 t.$$

However, in this case (see (1.44), (1.45), and (1.46)) we shall have $P_0 = A_1 + iA_2$, where the real matrix A_1 commutes with the matrix A_2, which has a purely diagonal canonical form, the characteristic numbers of which are equal to integers and numbers of the form $k + 1/2$, where k is an integer. Consequently,

$$\exp P_0 t = \exp A_1 t \cdot \exp \; iA_2 t.$$

Therefore, we may either set

$$W_0 = A_1 \text{ and } Z_0(t) = \exp \; iA_2 t$$

in (10.11) and (10.13) or introduce Y as defined by

$$X = Y \exp \; iA_2 t.$$

We note also that if we have $P_k^0 - P_l^0 = im$, then, in accordance with Theorem 2.3, Remark 2.3, and the example following it, in certain cases we can set

$$2\pi W_0 = \ln X_0(2\pi) = \ln \exp 2\pi P_0 + S_0 [2m_1 \pi i I_{\rho_1}, \ldots, 2m_\nu \pi i I_{\rho_\nu}] S_0^{-1},$$

in (10.11), where $\ln \exp 2\pi P_0$ is the principal value (see (2.11)). But here, W_0 may be complex.

11. Determination of the Coefficients in the Series Expansion of an Exponential Matrix

Let us find the coefficients in the expansions (10.11) and (10.13). If we substitute (10.3) into (10.1) and multiply on the left by exp $(-W(\varepsilon)t)$, we obtain

$$\frac{dZ(t, \varepsilon)}{dt} = Z(t, \varepsilon) \sum_{k=0}^{\infty} P_k(t) \varepsilon^k - W(\varepsilon) Z(t, \varepsilon). \tag{11.1}$$

If we substitute the expansions (10.11) and (10.13) into this and equate coefficients of like powers of ε, we obtain

$$\frac{dZ_k(t)}{dt} = Z_k(t) P_0(t) - W_0 Z_k(t) + \sum_{\nu=1}^{k} Z_{k-\nu}(t) P_\nu(t) - \sum_{\nu=0}^{k-1} W_{k-\nu} Z_\nu(t). \tag{11.2}$$

Let us assume that $X_0(2\pi)$ in (10.10) has no negative characteristic numbers. Then,

$$Z_0(0) = I, \quad Z_k(t + 2\pi) = Z_k(t) \tag{11.3}$$

and, in accordance with (10.11),

$$2\pi W_0 = 2\pi A_0 = \ln X_0(2\pi).$$

Let us write the system (11.2) more briefly in the form

$$\frac{dZ_k(t)}{dt} = Z_k(t) P_0(t) - A_0 Z_k(t) + F_k(t) - W_k Z_0(t), \tag{11.4}$$

where the periodic matrix $F_k(t)$ with period 2π is of the form

$$F_k(t) = \sum_{\nu=1}^{k} Z_{k-\nu}(t) P_\nu(t) - \sum_{\nu=1}^{k-1} W_{k-\nu} Z_\nu(t). \tag{11.5}$$

The general solution of the system

$$\frac{dY}{dt} = YP_0(t) - A_0Y \tag{11.6}$$

is

$$Y = \exp(-A_0t)\cdot CX_0(t), \tag{1.17}$$

where C is an arbitrary constant matrix and $X_0(t)$ is the solution of Eq. (10.8) given by formula (10.14).

We may seek a solution of the system (11.4) in the form

$$Z_k(t) = \exp(-A_0t)\cdot C(t)\, X_0(t). \tag{11.8}$$

If we substitute this into (11.4), on the basis of (10.8) and (10.14) we obtain

$$\frac{dC}{dt} = \exp(A_0t)\cdot[F_k(t) - W_kZ_0(t)]\, Z_0^{-1}(t)\cdot\exp(-A_0t).$$

From this, we obtain

$$C(t) = \int_0^t \exp A_0t\,[F_k(t)\, Z_0^{-1}(t) - W_k]\cdot\exp(-A_0t)\, dt.$$

If we substitute this into (11.8), we obtain

$$Z_k(t) = \exp(-A_0t)\int_0 \exp(A_0t)\,[F_k(t)\, Z_0^{-1}(t) - W_k]\times$$
$$\times\exp(-A_0t)\, dt\cdot\exp A_0t\cdot Z_0(t). \tag{11.9}$$

If we impose* on $Z_k(t)$ the requirement that

$$Z_k(t+2\pi) = Z_k(t),\ t = 0,$$

we obtain

$$\int_0^{2\pi} \exp A_0t\,[F_k(t)\, Z_0^{-1}(t) - W_k]\cdot\exp(-A_0t)\, dt = 0, \tag{11.10}$$

from which we find W_k.

---

*Essentially, Artem'yev was the first to use this method for determining $Z_k(t)$ and W_k [9]. Independently of him, this method appeared afterwards in [14] (October, 1942) and [10] (in this case, for systems of an even more general form).

Formula (11.9) gives a solution of Eq. (11.4) that satisfies the condition $Z_k(0) = 0$. We obviously have a solution satisfying the condition $Z_k(0) \neq 0$, in the form

$$Z_k(t) = \exp(-A_0 t) \int_0^t \exp A_0 t \cdot [F_k(t) Z_0^{-1}(t) - W_k] \times$$

$$\times \exp(-A_0 t)\, dt \cdot \exp A_0 t \cdot Z_0(t) + \exp(-A_0 t) \cdot Z_k(0) X_0(t). \tag{11.11}$$

From the condition that

$$Z_k(0) = Z_k(2\pi) \tag{11.11$_1$}$$

we find a W_k, such that $Z_k(t)$ will be periodic for arbitrary $Z_k(0)$. Conversely, we may choose W_k arbitrarily, for example,

$$W_{k_{\text{av}}} = \frac{1}{2\pi} \int_0^{2\pi} F_k(t)\, dt,$$

and find $Z_k(0)$ from (11.11$_1$). Then $Z_k(t)$ will again be periodic with period 2π.

For $Z_0(t) = I$ and $Z_k(0) = 0$, we find the matrix W_k from the equation

$$\int_0^{2\pi} \exp A_0 t \cdot [F_k(t) - W_k] \exp(-A_0 t)\, dt = 0\,. \tag{11.11$_2$}$$

Let us examine in greater detail the particular case in which the matrix $P_0(t) = P_0$ in the system (10.1) is constant.

Suppose that the matrix $\exp 2\pi P_0$ has no negative characteristic numbers and that $2\pi P_0 = \ln \exp 2\pi P_0$ is the principal value. Thus, we may set $W_0 = P_0$ and $Z_0(t) = I$.

We shall study in greater detail the equation (11.4), in which we now set $Z_0(t) = I$ and $P_0(t) = P_0 = A_0$. We denote by λ_m the characteristic numbers of the matrix P_0. Let J be the canonical matrix: $J = S^{-1}P_0S$ and suppose that $W = S^{-1}W_kS$, $Z = S^{-1}Z_kS$ and $F = S^{-1}F_kS$. If we multiply Eq. (11.4) on the left by S^{-1} and on the right by S, we obtain an equation of the form (11.4), where we only need to replace P_0 with J, W_k with W, Z_k with Z, and F_k with F:

$$\frac{dZ}{dt} = ZJ - JZ + F(t) - W. \tag{11.12}$$

If in general we denote by b_{kl} the elements of the matrix B, we can write (11.12) in an expanded form:

$$\frac{dz_{k,l}}{dt} = -\delta_k z_{k-l,l} - \lambda_k z_{k,l} + \lambda_l z_{k,l} + z_{k,l+1}\delta_l + F_{k,l} - \qquad (11.13)$$
$$- w_{k,l}.$$

Here, the numbers δ_m are equal to zero and unity. They are equal to zero if the elementary divisor of the root λ_m is a prime or if $z_{k,l}$, at the vertex of the Jordan cell on the principal diagonal corresponding to the root λ_m, is defined. If.

$$\lambda_k \neq \lambda_l + mi \quad (m = 0, \pm 1, \pm 2, \pm \ldots),$$

the $z_{k,l}$ are found from (11.13) to be periodic for arbitrary* $w_{k,l}$:

$$z_{k,l} = \exp[(\lambda_l - \lambda_k)t]\cdot[c + \int_0^t f(t)\exp(-(\lambda_l - \lambda_k)t)\,dt], \qquad (11.14)$$

where

$$f(t) = -\delta_k z_{k-l,l} + \delta_l z_{k,l+1} + F_{k,l} - w_{k,l}$$

is a periodic function and the constant c is determined by the equation

$$(\exp[(\lambda_l - \lambda_k)2\pi] - 1)c - \int_0^{2\pi} f(t)\exp(-(\lambda_l - \lambda_k)t)\,dt = 0. \qquad (11.15)$$

If we set $c = 0$ and find $w_{k,l}$ from Eq. (11.15), then we obtain $z_{k,l}(t)$ periodic and $z_{k,l}(0) = 0$.

We can take c arbitrarily in (11.14) and we can take $w_{k,l}$ so that $z_{k,l}(t)$ will be periodic. Finally, we can take

$$w_{k,l_{\text{av}}} = \frac{1}{2\pi}\int_0^{2\pi} F_{k,l}\,dt,$$

and we can choose c so that $z_{k,l}$ will be periodic.

For $\lambda_k = \lambda_l = \lambda$, the element $z_{k,l}$, corresponding to the vertex of the Jordan cell of the nonprincipal diagonal corresponding to the root λ is found from Eq. (11.13) with $\delta_k = \delta_l = 0$; that is,

$$z_{k,l} = \int_0^t (F_{k,l} - w_{k,l_{\text{av}}})\,dt + c_{k,l}, \qquad (11.16)$$

where $c_{k,l}$ is an arbitrary constant.

---

*Including the case in which $w_{k,l} = \frac{1}{2\pi}\int_0^{2\pi} F_{k,l}\,dt$.

For $c_{k,l}=0$, the function $z_{k,l}$ is periodic and $z_{k,l_{av}}=0$. The remaining elements $z_{k,l}$ of this square are found from Eq. (11.13) in the form (for $\lambda_k=\lambda_l$):

$$z_{k,l}=\int_0^t[-\delta_k z_{k-i,l}+z_{k,l+1}\delta_l+F_{k,l}-w_{k,l_{av}}]\,dt+c_{k,l}, \qquad (11.17)$$

where $c_{k,l}$ is an arbitrary constant. For $c_{k,l}=0$, the element $z_{k,l}$ is periodic with average value equal to 0.

Thus, in (11.12), we can always take* W_{av} and can find a C such that $Z(t)$ is periodic with period 2π or we can set** $C=0$ and can find a W so that $Z(t)$ will be periodic. Or, finally, we can take $Z(0)$ arbitrarily (choosing C accordingly) and can find a W such that $Z(t)$ will be periodic. This W will be unique. However, it should be noted that, when we set $Z_k(0)=0$ in (11.4) (that is, when we set $C_k=0$) and determine W_k in such a way that the $Z_k(t)$ will be periodic with period 2π, we obtain convergent series (10.11) and (10.13) (in the region mentioned in Theorem 2.1 and Remark 2.2).

Remark 11.1. If $X(t,\varepsilon)$ is a normalized integral matrix, that is, if $X(0,\varepsilon)=I$ or $Z_0(0)=I$ and $Z_k(0)=0$ (for $k\geqslant 1$), then, as was shown by Artem'yev [9],

$$Y=\sum_{k=0}^{\infty}A_k\varepsilon^k\cdot X(t,\varepsilon)$$

is an integral matrix***[9, 7, 12, 13] such that $Z_k(0)=A_k$ (for $k\geqslant 1$), where $A_0=I$. We assume that the series $A=\sum_{k=0}^{\infty}A_k\varepsilon^k$ converges. The exponential matrix $\overline{W}$ of the integral matrix

$$Y=\exp(\overline{W}(\varepsilon)\,t)\cdot\overline{Z}(t,\varepsilon)$$

is determined by the equation

$$\overline{W}(\varepsilon)=\left(\sum_{k=0}^{\infty}A_k\varepsilon^k\right)\sum_{k=0}^{\infty}W_k\varepsilon^k\left(\sum_{k=0}^{\infty}A_k\varepsilon^k\right)^{-1}. \qquad (*)$$

If $Z_k(0)=0$ (for $k\geqslant 1$), the series for W and Z will, in the case of a periodic matrix $P(t)$, converge when the conditions stated above

---

* $W_{av}=\frac{1}{2\pi}\int_0^{2\pi}F(t)\,dt$

**That is, $Z(0)=0$.

***The analysis given below was carried out in [13].

with regard to P_0 are satisfied. However, if we choose another value for $Z_k(0)$ (fixing W_k in some way as we do so), there is no guarantee that the series (10.11) and (10.13) will converge. If we take $A = \sum_{k=0}^{m} A_k \varepsilon^k$, that is, a polynomial in ε, then the series corresponding to $\overline{W}(\varepsilon)$ will converge and $\overline{Z}_k(0) = 0$ for $k \geqslant m+1$. In other words, if we take for W_k (where $k = 1, \ldots, m$) the mean* values of the corresponding functions and then take W_k (for $k = m+1, \ldots$) corresponding to the values of $Z_k(0) = 0$ (for $k = m+1, \ldots$), then the series (10.11) and (10.13) will still converge. However, let us suppose that nonzero values are chosen for $Z_k(0)$ (for $k = 1, 2, \ldots$) (and that the W_k are therefore unique) or, for example, let us choose for all the W_k (for $k = 1, 2, \ldots$) the corresponding average values (in which case, the $Z_k(0)$ will be unique and, in general, nonzero). Then, the series

$$A = \sum_{k=0}^{\infty} A_k \varepsilon^k \tag{**}$$

may diverge. The series $\overline{W}(\varepsilon)$ may also diverge. However, the invariants of the characteristic equation of the matrix $\overline{W}(\varepsilon)$ will, by virtue of the formula (*), coincide with the invariants of the characteristic equation of the matrix $W(\varepsilon)$ and therefore they will be convergent series in terms of ε. However,

$$Y_n(t, \varepsilon) = \exp\left(\sum_{k=0}^{m} \overline{W}_k \varepsilon^k t\right) \cdot \sum_{k=0}^{m} \overline{Z}_k(t) \cdot \varepsilon^k$$

will now obviously be a poor approximation** of the value of the integral matrix Y. In fact, there may not be an integral matrix Y with such value of $Z_k(0)$ (if the series (**) diverges).

Thus, we have obtained the following rule. Suppose that $2\pi P_0 = \ln \exp 2\pi P_0$ (principal value) and suppose that the matrix $\exp 2\pi P_0$ has no negative characteristic numbers. Then, we have the integral matrix X of Eq. (10.1) that is normalized at the point $t = 0$ in the form

$$X(t, \varepsilon) = \exp(W(\varepsilon)\, t) \cdot Z(t, \varepsilon), \tag{10.3}$$

---

*In [10], W_k was originally defined as the average value, but then convergence of the series (10.11) was not required. See Sect. 20 of the present book.

**As we have noted, these are still segments of convergent series if we take $\overline{Z}_k(0) = 0$ (where $k = m+1, m+2, \ldots$).

where $W(\varepsilon)$ is a real constant matrix that can be represented by the convergent series

$$W(\varepsilon) = \sum_{k=0}^{\infty} W_k \varepsilon^k, \tag{10.11}$$

and a real periodic matrix $Z(t, \varepsilon)$ that can be represented by a convergent series

$$Z(t, \varepsilon) = \sum_{k=0}^{\infty} Z_k(t) \varepsilon^k. \tag{10.13}$$

Here, $W_0 = P_0$, $Z_0 = I$, and W_k and $Z_k(t)$ (for $k \geqslant 1$) are obtained from Eqs. (11.4) (or with the aid of (11.12)) under the condition that the $Z_k(t)$ must be periodic with period 2π and that $Z_k(0) = 0$. Suppose that $2\pi P_0 = \ln \exp 2\pi P_0$ is the principal value but that the matrix exp $2\pi P_0$ has negative characteristic numbers. Then, the matrix exp $4\pi P_0$ does not have negative characteristic numbers and, if

$$4\pi P_0 = \ln \exp 4\pi P_0$$

is the principal value, then, in (10.11), we should take

$$4\pi W_0 = \ln \exp 4\pi P_0 = 4\pi P_0, \quad W_0 = P_0,$$

and find the W_k (for $k \geqslant 1$) from (10.5) (or with the aid of (11.12)) under the condition that the $Z_k(t)$ are periodic with period 4π. On the other hand, if $2\pi P_0$ is not the principal value of ln exp $2\pi P_0$, we need to proceed as was shown above (see Sect. 10).

We now note that the expansions (10.11) and (10.13) represent the matrices $W(\varepsilon)$ and $Z(t, \varepsilon)$ in the above-mentioned neighborhood of $\varepsilon = 0$.

Formulas (1.40), (1.41), and (1.39) enable us to represent $W(\varepsilon)$ throughout the entire region in which ε exists (thus providing ourselves with a representation of $Z(t, \varepsilon)$ for all possible values of ε), where the characteristic numbers of the matrix $X(2\pi, \varepsilon)$ are nonnegative. On the other hand, if the matrix $X(2\pi, \varepsilon)$ has negative characteristic numbers, we again obtain (10.3), (10.11) and (10.13) with the aid of formula (1.39) for all values of ε at which the coefficient matrix in (10.9) is given, but $Z(t, \varepsilon)$ will be of period 4π and $W(\varepsilon)$ can be constructed in accordance with (1.31) on the basis of the formula

$$4\pi W(\varepsilon) = \ln X(4\pi, \varepsilon). \tag{11.18}$$

Here, it is assumed that the matrix $X(4\pi, \varepsilon)$ has no negative characteristic numbers. For those values of ε at which the characteristic numbers of the matrix $X(2\pi, \varepsilon)$ or, correspondingly, $X(4\pi, \varepsilon)$ coincide, we need to take the limiting value of Lagrange's formula. We can obtain this limiting form of Lagrange's formula both from (1.31) and with the aid of the minimum polynomial (1.7), where it is shown below formula (1.7) how to find $\varphi_k(\lambda_1, \ldots, \lambda_m)$. Also, a way of finding $\varphi_k(\lambda_1, \ldots, \lambda_m)$ is given in Sect. 2, based on (2.4). Sometimes it is possible to find a bound for the radius of convergence of the series (10.11) on the basis of the bound for the coefficient matrix of Eq. (10.1). Thus, for example, (see p. 88 of [14]) for the system

$$\frac{dX}{dt} = XP(t),$$

where the characteristic numbers $p_k(t)$ of the matrix $P(t)$ satisfy the inequality $|p_k(t)| \leqslant a$, the series (10.11) will definitely converge*

for $|\varepsilon| < \frac{\ln 2}{2\pi a} = \varepsilon_1$. For $2\pi a < \ln 2$, we have the region of convergence

of the series (10.11): $|\varepsilon| < \varepsilon_1 > 1$. On the other hand, if

$$P(t) = \begin{Vmatrix} 0 & p_{12} \\ p_{21} & 0 \end{Vmatrix} \text{ and } |p_{12}| \leqslant a_2, \quad |p_{21}| \leqslant a_1,$$

then the series (10.11) will converge for

$$|\varepsilon| < \frac{\ln 2}{2\pi\sqrt{a_1 a_2}}.$$

For $2\pi\sqrt{a_1 a_2} < \ln 2$ we have $|\varepsilon| < \varepsilon_1 > 1$.

12. Approximate Integration of Equation (10.1)

For Eq. (10.1), we have obtained** a solution of the form

---

*This follows from the fact that the series $\ln X(2\pi, \varepsilon)$ converges if the maximum absolute value of any of the characteristic numbers of the matrix $X(2\pi, \varepsilon) - I$ | is less than unity. This maximum absolute value does not exceed the maximum absolute value of the characteristic numbers of $|\exp 2\pi P - I|$, where $|P(t, \varepsilon)| \leqslant P$ and the matrix P is constant. Let a denote the characteristic number of the matrix P with the greatest absolute value. Then, the characteristic number of the matrix $|\exp 2\pi\varepsilon P - I|$ with greatest absolute value does not exceed $(\exp 2\pi\varepsilon a - 1)$. From this, we have the region of convergence $|\varepsilon| < \frac{\ln 2}{2\pi a}$ since, here, $(\exp 2\pi a \varepsilon - 1) < 1$.

**The continuity of the characteristic numbers of the matrix W at the point $\varepsilon_1 = 0, \ldots, \varepsilon_m = 0$ is proven in [8] for the case in which the coefficient matrix of the linear system $P(t, \varepsilon_1, \ldots, \varepsilon_m)$ is continuous at the point $\varepsilon_1 = \ldots = \varepsilon_m = 0$ and is periodic with respect to t.

$$X(t, \varepsilon) = \exp(W(\varepsilon)t) \cdot Z(t, \varepsilon), \tag{10.3}$$

where $W(\varepsilon)$ and $Z(t, \varepsilon)$ are given in the form of series

$$W(\varepsilon) = \sum_{k=0}^{\infty} W_k \varepsilon^k, \tag{12.1}$$

$$Z(t, \varepsilon) = \sum_{k=0}^{\infty} Z_k(t) \varepsilon^k, \tag{12.2}$$

that converge for $|\varepsilon| < R$.

We define

$$W_m(\varepsilon) = \sum_{k=0}^{m} W_k \varepsilon^k, \tag{12.3}$$

$$Z_m(t, \varepsilon) = \sum_{k=0}^{m} Z_k(t) \varepsilon^k. \tag{12.4}$$

Then (see [4]),

$$X_m(t, \varepsilon) = \exp(W_m(\varepsilon)t) \cdot Z_m(t, \varepsilon) \tag{12.5}$$

will be an approximate value of the solution (10.3). Here, we construct $W(\varepsilon)$ and $Z(t, \varepsilon)$ in such a way that they will be real.

It may happen that the given system

$$\frac{dX}{dt} = XP(t) \tag{12.6}$$

can be written in the form

$$\frac{dX}{dt} = X(P_0(t) + P_1(t)\varepsilon), \tag{12.7}$$

so that, for $\varepsilon = 0$, we obtain

$$\frac{dX_0}{dt} = X_0 P_0(t), \tag{12.8}$$

the integral matrix of which is known:

$$X_0(t) = \exp W_0 t \cdot Z_0(t), \quad Z_0(t) = I, \tag{12.9}$$

and, for $\varepsilon = 1$, we obtain (12.6). Then, we have the integral matrix of the system (12.7) in the form of a series

$$X(t, \varepsilon) = \sum_{k=0}^{\infty} X_k(t)\, \varepsilon^k, \tag{12.10}$$

which converges for all finite ε. Now, we can find $X(t, \varepsilon)$ in the form (10.3). If the series (12.1) and (12.2) converge for $\varepsilon = 1$, we shall obtain an approximate solution in the form (12.5). As we have seen, it is sometimes possible to establish the convergence of the series (12.1) and (12.2) on the basis of bounds of the elements of the matrix $P(t)$. In particular, these series will converge for $\varepsilon = 1$ if (see Sect. 9) $P(t)$ is a second-order matrix (see p. 86 of [14]) and if

$$\sigma^2(X(2\pi, \varepsilon)) - 4 \exp \int_0^{2\pi} [\sigma(P_0(t)) + \sigma(P_1(t))\,\varepsilon]\, dt \neq 0$$

for $0 < |\varepsilon| \leqslant 1$ since, when this condition holds in the circle $|\varepsilon| \leqslant 1$, the matrix $X(2\pi, \varepsilon)$ has no multiple characteristic numbers. Here, we assume that the matrix $X_0(2\pi)$ has no negative characteristic numbers. For $P_0(t)$, we may take one of the matrices for which the integral matrix has been found in the preceding sections. Or, in the case of a second-order matrix $P(t)$, we may write the system (12.6) in the form

$$\frac{dX}{dt} = X\left[\begin{Vmatrix} p_{11} & 0 \\ 0 & p_{22} \end{Vmatrix} + \begin{Vmatrix} 0 & p_{12} \\ p_{21} & 0 \end{Vmatrix} \varepsilon\right]. \tag{12.11}$$

In particular, it is convenient to introduce this system in the case in which the average integral values (over the period) of the functions $p_{11}(t)$ and $p_{22}(t)$ are nonzero but those of the functions p_{12} and p_{21} are zero.

In general, for any matrix $P_0(t)$ such that the integral matrix Y of the system

$$\frac{dY}{dt} = YP_0(t) \tag{12.12}$$

is known, we obtain the system (12.7) in the form (see (31.30))

$$\frac{dX}{dt} = X\,[P_0(t) + (P(t) - P_0(t))\,\varepsilon], \tag{12.13}$$

that is, here, $P_1(t) = P(t) - P_0(t)$.

For $P_0(t)$ it is convenient to take a matrix such that the matrix Y is already a good approximation of the matrix X. For example, for Y, we may take the matrix

$$Y = X_m(t, 1) = \exp \sum_{k=0}^{m} A_k t \cdot Z_m(t, 1), \tag{12.14}$$

where $X_m(t, 1)$ is the approximate value of the integral matrix of a system of the form (12.7) or that of a system of the form

$$\frac{dX}{dt} = XP(t)\varepsilon \text{ for } \varepsilon = 1. \tag{12.15}$$

If we choose Y this way in advance, we easily find the corresponding periodic solution

$$P_0(t) = Z_m^{-1} B_m Z_m + Z_m^{-1} \frac{dZ_m}{dt}, \quad B_m = \sum_{k=0}^{m} A_k$$

or, we may choose $P_0(t)$ in such a way that $P(t) - P_0(t)$ is small over a large region of variation of t.

If we choose $P_0(t)$ in one way or another and then evaluate some terms of the series for $W(\varepsilon)$, and $Z(t, \varepsilon)$ for $\varepsilon = 1$, we evaluate a partial sum of the series representing $W(\varepsilon)$ and $Z(t, \varepsilon)$ for the system (12.15) for $\varepsilon = 1$ if these series converge and, of course, if the series representing $W(\varepsilon)$ and $Z(t, \varepsilon)$ for the system (12.13) converge. On the other hand, if they diverge but if the series representing $W(\varepsilon)$ and $Z(t, \varepsilon)$ for the system (12.13) converge, then the approximate values of $W_m(\varepsilon)$ and $Z_m(t, \varepsilon)$ for (12.13) provide, for $\varepsilon = 1$ approximate values of $W(\varepsilon)$ and $Z(t, \varepsilon)$ for their analytic continuation corresponding to the system (12.15) with $\varepsilon = 1$.

13. The Case in Which $P_0(t), P_1(t), \ldots, P_m(t)$ in Equation (10.1) Are Constants

Let us now consider the particular case of the system (10.1)

$$\frac{dX}{dt} = X \sum_{k=0}^{\infty} P_k(t) \varepsilon^k, \tag{13.1}$$

where (see [31]) the matrices $P_0(t), P_1(t), \ldots, P_m(t)$ are constants. Let us suppose also that the matrix P_0 has no characteristic numbers p_k, p_l such that $p_k - p_l = \nu i$ (where ν is an integer) or, in other words,

$$2\pi P_0 = \ln \exp 2\pi P_0$$

is the principal and regular value. Consequently, in the expansions (10.9) and (10.11), we can set $W_0 = P_0$ and $Z_0 = I$.

To determine W_k and Z_k (for $k \geqslant 1$), we have equations (11.2):

$$\frac{dZ_k}{dt} = \sum_{\nu=0}^{k} Z_{k-\nu} P_\nu - \sum_{\nu=0}^{k} W_{k-\nu} Z_\nu \,. \tag{13.2}$$

We need to find Z_k that are periodic with period 2π such that $Z_k(0) = 0$. We see from (13.2) that $Z_k = 0$ and $W_k = P_k$ (for $k = 1, \ldots, m$).

Thus, we have

$$W(\varepsilon) = \sum_{k=0}^{m} P_k \varepsilon^k + \sum_{k=m+1}^{\infty} W_k \varepsilon^k \,, \tag{13.3}$$

$$Z(t, \varepsilon) = I + \sum_{k=m+1}^{\infty} Z_k(t) \varepsilon^k \,. \tag{13.4}$$

We may also proceed this way: Let us write the system (13.1) in the form

$$\frac{dX}{dt} = X\,[P(\varepsilon) + P_1(t, \varepsilon)], \tag{13.5}$$

$$P(\varepsilon) = \sum_{k=0}^{m} P_k \varepsilon^k \,, \quad P_1(t, \varepsilon) = \sum_{k=m+1}^{\infty} P_k(t) \varepsilon^k \,,$$

and let us look at the auxiliary system

$$\frac{dX}{dt} = X\,[P(\varepsilon) + P_1(t, \varepsilon)]\,\lambda \tag{13.6}$$

where λ is a parameter. We seek a solution of this system in the form

$$X = \exp A(\lambda) t \cdot Z(t, \lambda), \tag{13.7}$$

$$A(\lambda) = \sum_{k=1}^{\infty} A_k \lambda^k \,, \quad Z(t, \lambda) = I + \sum_{k=1}^{\infty} Z_k(t) \lambda^k \,. \tag{13.8}$$

To determine Z_k and A_k, we have the equations

$$\frac{dZ_k}{dt} = Z_{k-1}\,[P(\varepsilon) + P_1(t,\,\varepsilon)] - A_k - \sum_{l=1}^{k-1} A_l Z_{k-l}, \tag{13.9}$$

$$\frac{dZ_1}{dt} = P(\varepsilon) + P_1(t,\,\varepsilon) - A_1.$$

From them, we obtain

$$A_1 = \frac{1}{2\pi}\int_0^{2\pi} P_1(t,\,\varepsilon)\,dt + P(\varepsilon),\quad Z_1 = \int_0^t P_1(t,\,\varepsilon)\,dt - \frac{t}{2\pi}\int_0^{2\pi} P_1(t,\,\varepsilon)\,dt.$$

We see that $Z_1(t), Z_2(t), \ldots,$ and also $A_2,\ A_3, \ldots$ are infinitesimals of order $m+1$ with respect to ε. If it turns out that the matrix $P(\varepsilon)$, for small $\varepsilon \neq 0$, has distinct characteristic numbers whose order of smallness $\leqslant m$, then the matrix $A(\varepsilon) = \sum_{k=1}^{\infty} A_k \lambda^k$, will not have multiple characteristic numbers for small values of ε if $|\lambda| \leqslant 1$ (or, in general, if $|\lambda| \leqslant M$) since the characteristic numbers μ of this matrix will be determined up to ε^m for small values of ε from the equation

$$|\lambda P(\varepsilon) - \mu| = 0,\quad |P(\varepsilon) - \bar{\mu}| = 0,\quad \bar{\mu} = \mu\lambda^{-1}.$$

But under these conditions, the series (13.8) will, in accordance with Theorem 2.1 and Remark 2.2 following it, converge also for $\lambda = 1$. Consequently, for small values of ε, we have for the system (13.5)

$$A(\varepsilon) = \sum_{k=1}^{\infty} A_k,\ Z(t,\,\varepsilon) = \mathrm{I} + \sum_{k=1}^{\infty} Z_k(t,\,\varepsilon). \tag{13.10}$$

Here, $Z_k(t,\,\varepsilon) = Z_k(t)$ in accordance with (13.8).

In our reasoning here, $P_1(t,\,\varepsilon)$ is an infinitesimal of order ε^{m+1} and is not necessarily a series in terms of ε.

Of course, we can also proceed in the following way: If we write Eq. (13.5) in the form

$$\frac{dX}{dt} = X\,[P(\varepsilon) + \lambda P_1(t,\,\varepsilon)],\quad P(\varepsilon) = P_0, \tag{13.11}$$

we find

$$X = \exp\,(W(\lambda)t)\cdot Z(t,\,\lambda), \tag{13.12}$$

$$W(\lambda) = \sum_{k=0}^{\infty} W_k \lambda^k, \quad Z(t, \lambda) = \sum_{k=0}^{\infty} Z_k(t) \lambda^k. \tag{13.13}$$

If we now assume that the matrix $P(\varepsilon)$ does not have characteristic numbers $p_k(\varepsilon), p_l(\varepsilon)$, such that

$$p_k(\varepsilon) - p_l(\varepsilon) = i\nu \tag{13.14}$$

where ν is an integer, we may set

$$W_0 = P(\varepsilon), \quad Z_0(t) = I. \tag{13.15}$$

We find $Z_k(t)$ and W_k from the equations

$$\frac{dZ_k}{dt} = Z_k P + Z_{k-1} P_1 - \sum_{\nu=0}^{k} W_{k-\nu} Z_\nu, \tag{13.16}$$

$$\frac{dZ_1}{dt} = Z_1 P(\varepsilon) - P(\varepsilon) Z_1 + P_1(t, \varepsilon) - W_1. \tag{13.17}$$

If we define W_1 from (13.17), we find, on the basis of (11.11_2),

$$\int_0^{2\pi} \exp P(\varepsilon) t \cdot W_1 \exp(-P(\varepsilon) t)\, dt = \int_0^{2\pi} \exp P(\varepsilon) t \cdot P_1(t, \varepsilon) \exp(-P(\varepsilon) t)\, dt.$$

To determine the elements of the matrix W_1, we obtain from this a system of linear equations with nonzero determinant since the elements of the matrix W_1 are, as we have seen, uniquely determined. The elements of the matrix $P_1(t, \varepsilon)$ are infinitesimals of order $m + 1$, or greater with respect to ε. Therefore, the elements of the matrix W_1 are also infinitesimals of order $m + 1$ or greater with respect to ε, and the same is true of the elements of the matrix $Z_1(t)$. We see from Eq. (13.16) that the elements of the matrices W_k and $Z_k(t)$ are in general infinitesimals of order $k(m + 1)$ or greater with respect to ε.

Consequently, we have

$$W(\lambda) = \sum_{k=1}^{\infty} W_{k(m+1)}(\varepsilon) \lambda^k + P(\varepsilon), \tag{13.18}$$

where the index $k(m+1)$ indicates the order of smallness with respect to ε. This series also converges for $|\lambda| \leqslant 1$ and for sufficiently small ε if the matrix $P(\varepsilon)$ has distinct characteristic numbers for $\varepsilon \neq 0$ that are of an order of smallness $\leqslant m$. Here, for the system (13.5), we have $W(\varepsilon)$ in the form of a convergent series

$$W(\varepsilon) = P(\varepsilon) + \sum_{k=1}^{\infty} W_{k(m+1)}(\varepsilon), \tag{13.19}$$

and $Z(t)$ in the form

$$Z(t) = \sum_{k=0}^{\infty} Z_{k(m+1)}(\varepsilon, t), \quad Z_0 = I. \tag{13.20}$$

In these considerations, again $P_1(t, \varepsilon)$ is an infinitesimal of order no greater than $m+1$ with respect to ε and is not necessarily holomorphic in the region $|\varepsilon| \leqslant r$.

We note again that the series (13.19) and (13.20) converge for those ε for which the characteristic numbers of the matrix $W(\lambda)$ (see (13.18))

$$p_k(\varepsilon) = p_k^{(m)}(\varepsilon) + p_k^{(m+1)}(\varepsilon) + p_k^{(m+1)}(\varepsilon, \lambda)$$

are distinct for all $|\lambda| \leqslant 1$. Here, $p_k^{(m+1)}(\varepsilon)$ is an infinitesimal of order $m+1$ generated by $P(\varepsilon)$ and $p_k^{(m+1)}(\varepsilon, \lambda)$ is a quantity generated by the expression

$$\sum_{k=1}^{\infty} W_{k(m+1)}(\varepsilon) \lambda^k .$$

The quantity $p_k^{(m)}(\varepsilon)$, although infinitesimal, of of order $\leqslant m$. If the $p_k^{(m)}(\varepsilon)$ (for $k = 1, \ldots, n$) are distinct and if

$$|p_k^{(m)}(\varepsilon)| > |p_k^{(m+1)}(\varepsilon)| + |p_k^{(m+1)}(\varepsilon, \lambda)|, \quad |\lambda| \leqslant 1,$$

then the series (13.19) and (13.20) converge (for small ε).

14. The Case in Which P_0 is Constant and $\exp P_0 t$ is a Periodic Matrix in Equation (10.1)

Consider the system

$$\frac{dX}{dt} = XP(t), \quad P(t) = \sum_{k=0}^{\infty} P_k(t)\varepsilon^k = P_0 + R(t, \varepsilon), \tag{14.1}$$

where the matrices P_k are periodic with period 2π and P_0 is constant. Suppose that the matrix $\exp P_0 t$ is periodic with period 2π. Then, before finding the series (10.9) and (10.11), we may proceed as follows.

We introduce* [31, Sect. 5] a new unknown matrix

$$X = Y \exp P_0 t = YX_0. \tag{14.2}$$

If we substitute this into (14.1), we obtain

$$\frac{dY}{dt} = Y\,[X_0 R(t, \varepsilon) X_0^{-1}] = YQ(t, \varepsilon). \tag{14.3}$$

Here, the matrix

$$Q(t, \varepsilon) = \sum_{k=1}^{\infty} Q_k(t)\,\varepsilon^k \tag{14.4}$$

is periodic with period 2π. Now, we may seek Y in the form

$$Y = \exp\left[\sum_{k=1}^{\infty} W_k \varepsilon^k t\right] \cdot \sum_{k=0}^{\infty} Z_k(t)\,\varepsilon^k, \quad Z_0 = I, \tag{14.5}$$

which simplifies the calculations in finding W_k and Z_k since $P_0 = W_0 = 0$ in Eq. (11.2).

15. An Example Illustrating Section 14

Example. Consider the system of two equations

$$\frac{dY}{dt} = Y\,[P_0 + \varepsilon P_1(t)] = YQ, \; P_0 = \left\|\begin{matrix} 0 & 1 \\ -1 & 0 \end{matrix}\right\|, \; P_1(t) = A \sin t + B \sin 2t, \tag{15.1}$$

where A and B are constant second-order matrices. Let us find a representation of the matrix

$$Y = \exp\,[W(\varepsilon)\,t] \cdot Z(t, \varepsilon), \quad Y_0(0) = I, \tag{15.2}$$

---

*Reference [31] also considers the more general case in which $P_0(t)$ is a matrix such that the integral matrix of the system $\frac{dX}{dt} = XP_0(t)$ is of the form (8.8), where the matrix W has purely imaginary characteristic numbers with prime elementary divisors.

where

$$W(\varepsilon) = \sum_{k=0}^{\infty} W_k \varepsilon^k, \tag{15.3}$$

$$Z(t, \varepsilon) = \sum_{k=0}^{\infty} Z_k(t) \varepsilon^k. \tag{15.4}$$

Here, the matrix P_0 has the characteristic numbers $p_1 = i$, $p_2 = -i$, $p_1 - p_2 = 2i$, and $2\pi P_0 = \ln \exp 2\pi P_0$ is not a regular value; that is, we may set $W_0 = P_0$.

First of all, let us find

$$Y = \sum_{k=0}^{\infty} Y_k \varepsilon^k. \tag{15.5}$$

To determine Y_0 and Y_1, we have the equations

$$\frac{dY_0}{dt} = Y_0 P_0, \quad \frac{dY_1}{dt} = Y_1 P + Y_0 P_1, \tag{15.6}$$

$$Y_0 = \exp P_0 t. \tag{15.7}$$

We seek Y_1 in the form

$$Y_1 = C(t) Y_0. \tag{15.8}$$

If we substitute this into (15.6), we obtain

$$\frac{dC}{dt} = Y_0 P_1 Y_0^{-1}, \quad C = \int_0^t Y_0 P_1 Y_0^{-1}\, dt. \tag{15.9}$$

On the basis of (1.14_1),

$$Y_0 = \sin t \cdot P_0 + \cos t, \quad Y_0^{-1} = -\sin t \cdot P_0 + \cos t. \tag{15.10}$$

On the basis of (15.7) and (17.8), we have

$$V = Y(2\pi) = I + \varepsilon C(2\pi) + \ldots \tag{15.11}$$

$$C(2\pi) = \int_0^{2\pi} [-P_0 P_1 P_0 \sin^2 t - P_1 P_0 \sin t \cdot \cos t +$$

$$+ P_0 P_1 \sin t \cdot \cos t + P_1 \cos^2 t]\, dt = \int_0^{2\pi} [-BP_0 + P_0 B]\, \frac{\sin^2 2t}{2}\, dt =$$

$$= \begin{Vmatrix} b_{21} + b_{12} & b_{22} - b_{11} \\ b_{22} - b_{11} & -(b_{12} + b_{21}) \end{Vmatrix} \frac{\pi}{2}, \tag{15.12}$$

where the b_{kl} are the elements of the matrix B. Consequently,

$$Y(2\pi)=\left\|\begin{matrix} 1+\varepsilon\frac{\pi}{2}(b_{12}+b_{21}) & \varepsilon\frac{\pi}{2}(b_{22}-b_{11}) \\ \varepsilon\frac{\pi}{2}(b_{22}-b_{11}) & 1-\frac{\pi\varepsilon}{2}(b_{12}+b_{21}) \end{matrix}\right\|+\varepsilon^2 Y_2+\ldots. \quad (15.13)$$

If we represent Y_0, defined in (15.7), in the form (10.7), we obtain

$$A_0=0,\ \ Z_0(t)=Y_0. \quad (15.14)$$

Here, $A_0=0=\ln\exp 2\pi P_0$ is the principal value and hence is regular. On the basis of formula (10.11), we obtain

$$W_0=0 \quad (15.15)$$

and, on the basis of (10.9), (15.14) and (15.7),

$$Z_0(t)=\exp P_0 t. \quad (15.16)$$

To determine the matrices W_k and $Z_k(t)$ (for $k\geqslant 1$), we have the equations (see (11.2), where $W_0=0$)

$$\frac{dZ_k}{dt}=Z_k(t)P_0+\sum_{\nu=1}^{k}Z_{k-\nu}(t)P_\nu(t)-\sum_{\nu=0}^{k-1}W_{k-\nu}Z_\nu(t). \quad (15.17)$$

Therefore,

$$\frac{dZ_1}{dt}=Z_1P_0+Z_0P_1-W_1Z_0. \quad (15.18)$$

We seek Z_1 in the form

$$Z_1=C\exp P_0t=CZ_0. \quad (15.19)$$

We have

$$\frac{dC}{dt}=(Z_0P_1-W_1Z_0)Z_0^{-1}=Z_0P_1Z_0^{-1}-W_1, \quad (15.20)$$

$$C=\int_0^t[Z_0P_1Z_0^{-1}-W_1]\,dt. \quad (15.21)$$

Since $Y_0=Z_0$, we have, on the basis of (15.10),

$$C = \int_0^t [-P_0P_1P_0 \sin^2 t + (P_0P_1 - P_1P_0) \sin t \cos t + P_1 \cos^2 t - W_1] \, dt.$$

Thus, we have found Z_1 in the form (15.19). To find W_1 we need to require that Z_1 satisfy

$$Z_1 (t + 2\pi) = Z_1 (t). \tag{15.22}$$

Then

$$W_1 = \frac{1}{2\pi} \int_0^{2\pi} [(P_0P_1 - P_1P_0) \sin t \cos t + \\ + P_1 \cos^2 t - P_0P_1P_0 \sin^2 t] \, dt.$$

Keeping the value of P_1 in mind, we obtain from (15.1)

$$W_1 = \frac{1}{4} [P_0B - BP_0]. \tag{15.23}$$

Similarly, we can easily find W_k and Z_k (for $k \geqslant 2$) from Eqs. (15.17). Specifically, to determine Z_k and W_k, we have

$$\frac{dZ_k}{dt} = Z_kP_0 + F_k(t) - W_kZ_0, F_k = \sum_{\nu=1}^{k} Z_{k-\nu}P_\nu - \sum_{\nu=1}^{k-1} W_{k-\nu}Z_\nu, \tag{15.24}$$

$$Z_k = C_k \exp P_0t = C_kZ_0, \tag{15.25}$$

$$\frac{dC_k}{dt} = \int_0^t (F_k(t) Z_0^{-1} - W_k) \, dt, \tag{15.26}$$

$$W_k = \frac{1}{2\pi} \int_0^{2\pi} F_k(t) Z_0^{-1} \, dt. \tag{15.27}$$

On the basis of Theorem 6.1, the series (15.5) converges for all finite values of ε. The series (15.3) and (15.4) converge at least in the region $|\varepsilon| < R$ in which the discriminant of the characteristic equation of the matrix (15.11)

$$\Delta(\varepsilon) = \sigma^2 (Y(2\pi)) - 4$$

has no more than one zero. Here, it is convenient to keep in mind that

$$D(Y(2\pi)) = \exp \int_0^{2\pi} \sigma(Q(t)) \, dt = 1.$$

We may proceed in a different way, following the lines shown in Sect. 14. Specifically, we introduce the matrix Y defined by

$$X = Y \exp P_0 t = YY_0. \tag{15.28}$$

If we substitute this into (15.1), we obtain

$$\frac{dY}{dt} = YY_0 P_1(t) Y_0^{-1} \varepsilon = YR(t)\varepsilon, \tag{15.29}$$

$$R(t) = Y_0 P_1(t) Y_0^{-1}. \tag{15.30}$$

If we use (15.10), we shall have

$$R(t) = -P_0P_1P_0 \sin^2 t + (P_0P_1 - P_1P_0)\sin t \cdot \cos t + P_1 \cos^2 t. \tag{15.31}$$

Now, we may seek Y in the form

$$Y = \exp \sum_{k=1}^{\infty} W_k \varepsilon^k t \sum_{k=0}^{\infty} Z_k(t) \varepsilon^k, \quad Z_0 = I. \tag{15.32}$$

In Eq. (15.24) we shall have $P_0 = 0$ and $Z_0 = I$, which simplifies the calculations.

We also obtain the integral matrix (15.5) in the form

$$Y = \exp\left(\sum_{k=0}^{\infty} W_k \varepsilon^k t\right) \cdot \sum_{k=0}^{\infty} Z_k(t) \varepsilon^k \tag{15.33}$$

on the basis of Theorem 2.3.

Let us first represent the matrix (15.13) in the form

$$Y(2\pi) = S \begin{Vmatrix} \lambda_1 & 0 \\ 0 & \lambda_2 \end{Vmatrix} S^{-1}. \tag{15.34}$$

We easily find

$$\lambda_1 = 1 + \varepsilon \frac{\pi}{2} M + \ldots, \quad \lambda_2 = 1 - \varepsilon \frac{\pi}{2} M + \ldots, \tag{15.35}$$

$$M = \sqrt{(b_{21} + b_{12})^2 + (b_{22} - b_{11})^2}.$$

Suppose that $M \neq 0$. Then,

$$S = S_0 + S_1\varepsilon + \dots, \quad S^{-1} = S_0^{-1} + \dots, \tag{15.36}$$

$$S_0 = \begin{Vmatrix} s_{11} & -\frac{A}{b} s_{22} \\ \frac{A}{b} s_{11} & s_{22} \end{Vmatrix},$$

$$S_0^{-1} = \begin{Vmatrix} s_{22} & \frac{A}{b} s_{22} \\ -\frac{A}{b} s_{11} & s_{11} \end{Vmatrix} \frac{1}{s_{11} s_{22}\left(1 + \frac{A^2}{b^2}\right)}, \tag{15.37}$$

where $A = M - (b_{12} + b_{21})$, $b = b_{22} - b_{11}$, and s_{11} and s_{22} are arbitrary nonzero numbers.

In accordance with the example following Theorem 2.3, we have

$$\ln Y(2\pi, \varepsilon) = \sum_{k=0}^{\infty} N_k \varepsilon^k, \tag{15.38}$$

where we may set

$$N_0 = S_0 [2k\pi i, \; -2k\pi i] S_0^{-1}, \tag{15.39}$$

k being an integer. Keeping the value of S_0 in mind, we obtain

$$N_0 = \frac{b^2 2k\pi i}{b^2 + A^2} \begin{Vmatrix} 1 - \frac{A^2}{b^2} & \frac{2A}{b} \\ \frac{2A}{b} & \frac{A^2}{b^2} - 1 \end{Vmatrix} = \frac{2k\pi i}{b^2 + A^2} \begin{Vmatrix} b^2 - A^2 & 2bA \\ 2bA & A^2 - b^2 \end{Vmatrix}. \tag{15.40}$$

It is easy to see that

$$b^2 - A^2 = 2(b_{12} + b_{21})A, \; b^2 + A^2 = 2MA.$$

Therefore, we have

$$N_0 = 2k\pi i \begin{Vmatrix} \sin\varphi & \cos\varphi \\ \cos\varphi & -\sin\varphi \end{Vmatrix}, \tag{15.41}$$

$$\sin\varphi = \frac{b_{12} + b_{21}}{M}, \quad \cos\varphi = \frac{b_{22} - b_{11}}{M},$$

$$M = \sqrt{(b_{12} + b_{21})^2 + (b_{22} - b_{11})^2}. \tag{15.42}$$

We recall that our assumption is that $M \neq 0$.

Consequently, on the basis of the example following Theorem 2.3, we have (15.33) for the matrix (15.5), where

$$W_0 = \frac{1}{2\pi} \ln Y(2\pi, 0) = \frac{N_0}{2\pi} = ki \begin{Vmatrix} \sin\varphi & \cos\varphi \\ \cos\varphi & -\sin\varphi \end{Vmatrix}. \quad (15.43)$$

To find $Z_0(t)$, we set $k = 0$ in (15.17). We obtain

$$\frac{dZ_0}{dt} = Z_0 P_0 - W_0 Z_0, \quad Z_0(0) = I, \quad (15.44)$$

$$Z_0 = \exp(-W_0 t) \cdot \exp P_0 t. \quad (15.45)$$

To determine Z_1 and W_1, we set $k = 1$ in (15.17). We have

$$\frac{dZ_1}{dt} = Z_1 P_0 - W_0 Z_1 + Z_0 P_1 - W_1 Z_0, \quad Z_1(0) = 0, \quad (15.46)$$

$$Z_1(t + 2\pi) = Z_1(t). \quad (15.46_1)$$

This equation is not an equation of the type (11.13) that we studied above since, in this case, the characteristic numbers of the matrix P_0 are $\lambda_1 = i$ and $\lambda_2 = -i$. Therefore, they do not possess the property that $\lambda_1 - \lambda_2 \neq mi$ for integral m since $\lambda_1 - \lambda_2 = 2i$. However, Theorem 2.3 assures us that, in this case, a solution satisfying condition (15.46_1) exists for a suitable choice of W_1. Let us seek a solution of Eq. (15.46) in the form (11.7)

$$Z_1 = \exp(-W_0 t) \cdot C \exp(P_0 t). \quad (15.47)$$

If we substitute this into (15.46), we obtain

$$\frac{dC}{dt} = \exp W_0 t \cdot [Z_0 P_1 - W_1 Z_0] \exp(-P_0 t), \quad (15.48)$$

$$C = \int_0^t \exp W_0 t \cdot [Z_0 P_1 - W_1 Z_0] \exp(-P_0 t)\, dt.$$

Since necessarily

$$Z_1(0) = Z_1(2\pi) = 0 \text{ and } \exp(-W_0 2\pi) = \exp 2\pi P_0 = I,$$

we have

$$C(2\pi) = \int_0^{2\pi} \exp W_0 t \cdot [Z_0 P_1 - W_1 Z_0] \exp(-P_0 t)\, dt = 0. \quad (15.49)$$

But

$$Z_0 = \exp(-W_0t)\cdot\exp P_0t.$$

Therefore,

$$C(2\pi) = \int_0^{2\pi} [\exp P_0t\cdot P_1\cdot\exp(-P_0t) - \\ - \exp W_0t\cdot W_1\exp(-W_0t)]\,dt = 0. \tag{15.50}$$

In accordance with (15.31), we have

$$\exp P_0t\cdot P_1\exp(-P_0t) = -P_0P_1P_0\sin^2 t + (P_0P_1 - P_1P_0)\sin t\cdot\cos t + P_1\cos^2 t,$$

or, substituting the value P_1 given by (15.1), we obtain

$$\exp P_0t\cdot P_1\cdot\exp(-P_0t) = -P_0AP_0\sin^3 t - P_0BP_0\sin 2t\cdot\sin^2 t + \\ + (P_0A - AP_0)\sin^2 t\cdot\cos t + (P_0B - BP_0)\sin t\cdot\cos t\cdot\sin 2t + \\ + A\sin t\cdot\cos^2 t + B\sin 2t\cdot\cos^2 t.$$

On the basis of (1.14₁), we also have

$$\exp W_0t\cdot W_1\cdot\exp(-W_0t) = -W_0W_1W_0\frac{\sin^2 kt}{k^2} + \\ + (W_0W_1 - W_1W_0)\frac{\sin kt\cdot\cos kt}{k} + W_1\cos^2 kt.$$

If we substitute this into (15.50), we obtain

$$\frac{P_0B - BP_0}{2} + \frac{W_0W_1W_0}{k^2} - W_1 = 0.$$

Here, W_0 is given by formula (15.43) and P_0 by (15.1).

Let us rewrite the last equation in the form

$$\frac{P_0B - BP_0}{2} = W_1 - \frac{W_0W_1W_0}{k^2} \tag{15.51}$$

and substitute the values of P_0, W_0, and

$$B = \begin{Vmatrix} b_{11} & b_{12} \\ b_{21} & b_{22} \end{Vmatrix},\quad W_1 = \begin{Vmatrix} w_{11} & w_{12} \\ w_{21} & w_{22} \end{Vmatrix}.$$

We obtain

$$\frac{M}{2}\begin{Vmatrix} \sin\varphi & \cos\varphi \\ \cos\varphi & -\sin\varphi \end{Vmatrix} = \begin{Vmatrix} \tau_{11} & \tau_{12} \\ \tau_{21} & \tau_{22} \end{Vmatrix}, \tag{15.52}$$

where M is given by formula (15.42) and

$$\begin{aligned}\tau_{11} &= w_{11}(1+\sin^2\varphi) + w_{12}\sin\varphi\cdot\cos\varphi + w_{21}\sin\varphi\cdot\cos\varphi + \\ &\quad + w_{22}\cos^2\varphi,\\ \tau_{12} &= w_{11}\sin\varphi\cdot\cos\varphi + w_{12}\cos^2\varphi + w_{21}\cos^2\varphi - w_{22}\sin\varphi\cdot\cos\varphi,\\ \tau_{21} &= w_{11}\sin\varphi\cdot\cos\varphi + w_{12}\cos^2\varphi + w_{21}\cos^2\varphi - w_{22}\sin\varphi\cdot\cos\varphi,\\ \tau_{22} &= w_{11}\cos^2\varphi - w_{12}\sin\varphi\cdot\cos\varphi - w_{21}\sin\varphi\cdot\cos\varphi + \\ &\quad + w_{22}(1+\sin^2\varphi).\end{aligned} \tag{15.53}$$

Consequently, we have

$$\frac{M}{2}\sin\varphi = \tau_{11},\quad \frac{M}{2}\cos\varphi = \tau_{12},\quad \frac{M}{2}\cos\varphi = \tau_{21},\ -\frac{M}{2}\sin\varphi = \tau_{22} \tag{15.54}$$

and

$$\tau_{12} = \tau_{21}. \tag{15.55}$$

If we add the first and fourth of Eqs. (15.54), we obtain

$$w_{11} + w_{22} = 0. \tag{15.56}$$

If we substitute $w_{22} = -w_{11}$ into the first and second of Eqs. (15.54), we have

$$\frac{M}{2}\sin\varphi = 2w_{11}\sin^2\varphi + w_{12}\sin\varphi\cdot\cos\varphi + w_{21}\sin\varphi\cdot\cos\varphi, \tag{15.57}$$

$$\frac{M}{2}\cos\varphi = 2w_{11}\sin\varphi\cdot\cos\varphi + w_{12}\cos^2\varphi + w_{21}\cos^2\varphi. \tag{15.58}$$

Here, the following cases are possible: 1) $\cos\varphi = 0$; 2) $\sin\varphi = 0$; 3) $\sin\varphi \times \cos\varphi \neq 0$.

In case 1), we have $4w_{11} = \pm M = \pm|b_{12} + b_{21}|$, and w_{12} and w_{21} are arbitrary.

In case 2), $2(w_{12} + w_{21}) = \pm M = \pm|b_{22} - b_{11}|$, and w_{11} and w_{12} are arbitrary.

In case 3), Eqs. (15.57) and (15.58) become

$$\frac{M}{2} = 2w_{11}\sin\varphi + (w_{12} + w_{21})\cos\varphi,\ \frac{M}{2} = 2w_{11}\sin\varphi + (w_{12} + w_{21})\cos\varphi. \tag{15.58$_1$}$$

Consequently, w_{12} and w_{21} may be considered arbitrary but w_{11} is uniquely determined. Z_1 is found in accordance with formula (15.47):

$$\begin{aligned} Z_1 &= \exp(-W_0 t)\cdot C(t)\exp(P_0 t),\\ C &= \int_0^t [\exp P_0 t\cdot P_1\exp(-P_0 t) - \\ &\quad - \exp W_0 t\cdot W_1 \exp(-W_0 t)]\,dt. \end{aligned}$$

Now, we can determine Z_2 and W_2 from (15.17) for $k=2$:

$$\frac{dZ_2}{dt} = Z_2P_0 - W_0Z_2 + Z_1P_1 - W_1Z_1 - W_2Z_0. \tag{15.59}$$

Z_2 can be sought in the form

$$Z_2 = \exp(-W_0t)\cdot C(t)\exp(P_0t).$$

To determine C, we obtain the equations

$$\frac{dC}{dt} = \exp W_0t\cdot[Z_1P_1 - W_1Z_1 - W_2Z_0]\exp(-P_0t),$$

$$C = \int_0^t \exp W_0t\cdot[Z_1P_1 - W_1Z_1 - W_2Z_0]\exp(-P_0t)\,dt.$$

If we require that $Z_2(2\pi) = Z_2(0) = 0$, we obtain $C(2\pi) = 0$. Then to determine the elements w_{kl} of the matrix W_2, we obtain equations whose right-hand members coincide with the right-hand members of Eqs. (15.53), but whose left-hand members are different and contain two arbitrary elements of the matrix W_1:

$$A_1 = w_{11}(1+\sin^2\varphi) + w_{12}\sin\varphi\cdot\cos\varphi + w_{21}\sin\varphi\cdot\cos\varphi + {}$$
$$+ w_{22}\cos^2\varphi, \tag{15.60}$$

$$A_2 = w_{11}\sin\varphi\cdot\cos\varphi + w_{12}\cos^2\varphi + w_{21}\cos^2\varphi - {}$$
$$- w_{22}\sin\varphi\cdot\cos\varphi,$$

$$A_3 = w_{11}\sin\varphi\cdot\cos\varphi + w_{12}\cos^2\varphi + w_{21}\cos^2\varphi - w_{22}\sin\varphi\cdot\cos\varphi.$$

$$A_4 = w_{11}\cos^2\varphi - w_{12}\sin\varphi\cdot\cos\varphi - w_{21}\sin\varphi\cdot\cos\varphi + {}$$
$$+ w_{22}(1+\sin^2\varphi).$$

In case 1) (where $\cos\varphi = 0$), we have $A_2 = A_3 = 0$, from which we find the arbitrary elements of the matrix W_1. In case 2) (where $\sin\varphi = 0$), we have $A_2 = A_3$, $A_1 = w_{11} + w_{22}$ and $A_4 = w_{11} + w_{22}$ from which we obtain $A_1 = A_4$. From these two equations, we again find the arbitrary elements of the matrix W_1. In case 3) (where $\sin\varphi\cdot\cos\varphi \neq 0$) we have

$$\frac{A_1 + A_4}{2} = w_{11} + w_{22}.$$

If we make the substitution

$$w_{22} = -w_{11} + \frac{A_1 + A_4}{2}$$

in the first and second of Eqs. (15.60), this gives us

$$M_1 = 2w_{11}\sin\varphi + (w_{12} + w_{21})\cos\varphi, \quad M_2 = 2w_{11}\sin\varphi + + (w_{12} + w_{21})\cos\varphi,$$

from which we get $M_1 = M_2$. Also, A_2 is obviously equal to A_3. From these two equations, we again find arbitrary elements of the matrix W_1. This follows from Theorem 2.3, which ensures uniqueness of the determination of the matrices W_k and Z_k.

Thus, in all cases, we finally find W_1 and Z_1. It is easy to see that we can also find W_k and Z_k (for $k \geqslant 2$).

We shall not complete the evaluation of W_1 and Z_1. We note now that the system (15.1) can be first replaced with the system

$$\frac{dX}{dt} = X\left[\begin{Vmatrix} i & 0 \\ 0 & -i \end{Vmatrix} + \varepsilon P(t)\right], \tag{15.61}$$

where

$$Y = XN, \tag{15.62}$$

$$N = \begin{Vmatrix} 1 & -i \\ -i & 1 \end{Vmatrix}, \quad N^{-1} = \begin{Vmatrix} 1 & i \\ i & 1 \end{Vmatrix}\frac{1}{2}, \quad P(t) = NP_1(t)N^{-1},$$

$$\begin{Vmatrix} i & 0 \\ 0 & -i \end{Vmatrix} = N\begin{Vmatrix} 0 & 1 \\ -1 & 0 \end{Vmatrix}N^{-1}.$$

For the solution X of the system (15.61), we easily find the representation

$$X = \exp W(\varepsilon)t \cdot Z(t, \varepsilon), \quad X(0) = \mathrm{I}, \quad W(\varepsilon) = \sum_{k=0}^{\infty} W_k\varepsilon^k, \quad Z(t, \varepsilon) = \sum_{k=0}^{\infty} Z_k\varepsilon^k,$$

after which we obtain such a representation for Y with $Y(0) = \mathrm{I}$ since

$$Y = N^{-1}XN = \exp[N^{-1}W(\varepsilon)Nt] \cdot N^{-1}ZN. \tag{15.63}$$

Remark 15.1. In accordance with Theorem 2.3 and the example following it, we may take, instead of (15.39),

$$N_0 = S_0[2m\pi i, \ 2n\pi i]S_0^{-1}, \tag{15.64}$$

where m and n are arbitrary integers. Correspondingly, instead of (15.43), we then need to set

$$W_0 = \frac{N_0}{2\pi} = S_0[mi, ni]S_0^{-1} =$$

$$= \begin{Vmatrix} m\sin^2\varphi + n\cos^2\varphi & (m-n)\sin\varphi\cos\varphi \\ (m-n)\sin\varphi\cdot\cos\varphi & m\cos^2\varphi + n\sin^2\varphi \end{Vmatrix} i, \tag{15.65}$$

where

$$\sin\varphi = \frac{b}{\sqrt{b^2+A^2}}, \quad \cos\varphi = \frac{A}{\sqrt{b^2+A^2}},$$

and the values of A and b are given in formula (15.37). After this, we would again find W_k (for $k \geqslant 1$) and Z_k (for $k \geqslant 0$) that appear in (15.33).

16. Canonical Systems [8, 9, 12, 13, 31, 33, 34, 67, 68]

Remark 16.1. Suppose that the characteristic equation of a real matrix $K(\varepsilon)$ of order $2n$ is of the form

$$D(\lambda, \varepsilon) = \lambda^{2n} + a_1\lambda^{2(n-1)} + \ldots + a_{n-1}\lambda^2 + a_n + \Phi(\lambda, \varepsilon) = 0, \tag{16.1}$$

where the coefficients $a_1, \ldots, a_n$ are independent of λ and ε and where $\Phi(\lambda, \varepsilon)$ is a polynomial in λ^2 of degree not exceeding $n-1$ with coefficients that are holomorphic functions of ε in a neighborhood of $\varepsilon = 0$ such that $\Phi(\lambda, \varepsilon) \to 0$ as $\varepsilon \to 0$. Then, if the roots of the equation [13]

$$D(\mu) = \mu^n + a_1\mu^{n-1} + \ldots + a_{n-1}\mu + a_n = 0 \tag{16.2}$$

are negative and distinct, the roots of Eq. (16.1) will be purely imaginary for real sufficiently small* values of ε; that is, $\lambda = \mu_k i + i\varphi_k(\varepsilon)$ (for $k = 1, \ldots, n$), where the μ_k are the roots of Eq. (16.2) and $\varphi_k(\varepsilon)$ is a real function that approaches 0 as $\varepsilon \to 0$. We note also that if the coefficients $a_1, \ldots, a_n$ are infinitesimals of lower order than the coefficients of $\Phi(\lambda, \varepsilon)$ for small values of ε, then, in the case of distinct $\mu_k < 0$, the roots of Eq. (16.1) will also be purely imaginary for small values of ε. We write the expression (16.1) in the form

$$D(\mu(\varepsilon)) = \mu^n + A_1(\varepsilon)\mu^{n-1} + \ldots + A_n(\varepsilon) = 0,$$
$$A_k(0) = a_k \quad (k = 1, \ldots, n). \tag{16.1$_1$}$$

Remark 16.2. Suppose that the roots $\mu_1, \ldots, \mu_n$ of Eq. (16.2) are negative but that some of them are multiple roots. Now, for all roots of (16.1) to be purely imaginary for small values

---

*And of course for $|\varepsilon| < r$, where r is the distance to the closest root of the equation $\Delta(K(\varepsilon)) = 0$. Here, $\Delta(K(\varepsilon))$ is the discriminant of Eq. (16.1). This follows from the fact that the complex roots of (16.1) arise immediately, in complex conjugate pairs, close to the multiple root if ε is real.

of ε, it is necessary and sufficient that all roots of equation (16.1_1) be negative* for small values of ε. But this will be the case if and only if all roots of (16.1_1) can be represented, for small values of ε, in the form

$$\mu_k(\varepsilon) = \mu_k + \sum_{l=1}^{\infty} \alpha_l^{(k)} \varepsilon^{\frac{l}{p}} \quad (k = 1, \ldots, n), \; p = 1 \text{ or } p = 2 \qquad (16.2_1)$$

with real** coefficients $\alpha_l^{(k)}$. If the discriminant $\Delta(K(\varepsilon))$ of equation (16.1_1) is not identically*** equal to 0, then the $\mu_k(\varepsilon)$ will be distinct. On the other hand, if there exist $\mu_k(\varepsilon)$, where p is an integer exceeding 2, some of the roots $\lambda(\varepsilon)$ will be such that $R(\lambda(\varepsilon)) > 0$ and others will be such that $R(\lambda(\varepsilon)) < 0$ since, in this case, there are complex $\mu_k(\varepsilon)$.

Suppose now that we are given the canonical system of $2n$ differential equations

$$\frac{dX}{dt} = X\left(P_0 + \sum_{k=1}^{\infty} P_k(t)\, \varepsilon^k\right), \quad |\varepsilon| < r, \qquad (16.3)$$

where the $P_k(t)$ are real continuous periodic matrices with period 2π, where ε is a numerical parameter and where P_0 is a real constant matrix. Thus, the system (16.3) corresponds to a system of the form

$$\frac{dx_s}{dt} = -\frac{\partial H}{\partial y_s}, \quad \frac{dy_s}{dt} = \frac{\partial H}{\partial x_s} \quad (s = 1, 2, \ldots, n),$$

where H is a quadratic**** form in the variables $x_1, \ldots, x_n, y_1, \ldots, y_n$, the coefficients of which are periodic functions of t. Let us suppose that $2\pi P_0 = \ln \exp 2\pi P_0$ is a regular value. Then,*****

---

*For the general solution of this problem, see [32] and Sect. 47 of the present book.

**If $\mu_k(\varepsilon) = \mu_k + \sum_{l=1}^{\infty} \alpha_l^{(k)} \varepsilon^l$ or $\mu_k(\varepsilon) = \mu_k + \sum_{l=1}^{\infty} \alpha_l^{(k)} \varepsilon^{l/2}$ and if there are complex $\alpha_l^{(k)}$, then $\mu_k(\varepsilon)$ will obviously also be complex.

***That is, if at least one coefficient in the expansion of the discriminant $\Delta(K(\varepsilon)) = \sum_{k=0}^{\infty} \Delta_k \varepsilon^k$ is nonzero.

****$H = \sum_{s=1}^{k} \sum_{\sigma=1}^{k} (p_{s\sigma} x_s x_\sigma + q_{s\sigma} y_s y_\sigma + r_{s\sigma} x_s y_\sigma)$.

*****It is shown in [33] that the system

$$\frac{dZ}{dt} = Z \sum_{k=0}^{\infty} W_k \varepsilon^k$$

is canonical.

$$X = \exp\left(\sum_{k=0}^{\infty} W_k \varepsilon^k t\right) \cdot \sum_{k=0}^{\infty} Z_k(t)\, \varepsilon^k, \quad W_0 = P_0, \quad Z_0 = 1,$$

$$Z_k(0) = 0 \quad (k \geqslant 1). \tag{16.4}$$

According to Lyapunov's theorem [26, p. 209], the characteristic equation of the matrix $\sum_{k=0}^{\infty} W_k \varepsilon^k$ is of the form

$$\mu^n + a_1(\varepsilon)\,\mu^{n-1} + \ldots + a_{n-1}(\varepsilon)\,\mu + a_n(\varepsilon) = 0, \tag{16.5}$$

where $\mu = \lambda^2$, where $a_1(0), \ldots, a_n(0)$ are the coefficients in the characteristic equation of the matrix P_0, and where the series $a_m(\varepsilon)$ converge (for $m = 1, \ldots, n$) at least in the region $|\varepsilon| < R < r$ in which the discriminant of the characteristic equation of the matrix

$$X(2\pi, \varepsilon) = \sum_{k=0}^{\infty} X_k(2\pi)\, \varepsilon^k, \quad X_0 = I \tag{16.6}$$

has no more than one zero.

Theorem 16.1 (See [8] and [13].) *If the roots of the equation*

$$\mu^n + a_1(0)\,\mu^{n-1} + \ldots + a_{n-1}(0)\,\mu + a_n(0) = 0 \tag{16.7}$$

are negative and distinct, then all solutions of Eq. (16.1) are bounded but do not approach zero; that is, they are bounded and oscillatory functions.

This theorem follows from Remark 16.1.

In [8], Artem'yev, studying canonical systems of the form (16.3) carried out detailed investigations* for a specific system of four equations.

Remark 16.3. If some of the roots of Eq. (16.7) are 0 (though none of them are positive), it is sometimes sufficient to examine the matrix W_1. Specifically, if the characteristic equation of the matrix $P_0 + W_1\varepsilon$

---

*Artem'yev's investigations [8, 9] were unknown to me at the time of completion of [14], which is a portion of the studies made in October-December 1942, when I had no access to mathematical literature (except for one book by Lyapunov, Obshchaya zadacha ob ustoychivosti dvizheniya [The General Problem of Stability of Motion]). The book [14] includes almost my complete doctoral dissertation, which was defended in July of 1943 at the University of Kazan. (A few sections of the dissertation were not included in that book and were published separately.)

$$\mu^n + b_1(\varepsilon)\mu^{n-1} + \ldots + b_{n-1}(\varepsilon)\mu + b_n(\varepsilon) = 0, \quad \mu = \lambda^2$$

is such that all $\mu < 0$ for small $\varepsilon \neq 0$ (for example, if the expansions of all roots have distinct coefficients of first powers of ε), then the roots of Eq. (16.5) will be negative for small values of ε and the characteristic numbers of the matrix $W = \sum_{k=0}^{\infty} W_k \varepsilon^k$ will be purely imaginary (and distinct) for small values of ε.

Remark 16.4. If the roots $\mu_1, \ldots, \mu_n$ of Eq. (16.7) are all negative but some of them coincide, then the solutions of the system (16.1) will be bounded but oscillatory if the μ_k are of the form (16.2$_1$) and $\Delta(K(\varepsilon)) \not\equiv 0$ (that is, if $\Delta = \sum_{k=0}^{\infty} \Delta_k \varepsilon^k$ and at least one of the $\Delta_k \neq 0$) since, in this case, $\mu_1(\varepsilon), \ldots, \mu_n(\varepsilon)$ are negative and distinct (for small values of ε).

Remark 16.5. On the basis of the preceding sections, we can also easily consider the case in which $2\pi P_0$ is not a regular value of $\ln \exp 2\pi P_0$. For example, we can, as a preliminary, transform the system (16.1) into a system for which $2\pi P_0$ is a regular value of $\ln \exp 2\pi P_0$. But we do not need to do this. Instead, we may simply take

$$W_0 = \frac{1}{2\pi} \ln \exp 2\pi P_0$$

which is a principal value. However, we need to keep in mind that if we take the irregular value

$$W_0 = \frac{1}{2\pi} \ln \exp 2\pi P_0$$

in accordance with Theorem 2.3, then the characteristic equation of the matrix $\sum_{k=0}^{\infty} W_k \varepsilon^k$ may fail to be of the form (16.5).

For example, if (15.1) is a canonical system and we take W_0 in the form (15.65), where $m \neq -n$, we do not obtain an equation of the form (16.5) since the roots of the characteristic equation of the matrix $\sum_{k=0}^{\infty} W_k \varepsilon^k$ obviously do not come in pairs of opposite sign. However, if we take

$$W_0 = \frac{1}{2\pi} \ln \exp 2\pi P_0$$

which is the principal value and is actually irregular, of the form (15.43) [on the basis of (15.39)], we obtain (16.5).

17. The System (16.3) With $P_0=P_1=\ldots=P_{m-1}=0$

Let us suppose that, in the system (16.3), $P_0=P_1=\ldots=P_{m-1}=0$ and that $P_m(t)\neq 0$. Then, in accordance with (13.3) and (13.4), we have

$$W(\varepsilon)=\sum_{k=m}^{\infty} W_k \varepsilon^k, \quad Z(t,\varepsilon)=I+\sum_{k=m}^{\infty} Z_k \varepsilon^k$$

where ε is real, and

$$\frac{dZ_m}{dt}=P_m(t)-W_m, \quad W_m=\frac{1}{2\pi}\int_0^{2\pi} P_m(t)\,dt, \quad Z_m=\int_0^t [P_m(t)-W_m]\,dt.$$

We have the characteristic equation for the matrix $M=W\varepsilon^{-m}$ in the form

$$\mu^{2n}+a_1\mu^{2(n-1)}+\ldots+\mu^2 a_{n-1}+a_n+P_{n-1}(\mu^2,\varepsilon)=0, \qquad (17.1)$$

where $a_1,\ldots,a_n$ are the coefficients of the characteristic equation for the matrix W_m and the coefficients of the $(n-1)$st polynomial $P_{n-1}(\mu^2,\varepsilon)$ converge to 0 as $\varepsilon\to 0$.

Theorem 17.1. *If the roots p_k of the equation*

$$p^n+a_1p^{n-1}+\ldots+pa_{n-1}+a_n=0, \quad p=\mu^2 \qquad (17.2)$$

are distinct and negative, that is, if $p_k=-b_k^2$, where each b_k (for $k=1,\ldots,n$) is positive, then the characteristic numbers of the matrix W are purely imaginary and distinct for small values of ε.

Proof: For the roots $p(\varepsilon)$ of Eq. (17.1), we have $p_k(\varepsilon)=-b_k^2+\varphi_k(\varepsilon)$ (where $k=1,\ldots,n$), where the real function $\varphi_k(\varepsilon)\to 0$ as $\varepsilon\to 0$. Consequently, for characteristic numbers λ_ν and $\lambda_{-\nu}$ (for $\nu=1,\ldots,n$) of the matrix W, we have

$$\lambda_\nu=i(b_\nu+\psi_\nu(\varepsilon))\varepsilon^m, \quad \lambda_{-\nu}=-i(b_\nu+\psi_\nu(\varepsilon))\varepsilon^m \quad (\nu=1,\ldots,n),$$

where the real function $\psi_\nu(\varepsilon)\to 0$ as $\varepsilon\to 0$.

This result is obtained in [34] by a different procedure for the system

$$\frac{dX}{dt}=XP(t)\varepsilon \quad (\text{i.e., } P_0=P_2=P_3=\ldots=0). \qquad (17.3)$$

Remark 17.1. Suppose that the roots of Eq. (17.2) are nonpositive numbers. Then, by considering W_{m+1}, we obtain the characteristic numbers of the matrix $W_m + W_{m+1}\varepsilon$. If it turns out that the p_k (for $k=1, \dots, n$) are distinct and negative, we again see that the characteristic numbers of the matrix W are purely imaginary for small values of ε. They remain purely imaginary for $|\varepsilon| < r$, where r is the smallest of the absolute values of the number ε_1 that are roots of the discriminant $\Delta(\varepsilon_1) = 0$ of the equation $(-1)^n D(X(2\pi, \varepsilon) - \lambda I) = 0$.

In [34] a general study is made of those intervals of values of ε in the system (17.3) for which the characteristic numbers of the matrix W are distinct and purely imaginary. It is also assumed that the characteristic numbers of the matrix W_1 are distinct and purely imaginary.

18. Artem'yev's Problem

In [8] Artem'yev examines the following problem. Consider the canonical system

$$\frac{dX}{dt} = XP(t, \mu_1, \dots, \mu_\nu, \varepsilon), \tag{18.1}$$

where the matrix of order $2n$

$$P(t + 2\pi, \mu_1, \dots, \mu_\nu, \varepsilon) = P(t, \mu_1, \dots, \mu_\nu, \varepsilon)$$

and $\mu_1, \dots, \mu_\nu, \varepsilon$ are parameters. Find those relationships between $\mu_1, \dots, \mu_\nu, \varepsilon$, under which the characteristic numbers of the matrix W of the system (18.1) will be purely imaginary. We note that, in accordance with Lyapunov's theorem, only in this case can the general solution of the system (18.1) be bounded. Artem'yev proposes to solve this problem thus:

According to Lyapunov's theorem, to each characteristic number σ of the matrix W, there exists a characteristic number $-\sigma$. Therefore, we have the following set of characteristic numbers $\sigma_k(\varepsilon)$ and $s_k(\varepsilon)$ of the exponential matrix W:

$$\sigma_1(\varepsilon) = \lambda_1(\mu_1, \dots, \mu_\nu, \varepsilon) + i\,\omega_1(\mu_1, \dots, \mu_\nu, \varepsilon)$$

$$\cdots\cdots\cdots\cdots\cdots\cdots\cdots$$

$$\sigma_n(\varepsilon) = \lambda_n(\mu_1, \dots, \mu_\nu, \varepsilon) + i\,\omega_n(\mu_1, \dots, \mu_\nu, \varepsilon)$$

$$\cdots\cdots\cdots\cdots\cdots\cdots\cdots$$

$$s_n(\varepsilon) = -\lambda_n(\mu_1, \dots, \mu_\nu, \varepsilon) - i\,\omega_n(\mu_1, \dots, \mu_\nu, \varepsilon).$$

From this, we obtain the relationships between $\mu_1, \ldots, \mu_\nu$, and ε from the equations

$$\lambda_1(\mu_1, \ldots, \mu_\nu, \varepsilon) = 0, \ldots, \lambda_n(\mu_1, \ldots, \mu_\nu, \varepsilon) = 0, \qquad (18.2)$$

the satisfaction of which makes it possible for the zero solution of the given linear system (18.1) to be stable. (We still require that the elementary divisors of the exponential matrix W be primes.)

In many specific problems, Artem'yev points out, it is possible to obtain the first few terms of the expansion of the quantities $\lambda_1, \ldots, \lambda_n$ in terms of a parameter ε and then calculate approximately the roots of Eqs. (18.2).

In line with this, note that, in this problem, we do not have equations* stating the relationships between the parameters $\mu_1, \ldots, \mu_\nu$ ε. Let us show this.

The characteristic equation of the matrix W of the system (18.1) is of the form

$$\mu^n + a_1(\mu_1, \ldots, \mu_\nu, \varepsilon)\mu^{n-1} + \ldots + a_n(\mu_1, \ldots, \mu_\nu, \varepsilon) = 0, \qquad (18.3)$$

where $\mu = \zeta^2$ and ζ is a characteristic number of the matrix W. From this we see that the characteristic numbers ζ of the matrix W are purely imaginary if and only if all roots of Eq. (18.3) are negative. But this will be the case if and only if Hurwitz' inequalities are satisfied [3, 35-37]. Let us agree to write these inequalities of Hurwitz in the form

$$b_1(\mu_1, \ldots, \mu_\nu, \varepsilon) > 0, \quad \ldots, \quad b_n(\mu_1, \ldots, \mu_\nu, \varepsilon) > 0. \qquad (18.4)$$

Thus, the region of values of the parameters $\mu_1, \ldots, \mu_\nu$, ε in which the characteristic numbers of the matrix W are purely imaginary is given by inequalities (18.4). If these inequalities are satisfied, then all the characteristic numbers of the matrix W will be purely imaginary. If they are also distinct (that is, if all negative roots of Eq. (18.3) are distinct), then the general solution of the system (18.1) will indeed be bounded and oscillatory (that is, it will not approach 0 asymptotically as $t \to \infty$). But if some of them are multiple, we need to show that all elementary divisors of the matrix W are primes since it is only when this condition is satisfied that the general solution will again be bounded and oscillatory.

From this it follows that the region (D) of values of the parameters $\mu_1, \ldots, \mu_\nu$, ε to which the bounded solutions of the system

*This is explained by the fact that the system (18.1) is not arbitrary but canonical. Therefore, certain equalities for the integral substitution $X(2\pi, \mu_1, \ldots, \mu_\nu, \varepsilon)$ of this system are already satisfied. (The characteristic equation for the matrix $X(2\pi, \mu_1, \ldots, \mu_\nu, \varepsilon)$ is, according to Lyapunov's theorem, reciprocal.)

(18.1) correspond is obtained by deleting from the region (18.4) that portion of it in which the characteristic numbers of the matrix W are multiple with nonprime elementary divisors. The region of values of the parameters $\mu_1, \ldots, \mu_\nu, \varepsilon$ to which multiple characteristic numbers of the matrix W correspond is given by the equation

$$\Delta(\mu_1, \ldots, \mu_\nu, \varepsilon) = 0, \quad (\Delta) \tag{18.5}$$

where Δ is the discriminant of Eq. (18.3).

Thus, the region (A) of values of the parameters $\mu_1, \ldots, \mu_\nu, \varepsilon$, which generates bounded solutions of the system (18.1) can be written in the form

$$(A) = (b) - (\Delta). \tag{18.6}$$

The boundary $(\bar{A}) - (A)$, where $(\bar{A})$ denotes the closure of (A), of this region will be the set of points $(\mu_1, \ldots, \mu_\nu, \varepsilon)$ to which the zero and multiple characteristic numbers of the matrix W correspond. However, this set $(\bar{A}) - (A)$ contains the set of points (C) corresponding to bounded solutions. These are those points that generate the matrix W with prime elementary divisors.

Thus, the entire region (D) corresponding to a bounded general solution can be written

$$(D) = (A) + (C). \tag{18.7}$$

The boundary $(\bar{D}) - (D)$ of this region will be the set of points $(\mu_1, \ldots, \mu_\nu, \varepsilon)$ corresponding to the matrix W with nonprime elementary divisors.

In this connection, the following problems arise:

I. Suppose that Hurwitz' conditions are satisfied for Eq. (18.3), that is, that all roots of this equation are negative. By using procedures familiar to us from algebra, we can find an interval $(-\omega, \omega)$ containing all the negative roots of Eq. (18.3). The question then arises: what are the conditions that the matrix $P(t, \mu_1, \ldots, \mu_\nu, \varepsilon)$ of the system (18.1) must satisfy to ensure that the roots of Eq. (18.3) do not lie outside the given interval $(-\omega, 0)$.

If we denote these roots by $-\omega_1^2, \ldots, -\omega_n^2$, we obtain the frequencies ω_m of the oscillatory solutions of the system (18.1). Specifically, if there is a frequency ω_m, then there exists a solution of the form

$$x = z_1(t) \cos \omega_m t + z_2(t) \sin \omega_m t,$$

where $z_1(t)$ and $z_2(t)$ are periodic vectors with period 2π.

II. Suppose that the point$(\mu_1^0, \ldots, \mu_\nu^0, \varepsilon^0)$ is such that the matrix W has multiple roots, whether with prime or nonprime elementary divisors. Then, the question may be asked, will the general solution of the system (18.1) be bounded in a neighborhood of this point? To answer this question, we need to express all the parameters $(\mu_1, \ldots, \mu_\nu, \varepsilon)$ as functions of some one parameter τ such that

$$\mu_1 = \mu_1(\tau), \ldots, \mu_\nu = \mu_\nu(\tau), \quad \varepsilon = \varepsilon(\tau) \tag{18.8}$$

and

$$\mu_1^0 = \mu_1(0), \ldots, \quad \mu_\nu^0 = \mu_\nu(0), \quad \varepsilon^0 = \varepsilon(0).$$

In particular, we may choose ε, for example, for the parameter τ or we may simply fix all values of the parameters but one and leave some one of them variable. For example, the functions (18.8) may be such that they satisfy the following equations (on the boundary of the region (18.4)):

$$b_1(\mu_1, \ldots, \mu_\nu, \varepsilon) = 0, \ \ldots, \ b_n(\mu_1, \ldots, \mu_\nu, \varepsilon) = 0. \tag{18.9}$$

For simplicity, suppose that the functions (18.8) are holomorphic in a neighborhood of $\tau = 0$. Then the coefficients of Eq. (18.3) will be holomorphic in a neighborhood of $\tau = 0$, and, for $\tau = 0$, Eq. (18.3) has multiple roots.

If it now turns out that all of the roots of Eq. (18.3) in a neighborhood of the point $\tau = 0$ are negative and simple, then, in a neighborhood of the point $\tau = 0$, we shall again obtain a system (18.1) whose general solution is bounded. It is possible to show, by using Hurwitz' inequalities and [32], in which methods are expounded enabling us to tell whether the roots will be simple and real or not, whether, with given functions (18.8), Eq. (18.3) has only simple negative roots. In this way, we can investigate the behavior of the general solution of the system (18.1) in a neighborhood of the point $(\mu_1^0, \ldots, \mu_\nu^0, \varepsilon^0)$ and, in particular, along the curve (18.8).

19. The Theory of Reducible Systems

Consider a reducible [14] system of n linear differential equations

$$\frac{dX}{dt} = XP(t) \tag{19.1}$$

and the corresponding reduced system

$$\frac{dY}{dt} = YB, \tag{19.2}$$

where $P(t)$ is a real matrix that is continuous and bounded in the region $t \geqslant 0$ and B is a real constant nth-order matrix. According to Remark 3 in [14], we may assume that B is canonical. According to Theorem 1 of [14], the system (19.1) has the solution

$$X = \exp Bt \cdot Z(t), \tag{19.3}$$

where $Z(t)$ and $Z^{-1}(t)$ are bounded matrices. The matrix $Z(t)$ maps the system (19.1) into the system (19.2) according to the formula

$$X = YZ(t). \tag{19.4}$$

Theorem 19.1. *There exist real bounded matrices $Z(t)$, such that $Z^{-1}(t)$ is also bounded, that map the system (19.1) into the system (19.2) according to formula (19.4).*

[We shall find all these matrices $Z(t)$.]

Proof: Suppose that $Z(t)$ in (19.3) is complex, $Z(t) = Z_1(t) + iZ_2(t)$, where $Z_1(t)$ and $Z_2(t)$ are bounded real matrices. Then, we have a real integral matrix of the system (19.1)

$$X(t, \alpha) = \exp Bt \cdot (Z_1(t) + \alpha Z_2(t)) = \exp Bt \cdot Z(t, \alpha),$$

where α is an arbitrary numerical parameter.

There exists a real value α such that $D(X(t, \alpha)) \neq 0$ where D is the symbol for a determinant. To see this, note that, since $D(Z^{-1}(t, i))$ is bounded, it follows that

$$D(Z(t, \alpha)) = \sum_{k=0}^{n} \alpha^k \beta_k(t) \neq 0 \text{ for } \alpha = i,$$

where the $\beta_k(t)$ are real bounded functions. Let us take some α at which $D(Z(t_0, \alpha)) \neq 0$. Then, in accordance with a familiar property of a fundamental system of solutions of the linear system (19.1), we have

$$D(Z(t, \alpha)) \neq 0. \tag{19.5}$$

From this it follows that there are no more than n values of the parameter α at which

$$D(Z(t, \alpha)) = 0. \tag{19.6}$$

In particular, (19.5) is satisfied for all sufficiently large and sufficiently small absolute values of α (except possibly $\alpha = 0$ if $D(Z_1) = 0$).

Thus, we have a real integral matrix of the system (19.1) in the form

$$X = \exp Bt \cdot Z(t, \alpha), \quad D(Z(t, \alpha)) \neq 0, \tag{19.7}$$

where α is an arbitrary real number not equal to a root of Eq. (19.6) for any $t = t_0$.

Let us show that the matrix $[Z(t, \alpha)]^{-1}$ is bounded in the region $t \geqslant 0$. From the Ostrogradskiy-Jacobi theorem for the solution of (19.7), we have

$$D(X) = \exp(\sigma(B)t) \cdot D(Z(t, \alpha)) = \quad c(\alpha) \exp\left(\int_{t_0}^{t} \sigma(P(t))\, dt\right),$$

where $\sigma(Y)$ is the trace of the matrix Y and $c(\alpha) = D(X(t_0)) \neq 0$. Therefore,

$$D(Z(t, \alpha)) = c(\alpha) \exp\left(\int_{t_0}^{t} \sigma(P - B)\, dt - \sigma(B) \cdot t_0\right).$$

Since the function $D(Z^{-1}(t, \alpha))$ is bounded for $\alpha = i$, it will also be bounded for all other values of α for which $D(Z(t, \alpha)) \neq 0$ since the function

$$\exp\left(\int_{t_0}^{t} \sigma(P - B)\right) dt$$

is independent of α. The boundedness of the function $D(Z^{-1}(t, \alpha))$ also follows directly from Theorem 3 of [14]. We in effect repeated the proof of that theorem.

Thus, we have shown that the real matrix $Z(t, \alpha)$ is, together with $Z^{-1}(t, \alpha)$, bounded and that it maps the system (19.1) into (19.2) for arbitrary real α not equal to a root of Eq. (19.6) for any $t = t_0$. According to (24) of [14], the general form of a real matrix mapping the system (19.1) into (19.2) can be written

$$Z = Z(t, \alpha) \exp(-Bt) \cdot C \exp(Bt),$$

where C is an arbitrary real matrix such that the matrix $\exp(-Bt) \cdot C \exp(Bt)$ is bounded and $D(C) \neq 0$. If the matrix P in the system (19.1) is constant, then, for a solution of (19.3), we may take

$$X = \exp Bt \cdot \exp([\beta_1, \ldots, \beta_n]\, it) S,$$

that is, we may have

$$Z = \exp([\beta_1, \ldots, \beta_n]\, it) S = Z_1(t) + iZ_2(t), \tag{19.8}$$

where $P = S^{-1}JS$ and B is the real part of the canonical Jordan form of the matrix P (i.e., the real part of the matrix J, where $J = B + [\beta_1, \ldots, \beta_n]\, i$.). Consequently, the matrices $Z_1(t)$ and $Z_2(t)$ are easily found. Here, $[\beta_1, \ldots, \beta_n]$ is a real diagonal matrix.

Remark 19.1. We see from (19.8) that the real matrices $Z(t, \alpha)$, which transform the system (19.1) with constant matrix P into the system (19.2), are of the form

$$Z(t, \alpha) = \| \delta \exp i \beta_k t \|,$$

where δ is a constant and the β_k are the imaginary parts of the characteristic numbers of the matrix P.

20. Shtokalo's Method [10, 38]

Consider the system

$$\frac{dX}{dt} = X \left[P_0 + \sum_{k=1}^{\infty} P_k(t)\, \varepsilon^k \right] = X P(t), \tag{20.1}$$

where P_0 is a real constant nth-order matrix and the real matrices $P_k(t)$ are of the form

$$P_k(t) = \sum C_{\mu_k}^{(k)} e^{i\mu_k t}. \tag{20.2}$$

Here, the $C_{\mu_k}^{(k)}$ are constant nth-order matrices and the μ_k are real numbers assuming a finite number of values. The series representing the bounded matrix $P(t)$ converges uniformly for $|\varepsilon| < r$ in the region $-\infty < t < \infty$. Here $P(t)$ will not be periodic if the numbers μ_k are not all commensurable.

Such systems were studied by Shtokalo [10]. We shall now follow his method. First, however, let us transform the system (20.1) to another system by means of the equation

$$Y = XZ, \tag{20.3}$$

where the elements of the real matrix Z, which, together with Z^{-1} is bounded, are of the form $\delta \exp(i\beta t)$. Here, δ is a constant number and β denotes the imaginary parts of the characteristic numbers of the matrix P_0,

$$Z^{-1} = Z_1(t, \alpha) = Z_1(t) + \alpha Z_2(t), \tag{20.4}$$

Z_1 and Z_2 are defined by Eq. (19.8) for $P = P_0$, and α is defined by the condition (19.5).

We denote by J the real part of the canonical form of the matrix P_0; that is, $P_0 = S^{-1} \bar{J} S$, where $\bar{J}$ is a canonical matrix, $\bar{J} = J + \beta i$, where in turn, β is a diagonal real matrix, $\beta = [\beta_1, \ldots, \beta_n]$.

For the matrix Y, we obtain the equation

$$\frac{dY}{dt} = Y\left[Z^{-1}\frac{dZ}{dt} + Z^{-1}P_0Z + Z^{-1}\sum_{k=1}^{\infty}P_k\varepsilon^k Z\right].$$

But obviously, in accordance with (20.3),

$$Z^{-1}\frac{dZ}{dt} + Z^{-1}P_0Z = J, \quad \frac{dZ}{dt} = ZJ - P_0Z,$$

since $Z(t, \alpha)$ is chosen on the basis of Remark 19.1. Since the elements of the matrix Z are of the form $\delta \exp(i\beta t)$, the matrices $\overline{P}_k(t) = Z^{-1}P_k(t)Z$ are again of the form (20.2) with variable μ_k. Thus, we may write

$$\frac{dY}{dt} = Y\left[J + \sum_{k=1}^{\infty} P_k(t)\varepsilon^k\right]. \tag{20.5}$$

Here, we again denote the matrices $\overline{P}_k(t)$ by $P_k(t)$. These matrices are of the form (20.2) and they are real.

For the system (20.5), we find the formal solution

$$Y = \exp\left(\sum_{k=0}^{\infty}W_k\varepsilon^k t\right)\cdot\sum_{k=0}^{\infty}Z_k(t)\varepsilon^k, \tag{20.6}$$

$$Z_k(0) = 0, \quad k \geqslant 1,$$

where the W_k are constant matrices independent of ε also and the $Z_k(t)$ are bounded matrices.

If we substitute (20.6) into (20.5) and multiply on the left by

$$\exp\left(-\sum_{k=0}^{\infty}W_k\varepsilon^k t\right)$$

we obtain

$$\sum_{k=0}^{\infty}W_k\varepsilon^k\sum_{k=0}^{\infty}Z_k(t)\varepsilon^k + \sum_{k=0}^{\infty}\frac{dZ_k}{dt}\varepsilon^k =$$

$$= \sum_{k=0}^{\infty}Z_k\varepsilon^k\sum_{k=0}^{\infty}P_k\varepsilon^k.$$

If we now equate the coefficients of like powers of ε, we obtain

$$\frac{dZ_0}{dt} = Z_0J - W_0Z_0. \tag{20.7}$$

$$\frac{dZ_k}{dt} = \sum_{\nu=0}^{k} Z_\nu P_{k-\nu} - \sum_{\nu=0}^{k} W_\nu Z_{k-\nu}. \tag{20.8}$$

Let us set

$$W_0 = J, \ Z_0 = I. \tag{20.9}$$

Shtokalo did not transform the system (20.1) into the system (20.5) but sought directly a formal solution (20.6) for the given system (20.1).

If we seek a formal solution (20.6) for the system (20.1), then, instead of (20.7), we obtain

$$\frac{dZ_0}{dt} = Z_0 P_0 - W_0 Z_0. \tag{20.10}$$

Let us look at this equation. Suppose that

$$P_0 = S^{-1}\bar{J}S = S^{-1}JS + S^{-1}\beta S i.$$

If we set $Z_0 = \exp(i\beta t)\cdot S$ into (20.10), we obtain

$$i\beta \exp(i\beta t)\cdot S = \exp(i\beta t)\cdot S\cdot S^{-1}\bar{J}S - W_0 \exp(i\beta t)\cdot S.$$

From this, we obtain

$$W_0 = [\exp(i\beta t)\cdot\bar{J}S - i\beta\exp(i\beta t)\cdot S]\cdot S^{-1}\exp(-i\beta t) =$$

$$= \exp(i\beta t)\cdot\bar{J}\exp(-i\beta t) - i\beta.$$

Obviously, the matrices β and $\bar{J}$ commute. Therefore, $W_0 = J$.

Thus, we have again obtained for the system (20.1) $W_0 = J$ but $Z_0 = \exp(i\beta t)\cdot S$ instead of $Z_0 = I$, as was the case with the system (20.5) in accordance with (20.9). This value of Z_0 may be complex.

Let us examine the system (20.5) further. We have (20.9). Let us find W_1 and Z_1 from Eq. (20.8) for $k = 1$:

$$\frac{dZ_1}{dt} = Z_1 J - JZ_1 + P_1 - W_1. \tag{20.11}$$

Suppose that the characteristic numbers (the real parts of the characteristic numbers of the matrix P_0) of the matrix J are λ_k (for $k = 1, \ldots, m$). Then, when $\lambda_k \neq \lambda_l$, the element $z_{k,l}^{(1)}$ of the matrix Z_1 can be found from formula (11.14):

$$z_{k,l}^{(1)} = \exp(\lambda_l - \lambda_k)t \cdot \int_0^t f(t)\exp(-(\lambda_l - \lambda_k)t)\,dt, \tag{20.12}$$

$$f(t) = \delta_l z_{k,l+1}^{(1)} - \delta_k z_{k-l,l}^{(1)} + p_{k,l}^{(1)} - w_{k,l}^{(1)}, \tag{20.13}$$

where the $p_{k,l}^{(1)}$ and the $w_{k,l}^{(1)}$ are elements of the matrices P_1 and W_1. Let us choose $w_{k,l}^{(1)}$ in such a way that $z_{k,l}^{(1)}$ will be of the form $\delta \exp(i\beta t)$. For this, it is necessary and sufficient that

$$\frac{1}{t}\int_0^t\left[\int_0^t f(t)\exp(-(\lambda_l-\lambda_k)t)\,dt\right]dt \longrightarrow 0 \tag{20.14}$$

as $t \to 0$. In other words, the second factor in the expression (20.12), which is of the form

$$\sum_\beta \delta\cdot\exp\left[i\beta t-(\lambda_l-\lambda_k)t\right]+M,$$

cannot have a free term M. On the other hand, if $\lambda_k = \lambda_l$, we find $z_{k,l}$ either from formula (11.6):

$$z_{k,l} = \int_0^t (p_{k,l}^{(1)} - w_{k,l}^{(1)})\,dt,\quad w_{k,l} = \lim_{t\to\infty}\frac{1}{t}\int_0^t p_{k,l}^{(1)}\,dt \tag{20.15}$$

or from formula (11.17),

$$z_{k,l} = \int_0^t \left[z_{k,l+1}\delta_l - \delta_k z_{k-l,l} + p_{k,l}^{(1)} - w_{k,l}\right]dt, \tag{20.16}$$

$$w_{k,l} = \lim_{t=\infty}\frac{1}{t}\int_0^t \left[z_{k,l+1}\delta_l - \delta_k z_{k-l,l} + p_{k,l}^{(1)}\right]dt, \tag{20.17}$$

as the case requires. We can also find a solution to Eq. (20.11) from the general formula (11.9):

$$Z_1 = \exp(-Jt)\int_0^t \exp(Jt)(P_1 - W_1)\exp(-Jt)\,dt\cdot\exp(Jt), \tag{20.18}$$

where W_1 is defined by

$$\lim_{t\to\infty}\frac{1}{t}\int_0^t \exp(Jt)\cdot(P_1 - W_1)\exp(-Jt)\,dt = 0. \tag{20.19}$$

Obviously, we also find W_k and Z_k (for $k \geqslant 2$).

Thus, we have a formal solution (20.6), where $W_0 = J$ and $Z_0 = I$. We note that we could also have found Z_k and W_k (for $k \geqslant 1$) if $P_k(t)$ (for $k \geqslant 1$) had infinitely many terms in the sum (20.2), that is, if it were quasi-periodic.

We may also assume that the $P_k(t)$ are uniformly periodic functions [39] with exponents* $\Delta_l^{(k)} \longrightarrow \infty$ as $l \longrightarrow \infty$, and we can make various other assumptions.

Remark 20.1. We can find the coefficients W_1 and Z_1 in a very simple manner from the general formulas (20.18) and (20.19) when the matrix $J = 0$. Specifically,

$$Z_1 = \int_0^t (P_1 - W_1)\, dt \tag{20.20}$$

and

$$W_1 = \lim_{t \to \infty} \frac{1}{t} \int_0^t P_1 dt. \tag{20.21}$$

The W_k and Z_k (for $k \geqslant 2$) can also be found in this case. Also, if the matrix P_0 in the system (20.1) has purely imaginary simple characteristic numbers, then we do have the case $J = 0$. For example, if the system (20.1) is canonical, then P_0 has purely imaginary characteristic numbers. If they are simple, we have $J = 0$.

Let us now find the coefficients of the two series

$$W = \sum_{k=0}^{\infty} W_k \varepsilon^k, \quad W_0 = J, \tag{20.22}$$

$$Z = \sum_{k=0}^{\infty} Z_k(t) \varepsilon^k, \quad Z_0 = I \tag{20.23}$$

by another method, proposed by Shtokalo.

21. Determination of the Coefficients of the Series (20.22) and (20.23) by Shtokalo's Method [10, 38]

Consider an equation of the form (20.11)

$$\frac{dZ}{dt} = ZJ - JZ + P(t) - W, \tag{21.1}$$

*For simplicity, we assume that the set of exponents $\{\Delta_l^{(k)}\}_{l=1}^{\infty}$ of the matrices $P_k(t)$ are independent of k.

where J has its former value (a canonical real matrix), $P(t)$ is an expression of the form (20.2), and W is a constant matrix to be determined in such a way that Z will be of the form (20.2).

Suppose that

$$P(t) = \sum P_\mu \exp(i\mu t), \tag{21.2}$$

where the P_μ are constant matrices. Following Shtokalo, let us seek Z in the form

$$Z = \sum b_\mu \exp(i\mu t), \tag{21.3}$$

where b_μ is a constant matrix. Following Shtokalo, let us set

$$W = \lim_{t\to\infty} \frac{1}{t}\int_0^t P(t)\,dt = P_0. \tag{21.4}$$

Here, P_0 is the free term in (21.2). Then, (21.1) can be rewritten

$$\frac{dZ}{dt} = ZJ - JZ + \sum_{\mu\neq 0} P_\mu \exp(i\mu t). \tag{21.5}$$

If we substitute (21.3) into (21.5) and equate coefficients of like powers of $e^{i\mu t}$, we obtain

$$i\mu b_\mu = b_\mu J - Jb_\mu + P_\mu. \tag{21.6}$$

From this, we can find the matrix of the b_μ. Shtokalo proved this in the general case. The given expression was also studied in the book by Lappo-Danilevskiy [1], who not only proved the solvability of (21.6) but also gave several forms of the solution in the case in which the matrix J has distinct characteristic numbers. Equation (21.6) is studied in detail in the book by Gantmakher [3].

Following essentially the same lines as Shtokalo, let us prove that Eq. (21.6) can be solved.

If we multiply (21.6) by $\exp(i\mu t)$ and define

$$U = b_\mu \exp(i\mu t), \tag{21.7}$$

we obtain

$$\frac{dU}{dt} = UJ - JU + P_\mu \exp(i\mu t). \tag{21.8}$$

We have the general solution of Eq. (21.8) for $P_\mu = 0$ in the form

$$U = \exp(-Jt)C\exp(Jt), \tag{21.9}$$

where C is an arbitrary constant matrix.

If Eq. (21.6) has no solution or has more than one solution, then this expression has a solution $b_\mu \neq 0$ for $P_\mu = 0$. But then Eq. (21.8) for $P_\mu = 0$ has a solution $U = b_\mu \exp(i\mu t)$ with $b_\mu \neq 0$. Consequently, we obtain

$$\exp(-Jt)C\exp(Jt) = b_\mu \exp(i\mu t),$$

which is impossible since the matrix J is real.

Thus, we have proven that equation (21.6) has a unique solution. Now, let us find it.

Assuming that C is a function of t and substituting (21.9) into (21.8), we obtain

$$\exp(-Jt)\frac{dC}{dt}\exp(Jt) = P_\mu \exp(i\mu t). \tag{21.10}$$

From this, we obtain

$$C = \int_0^t \exp(Jt)P_\mu \exp(-Jt)\cdot\exp(i\mu t)\,dt + K. \tag{21.11}$$

Here, K is an arbitrary constant matrix. Let us set

$$K = -\lim_{t\to\infty}\frac{1}{t}\int_0^t\left[\int_0^t \exp(Jt)\cdot P_\mu \exp(-Jt)\times \times\exp(i\mu t)\,dt\right]dt. \tag{21.12}$$

In other words, K must cancel that constant matrix in (21.11) that is obtained by substitution of the lower limit of integration. We then have

$$U = \exp(-Jt)\cdot\left[\int_0^t \exp(Jt)\cdot P_\mu \exp(-Jt)\times \times\exp(i\mu t)\cdot dt + K\right]\exp(Jt) \tag{21.13}$$

and (21.14)

$$b_\mu = U\exp(-i\mu t).$$

If we chose K differently, there would be in the bracketed expression a free term that would generate a term different from $Ae^{i\mu t}$ in U and we would obtain for U the expression

$$U = b_\mu \exp(i\mu t),$$

the existence and uniqueness of which we have proven.

Thus, we can always find a solution of Eq. (21.1) in the form (21.3) by taking the matrices in (21.6) in the form (21.14). This enables us to find the W_k and Z_k (for $k \geqslant 1$) from (20.8) by Shtokalo's method, that is, by determining W from equations of the form (21.1) with the aid of formula (21.4) and by determining Z with the aid of (21.3) and (21.14).

The matrix (21.14) can easily be written in expanded form. For example, if $J=[\lambda_1, \ldots, \lambda_n]$, that is, if the matrix J is a diagonal matrix, then

$$\{\exp(Jt)\cdot P_\mu \exp(-Jt)\}_{kl} = p_{kl}^{(\mu)} \exp(\lambda_k - \lambda_l)\cdot t, \tag{21.15}$$

where the $p_{kl}^{(\mu)}$ are the elements of the matrix P_μ. From this and from (21.11), we have

$$\{C\}_{kl} = \frac{p_{kl}^{(\mu)} \exp(\lambda_k - \lambda_l + i\mu)t}{\lambda_k - \lambda_l + i\mu}$$

and, consequently, again on the basis of (21.15)

$$\{b_\mu\}_{kl} = \frac{p_{kl}^{(\mu)}}{\lambda_k - \lambda_l + i\mu}. \tag{21.16}$$

Finally, we have obtained Lappo-Danilevskiy's formula. The method of determining the coefficients in the series (20.22) and (20.23) is also applicable in the case in which the matrices $P_k(t)$ in (20.5) are periodic and can be represented in the form (20.2), where there may possibly be an infinite number of terms.

Also, if the matrices $P_k(t)$ in the system (20.1) are periodic, the transformation (20.3) may yield a system (20.5) in which the $P_k(t)$ are not periodic. This will be the case when the matrix P_0 has characteristic numbers whose imaginary parts β are not commensurable with the frequency of the periodic matrices of the system (20.1). But then, we can transform (20.1) to a system that will contain not the matrix P_0 but a constant matrix not possessing characteristic numbers λ_k and λ_l such that $\lambda_k - \lambda_l = 2\pi\omega k$, where k is an integer and $2\omega\pi$ is the period of the matrices $P_k(t)$ in the system (20.1). We can then seek the coefficients of the series (20.22) and (20.23) by Shtokalo's method since the solution of Eqs. (20.8) can be obtained by the given method even in this case in the form of periodic functions. [The numbers μ are commensurable in (21.2) (see (21.3)).]

We should, however, note the following. In determining W_k and Z_k by Shtokalo's method, we find Z_k in the form (21.3). Consequently, generally speaking, we shall not have $Z_k(0)=0$ (for $k \geqslant 1$). In particular, this is obvious from (21.11) and (21.12). But then, we shall obtain series (20.22) and (20.23) the convergence of which cannot be ensured even in the case in which the $P_k(t)$ in the system (20.1) are periodic matrices with a single period. But if we are concerned only with the fact of asymptotic stability of the zero solution of the system (20.1), the convergence of the series (20.22) and (20.23) is not required if we then follow Shtokalo's method.

Thus, we proceed to further observations of Shtokalo after the series (20.22) and (20.23) are obtained.

22. Approximate Solutions Obtained by Shtokalo's Method

Consider the system (20.5). We introduce the new unknown matrix X defined by

$$Y = X \sum_{k=0}^{m} Z_k(t)\,\varepsilon^k, \tag{22.1}$$

where the second factor is a segment of the formal series (20.23) and X satisfies the equation

$$\frac{dX}{dt} = X\left[\sum_{k=0}^{m} W_k\varepsilon^k + \varepsilon^{m+1}R_m(t, \varepsilon)\right], \tag{22.2}$$

in which the sum is a segment of the series (20.22) and $R_m(t, \varepsilon)$is a holomorphic function in the region $|\varepsilon| < R$. Let us find $R_m(t, \varepsilon)$. If we substitute (22.1) into (20.5) and then multiply the resulting equation on the left by X^{-1} we obtain

$$\left[\sum_{k=0}^{m} W_k\varepsilon^k + \varepsilon^{m+1}R_m(t, \varepsilon)\right]\left[\sum_{k=0}^{m} Z_k(t)\varepsilon^k\right] +$$

$$+\sum_{k=0}^{m}\frac{dZ_k(t)}{dt}\cdot\varepsilon^k = \sum_{k=0}^{m} Z_k(t)\,\varepsilon^k\left[J + \sum_{k=1}^{\infty} P_k(t)\,\varepsilon^k\right]. \tag{22.3}$$

From this, we have

$$\varepsilon^{m+1}R_m(t, \varepsilon) = \left[\sum_{k=0}^{m} Z_k\varepsilon^k \sum_{k=0}^{\infty} P_k(t)\,\varepsilon^k -\right.$$

$$\left.-\sum_{k=0}^{m} W_k\varepsilon^k\sum_{k=0}^{m} Z_k(t)\,\varepsilon^k - \sum_{k=0}^{m}\frac{dZ_k(t)}{dt}\varepsilon^k\right]\left[\sum_{k=0}^{m} Z_k\varepsilon^k\right]^{-1} =$$

$$= \left[\sum_{k=0}^{\infty}\left(\sum_{l=0}^{k\leqslant m} Z_lP_{k-l} - \sum_{l=0}^{k\leqslant m} W_lZ_{k-l} -\right.\right. \tag{22.4}$$

$$-\frac{dZ_k(t)}{dt}\Big)\varepsilon^k\Big]\Big[\sum_{k=0}^{m} Z_k\varepsilon^k\Big]^{-1}.$$

by virtue of (20.8). Therefore, if we divide (22.4) by ε^{m+1}, we obtain

$$R_m(t,\varepsilon)=\sum_{k=m+1}^{\infty}\Big(\sum_{l=0}^{m} Z_lP_{k-l}-\sum_{l=0}^{m} W_lZ_{k-l}\Big)\varepsilon^{k-m-1}\times\Big[\sum_{k=0}^{m} Z_k\varepsilon^k\Big]^{-1} \quad (22.5)$$

We have

$$\Big[I+\sum_{k=1}^{m} Z_k\varepsilon^k\Big]^{-1}=\sum_{k=0}^{\infty} M_k\varepsilon^k, \qquad (22.6)$$

and this series converges (see Sect. 1) for

$$\Big|\sum_{k=1}^{m} Z_k\varepsilon^k\Big|<\Big\|\frac{1}{n}\Big\|,$$

where n is the order of the matrices Z_k.

To find the M_k, we multiply Eq. (22.6) on the left by

$$I+\sum_{k=1}^{m} Z_k\varepsilon^k.$$

We obtain

$$I=\sum_{k=0}^{\infty}\Big(\sum_{l=0}^{k\leqslant m} Z_lM_{k-l}\Big)\varepsilon^k,\quad M_0=I,\ Z_0=I.$$

From this, we have

$$\sum_{l=0}^{k\leqslant m} Z_lM_{k-l}=0 \text{ for } k\geqslant 1$$

and, consequently,

$$M_k=-\sum_{l=1}^{k\leqslant m} Z_lM_{k-l}.$$

Now, we may rewrite $R_m(t, \varepsilon)$ in the form

$$R_m(t, \varepsilon) = \sum_{\nu=0}^{\infty} D_\nu \varepsilon^\nu \sum_{k=0}^{\infty} M_k \varepsilon^k = \sum_{\mu=0}^{\infty} R_\mu^{(m)} \varepsilon^\mu . \tag{22.7}$$

Here,

$$D_\nu = \sum_{l=0}^{m} (Z_l P_{\nu+m+1-l} - W_l Z_{\nu+m+1-l}), \qquad R_\mu^{(m)} = \sum_{\nu=0}^{\mu} D_\nu M_{\mu-\nu}.$$

The series (22.7) converges for $\left| \sum_{k=1}^{m} Z_k \varepsilon^k \right| < \frac{1}{n}$ and $|\varepsilon| < r$ [the region of convergence of the series in (20.1)].

We have proven formula (22.2).

We see from (22.1) that, if the matrix X is bounded, then the matrix Y is also bounded. Thus, a study of the question of stability of the zero solution of the system (20.5) leads to a study of this same question for the system (22.2). By omitting infinitesimals of order ε^m in the right-hand side of (22.2), we obtain

$$X \approx \exp\left\{ t \sum_{k=0}^{m} W_k \varepsilon^k \right\}$$

This gives an approximate value of Y.

23. Inequalities Following from Shtokalo's Method

Consider the first system

$$\frac{dY}{dt} = YQ, \tag{23.1}$$

where Q is an nth-order matrix with elements

$$\{Q\}_{kl} = q_{kl}.$$

Let us suppose that the real parts of the characteristic numbers of the matrix Q are negative. Then, there exists a positive quadratic form [26, Chap. II]

$$U = \sum_{k,l=1}^{n} \gamma_{kl} y_k y_l \tag{23.2}$$

such that

$$\sum_{k=1}^{n}(q_{1k}y_1 + q_{2k}y_2 + \ldots + q_{nk}y_n)\frac{\partial U}{\partial y_k} = -\sum_{l=1}^{n} y_l^2, \tag{23.3}$$

or, on the basis of the system (23.1),

$$\frac{dU}{dt} = -\sum_{l=1}^{n} y_l^2. \tag{23.4}$$

Consider now the system

$$\frac{dY}{dt} = Y[Q + \varepsilon R(t, \varepsilon)], \tag{23.5}$$

where the matrix Q is as before but the matrix $R(t, \varepsilon)$ with elements

$$\{R(t, \varepsilon)\}_{kl} = R_{kl}$$

is bounded: $|R_{kl}| < r$. Then, for every solution of the system (23.5), we have

$$\frac{dU}{dt} = \sum_{k=1}^{n}\frac{\partial U}{\partial y_k}\frac{dy_k}{dt} = \sum_{k=1}^{n}\frac{\partial U}{\partial y_k}[q_{1k}y_1 + q_{2k}y_2 + \ldots +$$

$$+ q_{nk}y_k + \varepsilon(R_{1k}y_1 + \ldots + R_{nk}y_n)]$$

or

$$\frac{dU}{dt} = -\sum_{l=1}^{n} y_l^2 + \varepsilon\sum_{l,k=1}^{n}\gamma_{kl}y_l(R_{1k}y_1 + \ldots + R_{nk}y_n). \tag{23.6}$$

This equation can be represented in the form

$$\frac{dU}{dt} = -\sum_{l=1}^{n} y_l^2 + \varepsilon\sum_{k,l=1}^{n}\delta_{kl}y_k y_l, \tag{23.7}$$

where the δ_{kl} are constituted in the form of a sum of products of the quantitites γ_{pq} and $R_{\mu\nu}$ and are bounded. Since

$$\left|\sum \delta_{kl}y_k y_l\right| \leqslant \delta\sum_{l=1}^{n} y_l^2, \tag{23.8}$$

where $\delta = n \max |\delta_{kl}|$, it follows from (23.7) that, for sufficiently small ε, we have

$$\frac{dU}{dt} \leqslant (\varepsilon\delta - 1)\sum_{l=1}^{n} y_l^2. \tag{23.9}$$

The asymptotic stability of the solutions of the system (23.5) follows from this.

Now, we shall obtain an obvious inequality. Suppose that

$$\sum y_l^2 \leqslant A \sum_{k,l} \gamma_{kl} y_k y_l,$$

where, for example,

$$A^{-1} = \max \left(\sum \gamma_{kl} y_k y_l\right) \text{ for } \sum_{l=1}^{n} y_l^2 = 1. \tag{23.9$_1$}$$

Then, from (23.9), we have

$$\frac{dU}{dt} \leqslant (\varepsilon\delta - 1) AU, \; U \leqslant U_0 \exp(\varepsilon\delta - 1) A (t - t_0) \tag{23.10}$$

and

$$\sum_{l=1}^{n} y_l^2 < U_0 A e^{(\varepsilon\delta - 1) A (t - t_0)}, \; U_0 = (U)_{t=t_0}. \tag{23.11}$$

Other and more precise inequalities regarding approximations of the solutions appear in Shtokalo's works [10, 38].

24. Shtokalo's Theorem. Inequalities Involving Approximate Solutions Found by Shtokalo's Method (for Linear and Nonlinear Systems). Particular Problems

Now, we shall study the system (22.2). The coefficients γ_{kl} of the quadratic form (23.2) are found from a linear nonhomogeneous system of algebraic equations that are obtained by equating the coefficients in the quadratic forms on the right and left sides of Eq. (23.3). The determinant of this system, as Lyapunov showed [26, Chap. II], is

$$\Delta = \Pi (m_1 \lambda_1 + \ldots + m_n \lambda_n) \quad (m_1 + \ldots + m_2 = 2, \; m_k \geqslant 0),$$

where $\lambda_1, \ldots, \lambda_n$ are the characteristic numbers of the matrix Q. The determinant Δ, which will appear in the denominator, is a symmetric function of $\lambda_1, \ldots, \lambda_n$. Consequently, it can be expressed as a rational combination of the coefficients of the characteristic equation of the matrix Q. We introduce the notation

$$Q = \sum_{k=0}^{m} \varepsilon^k W_k \tag{24.1}$$

and assume that the real parts of all the characteristic numbers of the matrix Q are negative for certain sufficiently large m and $0 < \varepsilon < \varepsilon^*$, where ε^* is chosen sufficiently small for the given set $m \geqslant N$. This will, as Shtokalo showed in his article [10, Theorem 3], be the case when the Hurwitz' determinants set up for the characteristic equation of the formal matrix

$$W = \sum_{k=0}^{\infty} W_k \varepsilon^k, \tag{20.22}$$

have positive coefficients for low powers of ε.

The characteristic numbers $\lambda_1, \ldots, \lambda_n$ of the matrix Q are algebraic functions of the parameter ε. Consequently, for small values of ε, the λ_k can be represented in the form of series of fractional powers of ε or integral powers of $\varepsilon_1 = \varepsilon^{1/p}$, where p is an integer. It is easy to see that the first nonzero coefficients in these expansions do not change with increasing m in formula (24.1), beginning, at least, with some m. From this it follows that if

$$\begin{aligned} \Delta = 2^n \lambda_1 \ldots \lambda_n (\lambda_1 + \lambda_2)(\lambda_1 + \lambda_3) \ldots (\lambda_1 + \lambda_n) \times \\ \times (\lambda_2 + \lambda_3) \ldots (\lambda_2 + \lambda_n) \ldots (\lambda_{n-1} + \lambda_n) \end{aligned} \tag{24.2}$$

converges to 0 as $\varepsilon \to 0$, then the order of smallness of Δ in a neighborhood of $\varepsilon = 0$ does not increase with increasing m in formula (24.1).

From this it follows that if the coefficients γ_{kl} in the quadratic form (23.2) approach ∞ as $\varepsilon \to 0$, then the order of infinity does not increase with increasing m.

For the system (22.2) we obtain, instead of (23.6), the equation

$$\frac{dU}{dt} = -\sum_{l=1}^{n} y_l^2 + \varepsilon^{m+1} \sum_{k,\, l=1}^{n} \gamma_{k,\, l}\, y_l (R_{1k} y_1 + \ldots + R_{nk} y_n). \tag{24.3}$$

instead of (23.7), we obtain

$$\frac{dU}{dt} = -\sum_{l=1}^{n} y_l^2 + \varepsilon^{m+1} \sum_{k,\, l=1}^{n} \delta_{kl}\, y_k y_l \tag{24.4}$$

and, instead of (23.9), we obtain

$$\frac{dU}{dt} \leqslant (\varepsilon^{m+1}\delta - 1) \sum_{l=1} y_l^2 \,. \tag{24.5}$$

Since the order of increase of γ_{kl} as $\varepsilon \to 0$ does not increase, the order of increase of δ does not increase either. (The quantities γ_{kl} and hence δ may fail to be bounded.) Therefore, for sufficiently large m, we have $\varepsilon^{m+1}\delta - 1 < 0$, from which follows the asymptotic stability of the zero solution of the system (22.2). Of course, we also obtain an inequality of the form (23.11):

$$\sum_{l=1}^{n} y_l^2 < U_0 A \exp\left[(\varepsilon^{m+1}\delta - 1) A (t - t_0)\right]. \tag{24.6}$$

But here, it is possible that $U_0 \to \infty$ and $A \to 0$ as $\varepsilon \to 0$. Also, as was shown above, it is possible that $\delta \to \infty$. However, since the order of increase of δ does not increase with increasing m, it follows that $\varepsilon^{m+1}\delta - 1 < 0$ for sufficiently large m.

All this proves

Theorem 24.1 (Shtokalo). Suppose that, for all $m \geqslant N$ and $0 < \varepsilon < \varepsilon^*$, the real parts of the characteristic numbers of the matrix (24.1) are negative, but the zero solution of the system (22.2) and hence of the system (20.5) are asymptotically stable.

Keeping inequality (24.6) in mind, we see that (22.1) provides us with an approximate solution of the system (20.5):

$$Y = X \sum_{k=0}^{m} Z_k \varepsilon^k. \tag{24.7}$$

Here, inequality (24.6) provides us with an approximation for X; that is, in (24.6), we need to replace the sum $\sum_{l=1}^{n} y_l^2$ [in the notations of (22.2) and (23.5)] with the sum $\sum_{l=1}^{n} x_l^2$. Here, $x_1, \ldots, x_l$ are the elements of an arbitrary row of the matrix X.

Suppose that $y_1, \ldots, y_n$ are the elements of a row (of a solution) of the matrix Y and that $x_1, \ldots, x_n$ are the elements of the same row of the matrix X. Then, from (24.7), we have

$$(y_1, \ldots, y_n) = (x_1, \ldots, x_n) \sum_{k=1}^{n} Z_k \varepsilon^k \tag{24.8}$$

and

$$\sum_{l=1}^{n} x_l^2 \leqslant U_0 A \exp\left[(\varepsilon^{m+1}\delta - 1) A (t - t_0)\right], \quad U_0 = (U)_{t=t_0}. \tag{24.9}$$

Here,

$$U = \sum_{k,\, l=1}^{n} \gamma_{kl} x_k x_l, \tag{24.10}$$

where the $\gamma_{k,l}$ are determined from the system obtained on the basis of (23.3) in terms of the elements of the matrix (24.1) and δ in terms of γ_{kl} and $R_{\mu\nu}$; A is given by formula (23.9_1).

If the matrix (24.1) has characteristic numbers with positive real parts, the zero solution of the system (20.5) is unstable [10.30].

Reference [30] takes up a nonlinear system of the form

$$\frac{dy_k}{dt} = \sum_{\nu=}^{n} y_\nu p_{\nu k} + R_k(y_1, \ldots, y_n, t) \quad (k = 1, \ldots, n), \tag{24.11}$$

where the matrix $P(t)$ of the coefficients $p_{\nu k}$ is of the form of the matrix of the system (20.5) and the R_k satisfy the inequality

$$|R_k(y_1, \ldots, y_n, t)| < K(y_1^2 + \ldots + y_n^2).$$

Then, under the condition of Shtokalo's theorem, the zero solution of the system (24.6) is asymptotically stable, and the equation of the type (24.8) provides us with an approximate solution satisfying inequalities of the form (24.9). It is also proven that the zero solution of (22.11) is unstable when the matrix (24.1) has characteristic numbers with positive real parts.

For the system (20.1), the following problems arise:

I. When do the series (20.22) and (20.23) converge for small ε?

II. What is the representation of the functions W and Z for arbitrary values of ε (when these series converge for small values of ε)?

III. When do the series (20.22) and (20.23) converge and when is Z a bounded matrix for $|t| \geqslant 0$? In this case (if the matrix Z^{-1} is also bounded), the system (20.1) will be reducible, by virtue of Theorem 3 in [14].

IV. What can be said about the stability of the zero solution of the system (20.1) or its boundedness in the case in which, for all m and arbitrarily small ε, the matrix (24.1) does not have characteristic numbers with positive real part but not all the real parts of the characteristic numbers are negative? For example, suppose that the characteristic numbers of the matrix (24.1) are distinct purely imaginary numbers for all m and sufficiently small ε. Even if the series (20.22) and (20.23) converge, this question can be answered only in the case in which the function (20.23) is bounded.

V. Show that the system (20.1) will always be regular. Obviously, this is the case.

The question of the reducibility of a system of equations of the form (20.1) was studied for special cases in [14] and for a system of two equations of a general type (20.1) in [40]. Specifically, Gel'man found two rather general sufficient conditions for reducibility of the system

$$\frac{dX}{dt} = XP(t), \tag{24.12}$$

where

$$P(t) = \sum_{k=0}^{\infty} P_k(t) \tag{24.13}$$

converges uniformly, $-\infty < t < \infty$,

$$P_k(t) = \sum_{|m_1| + \dots + |m_n| < k} B_{m_1 \dots m_n} e^{it(m_1\omega_1 + \dots + m_n\omega_n)} \tag{24.14}$$

and the B's are constant second-order matrices. He also showed that reducibility can be violated by an arbitrarily small change in one of the frequencies ω_i. In particular, when studying the system

$$\frac{dX}{dt} = XP(t), \tag{24.15}$$

$$P(t) = \left\| \begin{matrix} -a + \sin\alpha t & \sin\alpha t \\ \cos\beta t & \frac{1}{2} - \frac{\cos 2\alpha t}{2} \end{matrix} \right\|, \tag{24.16}$$

where α and β are incommensurable and $a>0$, he showed on the basis of his general tests that the system (24.16) is reducible if

$$\overline{\lim_{|m_1|+|m_2|\to\infty}} |m_1\alpha + m_2\beta|^{-1/(|m_1|+|m_2|)} < R,$$

where R is the smallest positive root of the equation

$$y + 2y^{3/2} + \frac{1}{2} y^2 = a + \frac{1}{2}.$$

This system is also reducible when α and β are algebraic incommensurable numbers and $a>3$.

It is possible to exhibit examples in which the series (20.22) terminates, that is, becomes a polynomial in ε. Then, the series (20.23) will converge for all ε. However, the questions of reducibility and boundedness of solutions and even the regularity of the system remain open. Shtelik [41] solves problems I-IV for certain systems of equations. See also [42-45].

25. Other Approximate Forms of Solutions That Arise From Shtokalo's and Bogolyubov's Methods

With regard to the approximate solution (24.7) or (24.8) in the case in which the matrix (24.1) has characteristic numbers with nonnegative real part for every m, the following can be said:

Consider Eq. (22.2), which was

$$\frac{dX}{dt} = X\left[\sum_{k=0}^{m} W_k \varepsilon^k + \varepsilon^{m+1} R_m(t, \varepsilon)\right]. \tag{25.1}$$

Here, the simplest case is that in which $W_0 = 0$ (see Remark 20.1). Here, Eq. (25.1) is rewritten in the form

$$\frac{dX}{dt} = XR(t, \varepsilon)\varepsilon, \quad R(t, \varepsilon) = \sum_{k=1}^{m} W_k \varepsilon^{k-1} + \varepsilon^m R_m(t, \varepsilon). \tag{25.2}$$

Along with (25.1), consider the equation

$$\frac{dY}{dt} = YR_0(\varepsilon)\varepsilon, \quad R_0 = \lim_{t\to\infty} \frac{1}{t}\int_0^t R(t, \varepsilon)\, dt. \tag{25.3}$$

Then, in accordance with a theorem of Bogolyubov [46, p. 370], for arbitrarily small ρ, and η and arbitrarily large L there exists a positive number ε_0 such that, if $y = y(t)$ is a vector-valued solution of Eq. (25.3), the inequality $0 < \varepsilon < \varepsilon_0$ in the interval $0 < t < L/\varepsilon$ implies the inequality

$$|x(t) - y(t)| < \eta, \tag{25.4}$$

where $x(t)$ is a vector-valued* solution of Eq. (25.2) that coincides with $y(t)$ for $t = 0$. This enables us to obtain an approximate solution of the system (20.1) in the form (24.8) by taking instead of X the solution of Eq. (25.3).

We may proceed in a different manner. Let W_0 in (25.1) be arbitrary, not necessarily equal to 0. Consider the equation

$$\frac{dX_0}{dt} = X_0 \sum_{k=0}^{m} W_k \varepsilon^k, \quad X_0 = \exp\left[\left(\sum_{k=0}^{m} W_k \varepsilon^k\right) t\right]. \tag{25.5}$$

obtained from (25.1) for $R_m = 0$. Consider also the matrix Y defined by

$$X = YX_0, \tag{25.6}$$

where the matrix X is a solution of Eq. (25.1). Then, for Y, we obtain the equation (see (14.3))

$$\frac{dY}{dt} = Y\,[X_0 R_m(t, \varepsilon) X_0^{-1}]\,\varepsilon^{m+1} = YR(t, \varepsilon)\,\varepsilon^{m+1}, \tag{25.7}$$

$$R(t, \varepsilon) = X_0 R_m(t, \varepsilon) X_0^{-1}. \tag{25.8}$$

Let us suppose that the matrix $\sum_{k=0}^{m} W_k \varepsilon^k$ has only purely imaginary characteristic numbers with simple elementary divisors for $0 < \varepsilon < \varepsilon^*$. Then, the limit

$$\lim_{t \to \infty} \frac{1}{t} \int_0^t R(t, \varepsilon)\, dt = R_0(\varepsilon) \tag{25.9}$$

exists. Instead of the solution of Eq. (25.7), let us take its approximate value (using Bogolyubov's theorem), namely, the solution of the system

$$\frac{dY_0}{dt} = Y_0 R_0(\varepsilon)\, \varepsilon^{m+1}. \tag{25.10}$$

---

*But by $x(t)$, $y(t)$, and η we may also understand respectively the matrices $x(t)$ in (25.2), $y(t)$ in (25.3) and $\eta = \|\tau\|$ where all elements of the matrix $\eta = \tau$.

We obtain instead of (25.6) the approximation

$$X = Y_0 X_0. \qquad (25.11)$$

We can substitute this into (24.8).

Now, let us suppose that the canonical form of the matrix $\sum_{k=0}^{m} W_k \varepsilon^k$ is of a general form. We note first of all that, for every M and T, there exists a positive constant M_m such that

$$|R_m(t, \varepsilon)| \leqslant M_m \qquad (25.12)$$

where $|t| \leqslant T$ and $|\varepsilon| \leqslant \varepsilon^*$, where ε^* is an arbitrary number in the region of convergence of the series $P(t)$ in (20.1). This is obvious from formulas (22.4) and (22.5). It follows from this that, in the interval T (which we choose arbitrarily), the solution of (25.7) or of the equation

$$Y = Y_0 + \int_0^t YR(t, \varepsilon)\, \varepsilon^{m+1}\, dt \qquad (25.13)$$

with initial conditions $Y(0) = Y_0$ will, up to

$$Y_0 (e^{M_m \varepsilon^{m+1} t} - I)$$

be equal to $Y = Y_0$ or

$$Y = Y_0 + \Delta(\varepsilon), \quad |\Delta(\varepsilon)| = |Y_0 (e^{M_m \varepsilon^{m+1} t} - I)|.$$

Consequently, it is possible to exhibit an ε^* such that $|\Delta(\varepsilon)|$ can be arbitrarily small for all $|t| \leqslant T$ simultaneously. Therefore, we have an approximation for the matrix X for small values of ε in the form (25.11), where Y_0 is the constant matrix in (25.13).

Finally, we have the matrix (24.7) in the form

$$\begin{aligned} Y &= Y_0 X_0 \sum_{k=0}^{m} Z_k \varepsilon^k + \Delta(\varepsilon) X_0 \sum_{k=0}^{m} Z_k \varepsilon^k = \\ &= Y_0 \exp\left(\sum_{k=0}^{m} W_k \varepsilon^k t\right) \cdot \sum_{k=0}^{m} Z_k \varepsilon^k + \\ &+ \Delta(\varepsilon) \exp\left(\sum_{k=0}^{m} W_k \varepsilon^k t\right) \cdot \sum_{k=0}^{m} Z_k \cdot \varepsilon^k, \end{aligned} \qquad (25.14)$$

that is, we may, as an approximation, take

$$Y = Y_0 \exp\left(\sum_{k=0}^{m} W_k \varepsilon^k t\right) \cdot \sum_{k=0}^{m} Z_k \varepsilon^k \tag{25.15}$$

for $|\varepsilon| \leqslant \varepsilon^*$ and $|t| \leqslant T$.

Thus, we have

Theorem 25.1 In a given interval $|t| \leqslant T$, the solution of the system (20.5) with initial conditions $Y(0) = Y_0$ is given approximately in the form (25.15) for sufficiently small ε^*. Here, the error Δ does not exceed

$$\Delta_1 = \Delta(\varepsilon) \exp\left(\sum_{k=0}^{m} W_k \varepsilon^k t\right) \cdot \sum_{k=0}^{m} Z_k \varepsilon^k,$$

$$\Delta(\varepsilon) = |Y_0(\exp M_m \varepsilon^{m+1} - I)|, \tag{25.16}$$

where M_m is given by inequality (25.12).

In certain cases, in finding the matrix M_m in (25.12), we may use the inequalities of Academician I. M. Vinogradov (for example, [47, 48]). Here, we need to set $\lambda_k t = F(k)$(for $k = 1, 2, \ldots, n$), where

$$F(x) = \sum_{m=1}^{n} a_m x^m, \qquad a_m = t \sum_{k=1}^{n} b_k \lambda_k$$

and the b_k are rational numbers. If the $\lambda_k = k$ are integers, then $a_1 = 1$ and $a_l = 0$ for $l > 1$.

26. Demidovich's Problem

Consider the system of n linear homogeneous differential equations

$$\frac{dX}{dt} = XP(t), \tag{26.1}$$

where $P(t)$ is an nth-order matrix that is continuous and periodic with period ω. Suppose that the limit

$$\lim_{\omega \to 0} \frac{1}{\omega} \int_0^{\omega} P(t)\, dt = M \tag{26.2}$$

exists. The problem is to answer the question of the stability of the zero solution of the system (26.1) for small values of ω. Demidovich obtained the following result:

Theorem (Demidovich). *The characteristic indices $\lambda = \lambda(\omega)$ of the system (26.1) approach the characteristic indices λ_0 of the matrix M for suitable choice of imaginary part of $\lambda(\omega)$.*

The author concludes from this that if the real parts of the characteristic indices λ_0 are negative, then, for sufficiently small values of ω, the solution of the system (26.1) is asymptotically stable, but if there is a purely imaginary number λ_0, we can say nothing regarding the stability.

Let us note first that this assertion regarding the stability of the zero solution can be obtained by using Bogolyubov's theorem [46, p. 419]. We shall, however, solve Demidovich's problem by a different method, one based on the theory expounded in the present book.

Let us make the substitution $t = \omega\tau$ in Eq. (26.1). Then, (26.1) can be rewritten

$$\frac{dX}{d\tau} = XP(\omega\tau)\,\omega. \tag{26.3}$$

The matrix X can, for small values of ω, be represented in the form*

$$X = \exp\left[\left(\sum_{k=1}^{\infty} W_k\,\omega^k\right) t\right] \cdot \sum_{k=0}^{\infty} Z_k\,\omega^k. \tag{26.4}$$

Here, $Z_0 = I$ and we can determine Z_1 and W_1 from the equation (see (9.15))

$$\frac{dZ_1}{dt} = P(\omega\tau) - W_1.$$

The matrix $P(\omega\tau)$ is of period 1 with respect to τ. Therefore, in accordance with (9.17),

$$W_1 = \int_0^1 P(\tau\omega)\,d\tau = \frac{1}{\omega}\int_0^{\omega} P(t)\,dt. \tag{26.5}$$

Demidovich's results follow.

---

*By considering the system $\frac{dX}{d\tau} = XP(\omega\tau)\,\varepsilon$ we can obtain

$$X = \exp\left[\left(\sum_{k=1}^{\infty} W_k(\omega)\,\varepsilon^k\right) t\right] \cdot \sum_{k=0}^{\infty} Z_k(\tau, \omega)\,\varepsilon^k,$$

and then set $\varepsilon = \omega$.

If, for arbitrarily small ω, the matrix W_1 has characteristic numbers with real parts equal to 0 (but none with positive real parts), then, by taking, in the expansion of the matrix

$$W = \sum_{k=1}^{\infty} W_k \omega^k \tag{26.6}$$

the following terms, one may again obtain a solution of Demidovich's problem as was shown in the preceding section. Here, the problem is solved by the limiting values of the matrices $W_1, W_2, W_3, \ldots$ as $\omega \to 0$. We shall not repeat the process.

27. Another Formulation of Certain Problems and Consequences of Them

Consider a system of the form

$$\frac{dX}{dt} = X \sum_{k=0}^{\infty} P_k(t, \delta) \varepsilon^k, \tag{27.1}$$

where $P_k(t + 2\pi, \delta) = P_k(t, \delta)$ and where the matrices $P_k(t, \delta)$ are uniformly continuous with respect to δ at the point $\delta = 0$ and are absolutely integrable with respect to t in the interval $(0, 2\pi)$, where the series

$$P(t, \delta, \varepsilon) = \sum_{k=0}^{\infty} P_k(t, \delta) \varepsilon^k$$

converges in the interval $0 \leqslant t \leqslant 2\pi$, $0 \leqslant \delta < \delta_0$, $0 \leqslant \varepsilon < \varepsilon_0$, and where $|P(t, \delta, \varepsilon)| \leqslant M$, (where M is a constant matrix with positive elements).

We obtain an integral matrix of the system (27.1) in the form

$$X(t, \delta, \varepsilon) = \sum_{k=0}^{\infty} X_k(t, \delta) \varepsilon^k, \tag{27.2}$$

$X_0(0, \delta) = I$, $X_k(0, \delta) = 0$, for $k \geqslant 1$, where $X_0(t, \delta)$ and $X_k(t, \delta)$ are defined by the equations

$$\frac{dX_0}{dt} = X_0(t, \delta) P_0(t, \delta),$$

$$\frac{dX_k}{dt} = X_k P_0(t, \delta) + X_{k-1} P_1(t, \delta) + \ldots + X_0 P_k(t, \delta),$$

$$X_k(t, \delta) = \int_0^t (X_{k-1} P_1 + \ldots + X_0 P_k)_{t=\tau} X_0^{-1}(\tau, \delta)\, d\tau\, X_0(t, \delta).$$

By Theorem 6.1, the series (27.2) converges for $0 \leqslant t \leqslant 2\pi$, $|\varepsilon| < \varepsilon_0$, $|\delta| < \delta_0$ and is a continuous function of δ at the point $\delta = 0$. If the matrix $P(t, \delta, \varepsilon)$ is holomorphic with respect to δ and ε in the neighborhood $|\varepsilon| < \varepsilon_0, |\delta| < \delta_0$, then the matrix $X(t, \delta, \varepsilon)$ will also be holomorphic with respect to δ and ε in that region. The matrices $X_k(t, \delta)$ will be holomorphic with respect to δ.

We seek an integral substitution of the matrix (27.2) in the form

$$X(2\pi, \delta, \varepsilon) = \sum_{k=0}^{\infty} X_k(2\pi, \delta)\, \varepsilon^k. \tag{27.3}$$

Let us write the characteristic equation of this matrix $X(2\pi, \delta, \varepsilon)$

$$D(xI - X(2\pi, \delta, \varepsilon)) = x^n + a_1(\delta, \varepsilon)\, x^{n-1} + \ldots + a_n(\delta, \varepsilon) = 0, \tag{27.4}$$

where

$$a_k(\delta, \varepsilon) = \sum_{k=0}^{\infty} \alpha_\nu^{(k)}(\delta)\, \varepsilon \quad (k = 1, \ldots, n)$$

and these series converge in the interval $|\varepsilon| < \varepsilon_0$. If the matrix $P(t, \delta, \varepsilon)$ is holomorphic in the region $|\varepsilon| < \varepsilon_0$, $|\delta| < \delta_0$, then the $a_k(\delta, \varepsilon)$ will also be holomorphic in that region. To answer the question of the stability of the zero solution of the system (27.1) or the boundedness of the matrix (27.2), we may, in accordance with Sects. 10 and 11, represent the matrix (27.2) in the form

$$X(t, \delta, \varepsilon) = \exp\left[\left(\sum_{k=0}^{\infty} W_k(\delta)\, \varepsilon^k\right) t\right] \cdot \sum_{k=0}^{\infty} Z_k(t, \delta)\, \varepsilon^k, \tag{27.4$_1$}$$

where the matrices $Z_k(t, \delta)$ are periodic with respect to t. If, for all sufficiently small values of δ and ε, the real parts of the characteristic numbers of the matrix are negative, then the matrix (27.2) will possess the property that

$$X(t, \delta, \varepsilon) \to \|0\| \text{ as } t \to \infty. \tag{27.6}$$

If the real parts of all the characteristic numbers of the matrix $W_0(0)$ are negative, then (27.6) holds for all sufficiently small values of δ and ε; if the zeros are also negative, then (27.6) is also valid for all sufficiently small values of δ and ε provided the real parts of all the characteristic numbers of the matrix

$$W_m(\delta, \varepsilon) = \sum_{k=0}^{m} W_k(\delta)\, \varepsilon^k \tag{27.7}$$

are negative for all sufficiently small values of δ and ε. We obtain this on the basis of Shtokalo's method even in the case in which the matrices $P_k(t, \delta)$ are only quasi-periodic or some of them are almost periodic [13].

On the basis of Theorem 24.1 (Shtokalo), we have the following result. If, for some δ and sufficiently large m, the real parts of the characteristic numbers of the matrix (27.7) are negative, then the real parts of the characteristic numbers of the matrix (27.5) will also be negative for that δ and for all sufficiently small ε. We recall that the real parts of all characteristic numbers of the matrix (27.5) are negative for all sufficiently small ε if the Hurwitz determinants of that matrix have positive coefficients for the lower powers of ε (that is, if the coefficients are positive only for sufficiently large m in the matrix (27.7) [10, Theorem 3].

We see how the question of the boundedness of the matrices (27.2) is answered when the system (27.1) is canonical. We have also considered Artem'yev's problem in this case for the system (18.1), a particular case of which is the system (27.1) if it is canonical. We shall return to these problems in Sect. 46, solving them on the basis of the matrix (27.3) and Eq. (27.4).

Now, we shall touch on a problem that is considered in [49] and in various works referred to therein.

Suppose that we have a set of periodic integrable matrices $P(t) = P(t + 2\pi)$. Let us take any one of these $P(t)$ and let us examine the system of linear homogeneous equations

$$\frac{dX}{dt} = XP(\omega t), \tag{27.8}$$

where the parameter ω is positive. Let us also consider the subset of this set that consists of matrices $P_1(t)$ possessing the property

$$\int_0^{2\pi} |P_1(t) - P(t)|\, dt \leqslant \varepsilon \|1\|, \tag{27.9}$$

where $\|1\|$ is the matrix all of whose elements are equal to 1 and $|P_1(t) - P(t)|$ is the matrix whose elements are the absolute values of the differences of the elements of the matrices $P_1(t)$ and $P(t)$. From (27.9), we see that the set of matrices $P_1(t)$ can be written

$$P_1(t) = P(t) + \varepsilon Q(t), \tag{27.10}$$

where the set of matrices $Q(t)$ is such that

$$\int_0^{2\pi} |Q(t)|\, dt \leqslant \|1\|. \tag{27.11}$$

Along with the system (27.8), let us consider the system

$$\frac{dX}{dt} = X\,[P((\omega+\delta)t) + \varepsilon Q((\omega+\delta)t)], \tag{27.12}$$

where δ is a parameter. Let us suppose that the zero solution of the system (27.8) is stable. The question* arises as to the conditions under which the zero solution of the system (27.12) will also be stable for sufficiently small values of δ and ε.

Let us introduce a new independent variable τ defined by $\tau = (\omega+\delta)t$ into equation (27.12). We obtain [13]

$$\frac{dX}{d\tau} = X\,[P(\tau) + \varepsilon Q(\tau)]\,\frac{1}{\omega+\delta}. \tag{27.13}$$

Now, for the system (27.13), the problem becomes the following: For $\varepsilon = \delta = 0$, the system has a bounded fundamental** integral matrix $X(\tau)$. Under what conditions will this fundamental integral matrix be bounded for all sufficiently small ε and δ?

The system (27.13) is a particular case of the system (27.1). We have the obvious result: If the integral matrix of (27.13) $X(\tau, \delta, \varepsilon) \to \|0\|$ as $\tau \to \infty$ when $\delta = \varepsilon = 0$, then $X(\tau, \delta, \varepsilon) \to \|0\|$ as $\tau \to \infty$ for all sufficiently small δ and ε. This follows from the fact that if $X(\tau, 0, 0) \to \|0\|$ as $\tau \to \infty$, then the real parts of all characteristic numbers of the matrix (27.5) for $\delta = \varepsilon = 0$ will be negative. But then, the real parts of the characteristic numbers of the matrix (27.5) will also be negative for all sufficiently small*** values of δ and ε. On the other hand, if the real parts of the characteristic numbers of the exponential substitution (27.5) are nonpositive numbers when $\delta = \varepsilon = 0$, we need to consider the characteristic numbers of the matrix (27.7). If, for all sufficiently small δ and ε, the real parts of the characteristic matrix (27.7) are negative, then $X(\tau, \delta, \varepsilon)$ will again approach $\|0\|$ as $\tau \to \infty$ for all sufficiently small δ and ε. Here, the matrices $P(\tau)$ and $Q(\tau)$ may be considered quasi-periodic or almost periodic. If, for $\delta = \varepsilon = 0$, the characteristic numbers of the exponential substitution (27.7) are nonpositive, we may consider the particular cases in which $\delta = \delta(\varepsilon) \to 0$ as $\varepsilon \to 0$ in accordance with what was said in Sect. 18. This is particularly convenient when (1) the real parts of all the characteristic numbers of the matrix $W_0(0)$ are equal to 0, (2) the matrices $P(\tau)$ and $Q(\tau)$ are

*Here, we pose a problem equivalent to the one examined in [49] although in a different formulation.

**That is, with $D(X(\tau)) \neq 0$, where D indicates a determinant.

***This was already pointed out in [9, p. 73], where it was assumed only that the coefficient matrix of the system (27.1) was a continuous function of δ and ε since the continuity of the characteristic numbers of the matrix (27.5) as functions of the δ and ε had been proven.

periodic, and (3) the system (27.13) is canonical. For example, we may consider the case of $\delta = \varepsilon$. Then, the system (27.13) can be written in the form

$$\frac{dX}{d\tau} = X \sum_{k=0}^{\infty} P_k(\tau)\, \varepsilon^k, \tag{27.14}$$

where

$$P_0(\tau) = \frac{P(\tau)}{\omega}. \tag{27.15}$$

Now, the problem for Eq. (27.14) becomes the following: for $\varepsilon = 0$, the integral matrix of the system (27.14) is bounded. Under what conditions will this integral matrix be bounded for all sufficiently small ε?

Obviously, if the real parts of the characteristic numbers of the system (27.8) (that is, the real parts of the characteristic numbers of the exponential matrix W) are negative, then for small values of ε, the integral matrix $X(\tau)$ of the system (27.14) possesses

$$X(\tau) \to \|0\| \text{ as } \tau \to \infty. \tag{27.15$_1$}$$

On the other hand, if the system (27.8) has characteristic numbers whose real parts are equal to zero (and none of the characteristic numbers have positive real parts), then the question is answered by the coefficients in the expansion of the exponential matrix

$$W = \sum_{k=0}^{\infty} W_k \varepsilon^k. \tag{27.16}$$

Suppose that $\delta = 0$ and $P(\omega t) = C$ is a constant matrix in the system (27.12). Then, we have the system

$$\frac{dX}{dt} = X\,[C + \varepsilon Q(\omega t)]. \tag{27.17}$$

In essence, such a system was considered in [49], pp. 37–39. In this case, the system (27.13) is of the form

$$\frac{dX}{d\tau} = X\,[C + \varepsilon Q(\tau)]\,\frac{1}{\omega}, \quad Q(\tau + 2\pi) = Q(\tau). \tag{27.18}$$

Let us suppose that this system is canonical and that $\frac{2\pi C}{\omega} = \ln \exp \frac{2\pi C}{\omega}$ is a regular value.* Then, if the matrix C has distinct,

*That is, $\frac{2\pi(\omega_k - \omega_l)}{\omega} \neq m$, where m is an integer and $\omega_k i$ and $\omega_l i$ are the characteristic numbers of the matrix C. The values $\omega = \frac{2\pi(\omega_k - \omega_l)}{m}$ are called "critical values" in [34, 49].

purely imaginary characteristic numbers, the zero solution of the system (27.18) is stable for sufficiently small ε [or the integral matrix of this system is bounded and oscillatory (i.e., does not approach 0 as $\tau\to\infty$)]. This follows from the Theorem 16.1 (Artem'yev's theorem).

Suppose that

$$2\pi(\omega_k - \omega_l) = \omega m. \tag{27.19}$$

Then, to solve the problem, we need to proceed as indicated in Sects. 10, 11, and 20-24.

Let us construct the integral matrix of the system (27.18):

$$X(\tau) = \sum_{k=0}^{\infty} X_k \varepsilon^k, \quad X(0) = I, \qquad X_0(\tau) = \exp\frac{C\tau}{\omega}, \tag{27.20}$$

$$X_1(\tau) = \int_0^{\tau} \frac{X_0(t)Q(t)X_0^{-1}(t)}{\omega}\, dt X_0(\tau)$$

and the integral substitution

$$V = X(2\pi) = \exp\left(\frac{2\pi C}{\omega}\right) + \varepsilon\int_0^{2\pi}\frac{X_0(t)Q(t)X_0^{-1}(t)}{\omega}\, dt X_0(2\pi) + \ldots \tag{27.21}$$

Following the methods explained in Sects. 10 and 11, we can represent the matrix $X(\tau)$ in the form

$$X(\tau) = \exp\left[\sum_{k=0}^{\infty} W_k \varepsilon^k \tau\right]\sum_{k=0}^{\infty} Z_k(\tau)\varepsilon^k. \tag{27.22}$$

Here, for example (see (10.14)), $2\pi W_0 = \ln\exp\left(\frac{2\pi C}{\omega}\right)$ is the principal value if the matrix $\exp\frac{2\pi C}{\omega}$ has no negative characteristic numbers. Then,

$$Z_0(\tau) = \exp(-W_0\tau)\cdot\exp\left(\frac{C\tau}{\omega}\right). \tag{27.23}$$

We showed in Sects. 10 and 11 how to calculate W_k and Z_k under all hypotheses regarding the matrix C. In particular, we found above that it is sometimes possible (see Theorem 2.3 and the example following it), when condition (27.19) is satisfied, to take

$$W_0 = S\frac{C}{\omega}S^{-1}, \tag{27.24}$$

where S is a constant matrix that does not depend on ε. In particular, this is possible in the case in which the characteristic numbers of the matrix (27.21) are holomorphic functions of ε and the elementary divisors are prime in a neighborhood of $\varepsilon = 0$. Let us suppose that the system (27.18) is canonical (the set $Q(\tau)$ is such a C). Then, for the exponential matrix $W(\varepsilon)$, we have the characteristic equation

$$\mu^n + a_1(\varepsilon)\mu^{n-1} + \ldots + a_{n-1}(\varepsilon)\mu + a_n(\varepsilon) = 0, \tag{27.25}$$

where $\mu = \lambda^2$, λ being a characteristic number of the matrix $W(\varepsilon)$.

It may happen that (27.19) is verified but all the characteristic numbers of the matrix $\frac{C}{\omega}$ (or of the matrix W_0) are purely imaginary and distinct. Then, if Theorem 2.3 is applicable*, the roots of Eq. (27.25) will all be negative and distinct for $\varepsilon = 0$. But then the roots of Eq. (27.25) will be negative and distinct for all sufficiently small ε. From this it follows that the integral matrix of the system (27.28) is bounded and oscillatory for small ε. For example, this will be the case if the system (27.18) is canonical and of the type (15.1). (In the system (15.1), the characteristic numbers of the matrix P_0 are i and $-i$.)

It may happen that Eq. (27.25) also has zero roots for $\varepsilon = 0$ but distinct negative roots for small $\varepsilon \neq 0$. Then, the integral matrix of the system (27.13) will again be bounded and oscillatory. Here, it is useful to recall Remark 16.3 and Theorem 24.1 (Shtokalo's theorem).

28. Solution of the Problems in Section 8 by Use of the Method of Solving the Poincaré–Lappo-Danilevskiy Problem and Lyapunov's Contributions

We shall now show that the complete solution of the Poincaré–Lappo-Danilevskiy problem is closely related to the problem of constructing the integral matrix X of the system

$$\frac{dX}{dt} = XP(t), \quad P(t+2\pi) = P(t) \tag{28.1}$$

in the form

$$X = e^{At}N(t), \tag{28.2}$$

*But, in applying Theorem 2.3, we need to keep Remark 16.5 in mind.

where A is a constant matrix and $N(t)$ is periodic with period 2π. The integral matrix (28.2) is in effect multiplied on the left by the matrix

$$V = e^{2\pi A} \tag{28.3}$$

when t is increased by 2π.

Suppose that the matrix* $P(t)$ is of the form

$$P(t) = b_0 + \sum_{k=1}^{m} b_k \cos kt + \sum_{k=1}^{m} a_k \sin kt, \tag{28.4}$$

where b_0, b_k, and a_k are constant matrices. If we make the substitutions

$$\sin kt = \frac{e^{kti} - e^{-kti}}{2i}, \quad \cos kt = \frac{e^{kti} + e^{-kti}}{2}$$

and $z = e^{ti}$, we can write Eq. (28.1) in the form

$$zi \frac{dX}{dz} = X \sum_{k=-m}^{m} P_k Z^k, \tag{28.5}$$

where

$$P_k = \frac{b_k - ia_k}{2}, \quad k \geqslant 1; \; P_k = \frac{b_{-k} + ia_{-k}}{2}, \quad k \leqslant -1, \quad P_0 = b_0.$$

We can write the system (28.5) in the form

$$\frac{dX}{dz} = X \sum_{k=-m-1}^{m-1} T_k z^k, \tag{28.6}$$

where

$$T_k = -iP_{k+1}, \; T_{-1} = -ib_0. \tag{28.7}$$

Thus, at a finite distance, the system (28.6) has one singular irregular point $z = 0$. Suppose that $X(t)$ is an integral matrix of the system (28.6) that is normalized at the point $z = 1$. In accordance with (7.7), we have

---

*In accordance with what was said above, our subsequent reasoning will remain valid for $m = \infty$ if the series $\sum_{-\infty}^{\infty} P_k z^k$ converges for $|z| < 1$.

$$X(z) = z^W N(z), \tag{28.8}$$

where W is a constant matrix and $N(z)$ is a single-valued matrix in a neighborhood of the point $z = 0$.

When we let the variable z move around the coordinate origin, the matrix $X(z)$ is multiplied on the left by the matrix

$$V = e^{2\pi iW}, \quad 2\pi iW = \ln V, \tag{28.9}$$

which, as we have seen, can be represented by series of matrices $T_{-m-1}, \ldots, T_{m-1}$, which converge (with exponential speed) at all finite values of these matrices. The matrix W can be represented in accordance with formula (7.15) for all values of these matrices $T_{-m-1}, \ldots, T_{m-1}$ if the matrix W is second-order, and it can be represented in accordance with (1.39) if it is of nth-order.

By making the substitution $z = e^{it}$, we may write

$$X(e^{it}) = e^{iWt} N(e^{it}). \tag{28.10}$$

Here, the matrix $N(e^{it})$ is periodic since $N(z)$ is single-valued in a neighborhood of the point $z=0$ with period 2π and

$$iW = A \tag{28.11}$$

is the matrix A that appears in formula (28.2). From this we see that the integral matrix $X(t)$ is multiplied on the left by the matrix

$$V = e^{2\pi iW} = e^{2\pi A} \tag{28.12}$$

when t is increased by the period 2π.

Consequently, finding the matrix V by which the integral matrix of the system of differential equations with periodic coefficients is multiplied when the independent variable t is increased by an amount equal to the period of the coefficient matrix, leads us to seek a matrix by which the integral matrix of the system of differential equations with singular irregular point $z=0$ is multiplied when the point z moves around the coordinate origin. Let us consider in greater detail the general representation of a second-order matrix A in terms of matrices that appear in the system of two differential equations with periodic coefficients. In accordance with (28.11) and (7.15), we have

$$A = iW = \frac{\ln(t + \sqrt{t^2 - 1})}{2\pi\sqrt{t^2 - 1}} \times [Ve^{-\pi i\sigma(T_{-1})} - t] + \frac{\sigma(T_{-1})}{2} i, \tag{28.13}$$

where

$$t = \frac{\sigma(V)}{2} e^{-\pi i\sigma(T_{-1})}. \tag{28.14}$$

On the basis of (28.7), we may also write

$$A = \frac{\ln(t + \sqrt{t^2 - 1})}{2\pi\sqrt{t^2 - 1}} [Ve^{-\pi\sigma(b_0)} - t] + \frac{\sigma(b_0)}{2}, \quad (28.15)$$

$$t = \frac{\sigma(V)}{2} e^{-\pi\sigma(b_0)}. \quad (28.16)$$

If

$$\sigma(b_0) = 0, \quad (28.17)$$

then

$$A = \frac{\ln\left(\frac{\sigma(V)}{2} + \sqrt{\frac{\sigma^2(V)}{4} - 1}\right)}{2\pi\sqrt{\frac{\sigma^2(V)}{4} - 1}} \left[V - \frac{\sigma(V)}{2}\right]. \quad (28.18)$$

To find A, we need to find V and $\sigma(V)$, since, on the basis of (28.4), $\sigma(b_0)$ is given together with the system (28.1). To find V, we need to proceed as follows: Using the notations $b_0 = U_1$, $b_1 = U_2$, ..., $b_m = U_{m+1}$, $a_1 = U_{m+2}$, ..., $a_m = U_{2m+1}$ we write the system (28.1) in the form

$$\frac{dX}{dt} = X \sum_{k=1}^{2m+1} \varphi_k(t) U_k, \quad (28.19)$$

where

$$\begin{aligned} &\varphi_1(t) = 1, \quad \varphi_k(t) = \cos(k-1)t \qquad (k = 2, \ldots, m+1), \\ &\varphi_k(t) = \sin(k-m-1)t \qquad (k = m+2, \ldots, 2m+1). \end{aligned} \quad (28.20)$$

Now, we can use formula (6.11) to find the matrix $X(t)$ in the form of a series of compositions of the matrices $U_1, \ldots, U_{2m+1}$ that converges for all finite $U_1, \ldots, U_{2m+1}$ and arbitrary finite t. We can also obtain $X(t)$ in the form (6.1), which amounts to the same thing.

When we have done this, we can easily obtain

$$V = X(2\pi), \quad \sigma(V) = \sigma(X(2\pi)) \quad (28.21)$$

in the form of convergent series.

However, we can also use the series (7.12), which represents V in the form of a series of compositions of $T_{-s}, \ldots, T_l$. The series (7.12) also converges for arbitrary finite values of these matrices. Here, we need to set $b = 1$.

The coefficients in the series (7.12) are polynomials in π with rational coefficients, where the rational numbers α and $\overset{*}{\alpha}$ are defined by Lappo-Danilevskiy's recursion formulas given above.

Since V is a real matrix, the coefficient of i in every sum

$$\sum_{p_1 \ldots p_\nu = -m-1}^{m-1} T_{p_1} \ldots T_{p_\nu} \sum_{\mu=0}^{\nu} \alpha^{*(0)}_{p_1 \ldots p_\mu} \sum_{\varkappa=0}^{\nu-\mu} \alpha^{(\varkappa)}_{p_{\mu+1} \ldots p_\nu} (2\pi i)^\varkappa$$

in (7.12) is equal to 0 when we substitute the values of $T_{-m-1}, \ldots, T_{m-1}$ given by (28.7).

A system of linear equations with periodic coefficients is a particular case of systems that can be reduced by Lyapunov's method [14]. $Z(t)$ is the matrix of the transformation of the given system with periodic coefficients into a system with constant coefficients and with coefficient matrix A, the general expression for which (as well as $Z(t)$), we shall now find.

Let us consider the case in which the characteristic numbers μ_1, and μ_2 of the matrix V are negative. Then, $\sigma(V) = \mu_1 + \mu_2 < 0$ and, in accordance with (28.16),

$$t = \frac{\sigma(V)}{2} e^{-\pi\sigma(b_0)} < 0.$$

From this it follows* that $t + \sqrt{t^2 - 1} < 0$ since $|t| > 1$.

Therefore, in accordance with (28.15), the matrix A is complex. Specifically,

$$A = \frac{\ln(-t - \sqrt{t^2 - 1}) + \pi i}{2\pi \sqrt{t^2 - 1}} \times$$

$$\times \left[V e^{-\pi\sigma(b_0)} - \frac{\sigma(V)}{2} e^{-\pi\sigma(b_0)} \right] + \frac{\sigma(b_0)}{2} =$$

$$= A_1 + \frac{i e^{-\pi\sigma(b_0)}}{2\sqrt{t^2 - 1}} \left| V - \frac{\sigma(V)}{2} \right| .$$

---

*It follows from (28.22) that $|t| > 1$ since $t = \dfrac{\mu_1 + \mu_2}{2\sqrt{\mu_1 \mu_2}}$.

where

$$A_1 = \frac{\ln(-t + \sqrt{t^2-1})}{2\pi\sqrt{t^2-1}}\left[V - \frac{\sigma(V)}{2}\right] e^{-\pi\sigma(b_0)} + \frac{\sigma(b_0)}{2}$$

is a real matrix.

The characteristic numbers μ_1 and μ_2 are roots of the equation

$$\mu^2 - \sigma(V)\mu + D(V) = 0.$$

In accordance with Jacobi's formula, we have, from Eq. (28.1),

$$\mu_1\mu_2 = D(V) = e^{\int_0^{2\pi}\sigma(P)dt} = e^{2\pi\sigma(b_0)}. \tag{28.22}$$

Therefore,

$$\mu_1 = \frac{\sigma(V) + \sqrt{\sigma^2(V) - 4e^{2\pi\sigma(b_0)}}}{2},$$

$$\mu_2 = \frac{\sigma(V) - \sqrt{\sigma^2(V) - 4e^{2\pi\sigma(b_0)}}}{2}$$

and

$$\mu_1 - \mu_2 = \sqrt{\sigma^2(V) - 4e^{2\pi\sigma(b_0)}} = 2e^{\pi\sigma(b_0)}\sqrt{t^2-1}.$$

Furthermore, we have

$$V - \frac{\sigma(V)}{2} = S[\mu_1, \mu_2]S^{-1} - \frac{\mu_1+\mu_2}{2} =$$

$$= S\left[\frac{\mu_1-\mu_2}{2}, \frac{\mu_2-\mu_1}{2}\right]S^{-1}.$$

It follows from this that

$$\frac{ie^{-\pi\sigma(b_0)}}{2\sqrt{t^2-1}}\left(V - \frac{\sigma(V)}{2}\right) = \frac{i}{2}S[1, -1]S^{-1},$$

$$A = A_1 + \frac{i}{2}S[1, -1]S^{-1}. \tag{28.23}$$

This enables us to write (28.2) in the form

$$X = e^{A_1 t}e^{\frac{i}{2}tS[1, -1]S^{-1}}N(t) \tag{28.24}$$

or

$$X = e^{A_1 t} N_1(t),$$

where

$$N_1(t) = e^{\frac{it}{2} S[1, -1] S^{-1}} N(t).$$

The matrix $N_1(t)$ is real (since the matrices X and A_1 are real) and is of period 4π since $N(t)$ is of period 2π but the function $e^{\frac{i}{2} tS[1, -1] S^{-1}}$ is of period 4π by virtue of the equation $e^{2\pi i S[1, -1] S^{-1}} = I$.

Earlier (see (9.3)), we had

$$X = e^{A_1 t} e^{\frac{i}{2} t} N(t),$$

instead of (28.4), but, in accordance with Remarks 1.3 and 1.4, even there we could have obtained (28.24).

Let us find the general representation of the matrix A for a system of n equations with the aid of formula (1.39).

It should be noted that Lyapunov in his dissertation [26, Chap. III, 53] exhibited a case of a linear system of differential equations with periodic coefficients such that finding the characteristic numbers of the matrix A leads to a simple algebraic problem. This is the case in which, in a system of $2n$ equations with unknowns $x_1, \ldots, x_n, y_1, \ldots, y_n$, the system is broken into two systems for unknowns $u_1, \ldots, u_n, v_1, \ldots, v_n$ after we introduce the new variables $u_s = x_s + iy_s$ and $v_s = x_s - iy_s$ (for $s = 1, \ldots, n$).

The first of these systems is such that the substitution $e^{it} = z$ leads to linear equations with regular singular point $z = 0$. Consequently, the characteristic numbers of the matrix A are found as the characteristic numbers of the matrix* that is the coefficient of z^{-1}.

A second system of equations with unknowns $v_1, \ldots, v_n$ also leads to a system with regular singular point $z = 0$ by means of the substitution $e^{-it} = z$. In the case of a system of two equations, this class of Lyapunov equations is an extremely simple particular case of a system in which the coefficient matrix $P(t)$ possesses the property

$$P(t) \int_0^t P(t)\, dt = \int_0^t P(t)\, dt\, P(t).$$

Thus, Lyapunov also turned his attention to the relationship between the theory of linear systems of differential equations with

*This is clear from the formula (see Sect. 7) $W = SU_{-1}S^{-1}$, in reference to Eq. (7.9).

periodic coefficients and the analytic theory of linear systems of differential equations.

We note that the invariants of the matrix W coincide with the invariants of the matrix H constructed by Lappo-Danilevskiy in the form

$$H=\sum_{\nu=1}^{\infty}\sum_{p_1\ldots p_\nu=-s}^{l} T_{p_1}\ldots T_{p_\nu}\,\delta^{(0)}_{p_1+\ldots+p_\nu+\nu}\,\alpha^{(1)}_{p_1\ldots p_\nu}, \tag{28.25}$$

where $\delta^{(0)}_p$ is the Kronecker delta and $\alpha^{(1)}_{p_1\ldots p_\nu}$ are defined by the formulas of Sect. 7. Here, H is the exponential substitution of the so-called metacanonical integral matrix [1]. The matrix H is similar to the matrix W.

29. Remarks on Bounded and Periodic Solutions of a System of Two Differential Equations With Periodic Coeffficients

In this section, we shall touch on the question of the existence of bounded and periodic solutions of a system of two linear homogeneous differential equations with periodic coefficient matrix $P(t)$

$$\frac{dX}{dt}=XP(t),\ P(t+2\pi)=P(t). \tag{29.1}$$

As we have seen, the integral matrix normalized for $t=0$ of such a system can be represented in the form

$$X=e^{At}Z(t), \tag{29.2}$$

where A is a real constant second-order matrix and $Z(t)$ is a periodic matrix with period either 2π or 4π. If $Z(t)$ is of period 4π, then $Z(t+2\pi)=-Z(t)$. When t is increased by an amount equal to the period 2π, the integral matrix $X(t)$ given by formula (29.2) is multiplied on the left by the matrix

$$V=X(2\pi)=e^{2\pi A}, \tag{29.3}$$

if $Z(t)$ is of period 2π and by the matrix

$$V=X(2\pi)=-e^{2\pi A}, \tag{29.4}$$

if the period of $Z(t)$ is 4π. Consequently, we have

$$X(t+2\pi n)=V^nX(t), \tag{29.5}$$

where n is an integer.

Let us suppose that the matrix V has the canonical form

$$V = S \begin{Vmatrix} \mu_1 & 0 \\ 0 & \mu_2 \end{Vmatrix} S^{-1}, \tag{29.6}$$

where μ_1, and μ_2 are roots of the equation

$$\mu^2 - \sigma(V)\mu + D(V) = 0 \tag{29.7}$$

and, according to Jacobi's formula

$$D(V) = e^{\int_0^{2\pi} \sigma(P)\,dt} \tag{29.7$_1$}$$

The matrix

$$X_1 = S^{-1}X \tag{29.8}$$

is also an integral matrix for the system (29.1) and is multiplied on the left by the matrix

$$J = \begin{Vmatrix} \mu_1 & 0 \\ 0 & \mu_2 \end{Vmatrix} \tag{29.9}$$

as t is increased by an amount 2π. This means that the solution in the first row of the integral matrix X_1 is multiplied by μ_1, and that the solution in the second row is multiplied by μ_2 as t increases by an amount 2π. This is true because

$$X_1(t + 2\pi) = \begin{Vmatrix} \mu_1 & 0 \\ 0 & \mu_2 \end{Vmatrix} X_1(t) \tag{29.10}$$

and hence

$$x_{k1}(t + 2\pi) = \mu_1 x_{k1}(t),\ x_{k2}(t + 2\pi) = \mu_2 x_{k2}(t)\ \ (k = 1,2) \tag{29.11}$$

where $x_{k1}(t)$, $x_{k2}(t)$ are the elements of the kth row of the matrix $X_1(t)$.

From a property of the roots of Eq. (29.7) and on the basis of (29.7$_1$), we have

$$\mu_1\mu_2 = e^{\int_0^{2\pi} \sigma(P)\,dt} \tag{29.12}$$

If

$$\int_0^{2\pi} \sigma(P)\,dt = 0,$$

then

$$\mu_1\mu_2 = 1. \tag{29.13}$$

We see from (29.11) that, if

$$|\mu_1| < 1, \tag{29.14}$$

the system of linear equations corresponding to the matrix equation (29.1) has a one-parameter family* of solutions $x_1(t)$ and $x_2(t)$ with the property that

$$|x_1(t)| + |x_2(t)| \to 0 \quad \text{as} \quad t \to \infty. \tag{29.15}$$

If μ_1 and μ_2 are less than unity in absolute value, then all solutions possess the property (29.15) and the zero solution $x_1 = x_2 = 0$ is obviously asymptotically stable in the sense of Lyapunov.

Let us suppose now that μ_1 and μ_2 are complex and that $|\mu_1| = |\mu_2| = 1$, that is, that

$$\mu_1 = e^{i\varphi}, \quad \mu_2 = e^{-i\varphi}. \tag{29.15$_1$}$$

If, on the basis of (29.6) and (29.15$_1$), we write (29.5) in the form

$$X(t + 2\pi n) = S\,[e^{in\varphi},\ e^{-in\varphi}]\,S^{-1}X(t), \tag{29.16}$$

we see that the matrix $X(t)$ is bounded and oscillatory as $t \to \infty$. Since every other integral matrix of equation (29.1) is of the form

$$X_1 = CX, \tag{29.17}$$

where C is a constant matrix, all solutions are bounded and oscillatory (except the zero solution).

If

$$k\varphi = 2\pi, \tag{29.18}$$

where k is an integer, then all solutions will be periodic with period $2\pi k$.

*That is, the family $x_1(t) = cx_{11}(t), x_2(t) = cx_{12}(t)$, where c is an arbitrary constant number.

For $\varphi = 2\pi$, we have $\mu_1 = \mu_2 = 1$. Therefore, all solutions are periodic with period 2π. On the other hand, if $\varphi = \pi$, then $\mu_1 = \mu_2 = -1$ and all solutions will be of period 4π.

Let us suppose now that the canonical form of the matrix V is of the form

$$V = S \left\| \begin{matrix} \mu & 0 \\ 1 & \mu \end{matrix} \right\| S^{-1}. \tag{29.19}$$

Then, we have

$$X(t + 2\pi n) = V^n X(t) = S \left\| \begin{matrix} \mu^n & 0 \\ n\mu^{n-1} & \mu^n \end{matrix} \right\| S^{-1} X(t). \tag{29.20}$$

Since $a\mu^a \to 0$ as $a \to \infty$ for $|\mu| < 1$, it follows that $X(t) \to 0$ as $t \to \infty$ if $|\mu| < 1$.

On the basis of (29.17), we conclude that all solutions of the system (29.1) possess the property (29.15).

If $\mu = 1$, the integral matrix (10.8) is multiplied on the left by the matrix

$$J_1 = \left\| \begin{matrix} 1 & 0 \\ 1 & 1 \end{matrix} \right\| \tag{29.21}$$

as t increases by 2π. It follows from this that the solution $x_{11}(t)$, $x_{12}(t)$ in the first row of the matix X_1 is periodic with period 2π. The second solution $x_{21}(t)$, $x_{22}(t)$, in the second row, possesses the property

$$x_{21}(t + 2\pi n) = x_{21}(t) + nx_{22}(t), x_{22}(t + 2\pi n) = x_{22}(t).$$

Thus, for $\mu = 1$, we have only a one-parameter family of periodic solutions with period 2π; the remaining solutions are unbounded. For $\mu = -1$, we have a one-parameter family of periodic solutions with period 4π.

If $|\mu| > 1$ in (29.19) or if $|\mu_1| > 1$ and $|\mu_2| > 1$ in (29.10), then all solutions of the system (29.1) are unbounded as $t \to \infty$.

We note that when the condition

$$\int_0^{2\pi} \sigma(P)\, dt > 0 \tag{29.21$_1$}$$

is satisfied, not all the solutions can be bounded since, in accordance with (29.12), we have $|\mu_1| > 1$.

Suppose now that

$$\int_0^{2\pi} \sigma(P)\, dt < 0, \qquad (29.22)$$

that is,

$$0 < D(V) = e^{\int_0^{2\pi} \sigma(P)dt} < 1. \qquad (29.23)$$

Then, on the basis of (29.7), we conclude that, if

$$\sigma(V) > 0,\ \sigma^2(V) - 4D(V) > 0, \qquad (29.24)$$

then the case

$$0 < \mu_1 < 1,\ 0 < \mu_2 < 1 \qquad (29.25)$$

will occur if

$$\sigma(V) < 1 + D(V) < 2. \qquad (29.26)$$

If we have

$$\sigma(V) < 0,\ \sigma^2(V) - 4D(V) > 0, \qquad (29.27)$$

then, for

$$0 < 1 + \sigma + D \qquad (29.28)$$

we have

$$1 < \mu_1 < 0,\ -1 < \mu_2 < 0. \qquad (29.29)$$

Consequently, when conditions (29.24) and (29.26) or (29.27) and (29.28) are satisfied, all solutions of the system (29.1) possess property (29.15).

Suppose now that we have (29.23) and

$$\sigma^2(V) - 4D(V) = 0.$$

Then,

$$\mu = \mu_1 = \mu_2 = \frac{\sigma(V)}{2} = \pm \sqrt{D(V)}. \qquad (29.31)$$

On the basis of what was said above and inequality (29.23), all solutions of the system (29.1) possess the property (29.15) independently of the canonical form of the matrix V.

Let us suppose now that we have (29.23) and

$$\sigma^2(V) - 4D(V) < 0. \tag{29.32}$$

Then, μ_1 and μ_2 are complex and, since $\mu_1\mu_2 = D(V) < 1$, it follows that $|\mu_1| = |\mu_2| < 1$. Consequently, when conditions (29.23) and (29.32) are satisfied, all solutions of the system (29.1) possess the property (29.15).

Let us now consider the case

$$\int_0^{2\pi} P(t)\,dt = 0, \quad D(V) = 1. \tag{29.33}$$

Suppose also that

$$\sigma^2(V) - 4 > 0. \tag{29.34}$$

Then, when

$$\sigma(V) > 0 \tag{29.35}$$

we have

$$\mu_1 = \frac{\sigma(V) + \sqrt{\sigma^2(V) - 4}}{2} > 1 \tag{29.36}$$

and

$$0 < \mu_2 = \frac{\sigma(V) - \sqrt{\sigma^2(V) - 4}}{2} < 1, \tag{29.37}$$

and when

$$\sigma(V) < 0 \tag{29.38}$$

$$-1 < \mu_1 < 0, \quad \mu_2 < -1. \tag{29.39}$$

If (29.33) holds and

$$\sigma^2(V) - 4 < 0, \tag{29.40}$$

then μ_1 and μ_2 are complex numbers of absolute value 1; that is, we have the case (29.15_1).

Thus, when conditions (29.33) and (29.40) are satisfied, all solutions of the system (29.1) will be bounded and oscillatory.

Suppose now that we have (29.33) and

$$\sigma^2(V) - 4 = 0. \tag{29.41}$$

Then,

$$\mu_1 = \mu_2 = 1, \tag{29.42}$$

if condition (29.35) is satisfied; conversely,

$$\mu_1 = \mu_2 = -1 \tag{29.43}$$

if condition (29.38) is satisfied.

If we have (29.42), then there exists a one-parameter family of periodic solutions of the system (29.1) with period 2π. On the other hand, if (29.43) is satisfied, then there exists a one-parameter family of periodic solutions of the system (29.1) with period 4π.

The question of the boundedness (and, in the present case, of the periodicity) of all solutions of the system (29.1) is answered, as we have seen, by the canonical form of the matrix V. Specifically, if V is of the form (29.19), where μ is now ± 1, then not all solutions of the system (29.1) will be bounded.

Let us give a necessary condition for the existence of a periodic solution of the system (29.1) with period 2π.

Since the condition

$$\mu_1 = 1, \tag{29.44}$$

is necessary and sufficient for the existence of a periodic solution, we have, by virtue of the property of the roots of a quadratic equation and (29.7),

$$\mu_2 = D(V) = e^{\int_0^{2\pi} \sigma(P)\,dt} \tag{29.45}$$

and

$$1 + \mu_2 = \sigma(V). \tag{29.46}$$

If we eliminate μ_2 from these equations, we obtain a necessary and sufficient condition for the existence of a solution

$$1 + e^{\int_0^{2\pi} \sigma(P)\,dt} = \sigma(V) \tag{29.47}$$

that is periodic with period 2π. To see this, note that if

$$1 + D(V) = \sigma(V), \tag{29.47$_1$}$$

then, by substituting $D(V) = \sigma(V) - 1$ into (29.7), we obtain

$$\mu^2 - \sigma(V)\mu + \sigma(V) - 1 = 0.$$

From this we see that $\mu = 1$ is a root of Eq. (29.7). Consequently, if

$$1 + e^{\int_0^{2\pi} \sigma(P)\,dt} \neq \sigma(V), \tag{29.47$_2$}$$

then the system (29.1) has no periodic solution with period 2π.

If, in particular, condition (29.33) is satisfied, there is no such periodic solution for $2 \neq \sigma(V)$ but there is such a solution for

$$\sigma(V) = 2. \tag{29.48}$$

Suppose that

$$P(t) = \begin{Vmatrix} 0 & p(t) \\ q(t) & 0 \end{Vmatrix},$$

in the system (29.1), where $p(t)$ and $q(t)$ are periodic nonnegative functions with period 2π. In this case, as is easily seen, in formula (6.1),

$$\sigma(X_{2k+1}(t)) = 0 \text{ and } \sigma(X_{2k}(t)) > 0. \tag{29.49}$$

From this it follows that

$$\sigma(V) = \sigma(X(2\pi)) = 2 + \sum_{k=1}^{\infty} \sigma(X_k(2\pi)) > 2$$

and, consequently, there are no periodic functions of period 2π.

Remark 29.1. If we make the substitution $t = k\tau$, in (29.1), we obtain

$$\frac{dX}{d\tau} = Xp(\tau), \quad p(\tau) = P(k\tau)\,k, \tag{29.50}$$

where $p(\tau) = p(\tau + 2\pi)$. If we now write condition (29.47) for Eq. (29.50), we obtain a necessary and sufficient condition for the existence of periodic solutions of Eq. (29.1) of period $2\pi k$.

There are no periodic solutions of the system (29.1) with period incommensurable with 2π (see Sect. 36).

30. Periodic and Bounded Solutions of the Systems of Equations Considered in Sections 3 and 4

Suppose that the periodic matrix $P(t)$ in the system (29.1) possesses the property (4.6). Then, in accordance with (4.7),

$$X(t) = e^{\int_0^t P(t)\,dt} \tag{30.1}$$

or, since $P(t)$ is of the form (4.11), we have

$$\int_0^t P(t)\,dt = \begin{Vmatrix} \bar{\varphi}_1(t) + b_1\bar{\varphi}_2(t) & \bar{\varphi}_2(t) \\ b_2\bar{\varphi}_2(t) & \bar{\varphi}_1(t) \end{Vmatrix}, \tag{30.1$_1$}$$

where

$$\int_0^t \varphi_k(t)\,dt = \bar{\varphi}_k(t) = \bar{\varphi}_k\,. \tag{30.2}$$

The characteristic numbers of the matrix (30.1$_1$) are

$$\begin{aligned} 2\lambda_1(t) &= 2\bar{\varphi}_1 + b_1\bar{\varphi}_2 + \bar{\varphi}_2\sqrt{b_1^2 + 4b_2}\,, \\ 2\lambda_2(t) &= 2\bar{\varphi}_1 + b_1\bar{\varphi}_2 - \bar{\varphi}_2\sqrt{b_1^2 + 4b_2}\,. \end{aligned} \tag{30.3}$$

Consequently,

$$\sigma(V) = e^{\lambda_1(2\pi)} + e^{\lambda_2(2\pi)} \tag{30.4}$$

or

$$D(V) = e^{\lambda_1(2\pi)+\lambda_2(2\pi)}\,. \tag{30.5}$$

If we substitute (30.4) and (30.5) into (29.47), we get

$$1 + e^{\lambda_1(2\pi)+\lambda_2(2\pi)} = e^{\lambda_1(2\pi)} + e^{\lambda_2(2\pi)}$$

or

$$[1 - e^{\lambda_1(2\pi)}]\,[1 - e^{\lambda_2(2\pi)}] = 0. \tag{30.6}$$

Thus, the condition for the existence of a periodic solution of the present system of two equations with period 2π consists in the requirement that at least one of the two equations

$$\left.\begin{aligned} 2\int_0^{2\pi}\varphi_1(t)\,dt + \left(b_1 + \sqrt{b_1^2 + 4b_2}\right)\int_0^{2\pi}\varphi_2(t)\,dt = 0 \\ 2\int_0^{2\pi}\varphi_1(t)\,dt + \left(b_1 - \sqrt{b_1^2 + 4b_2}\right)\int_0^{2\pi}\varphi_2(t)\,dt = 0 \end{aligned}\right\} \tag{30.7}$$

be satisfied or that, simultaneously,

$$\left.\begin{aligned} 2\int_0^{2\pi}\varphi_1(t)\,dt + b_1\int_0^{2\pi}\varphi_2(t)\,dt = 0 \\ \left[\int_0^{2\pi}\varphi_1(t)\,dt\right]^2 + b_1\int_0^{2\pi}\varphi_1(t)\,dt\int_0^{2\pi}\varphi_2(t)\,dt - b_2\left[\int_0^{2\pi}\varphi_2\,dt\right]^2 = \\ = 4n^2\pi^2 \end{aligned}\right\}, \qquad (30.7_1)$$

since we now have $\lambda_1(2\pi) = 2\pi ni$ and $\lambda_2(2\pi) = -2\pi ni$, where n is an integer. If neither of equations (30.7) is satisfied, there will be no periodic solutions of period 2π.

Let us now consider the system (5.1), where U_1 and U_2 are second-order matrices possessing properties (5.2) and (5.3) and where $\varphi_1(t)$ and $\varphi_2(t)$ are periodic functions with period 2π. Suppose that the matrices U_1 and U_2 are of the form (5.6). Then, as we have seen, $\sigma(V)$ and $D(V)$ can be obtained from formulas (5.8) and (5.9) for $t = 2\pi$. If we substitute these values of $\sigma(V)$ and $D(V)$ into (29.47), we easily find

$$\left[1 - e^{a\int_0^{2\pi}\varphi_1(t)dt + b_1\int_0^{2\pi}\varphi_2(t)dt}\right]\left[1 - e^{a\int_0^{2\pi}\varphi_1(t)dt + b_2\int_0^{2\pi}\varphi_2(t)dt}\right] = 0. \qquad (30.8)$$

Thus, there will be a periodic solution with period 2π only in the case in which one of the two equations

$$\int_0^{2\pi}[a\varphi_1(t) + b_1\varphi_2(t)]\,dt = 0 \qquad (30.9)$$

or

$$\int_0^{2\pi}[a\varphi_1(t) + b_2\varphi_2(t)]\,dt = 0 \qquad (30.10)$$

is satisfied.

Let us now suppose that the matrices U_1 and U_2 in the system (5.1) are of the form (5.11). Then, in accordance with (5.16) and (5.17),

$$\sigma(V) = e^{(a+cm)L_1(2\pi)+(b+mn)L_2(2\pi)} + e^{(a+cm)L_1(2\pi)+(b-mn)L_2(2\pi)}$$

and

$$D(V) = e^{2(a+cm)L_1(2\pi)+2bL_2(2\pi)}$$

If we substitute this into the condition for periodicity of the solutions (29.47), we find*

$$[1 - e^{(a+cm)L_1(2\pi)+(b+mn)L_2(2\pi)}]\,[1 - e^{(a+cm)L_1(2\pi)+(b-mn)L_2(2\pi)}] = 0.$$

The system in question has a periodic solution with period 2π only when one of the following equations is satisfied:

$$\left.\begin{aligned}\int_0^{2\pi}[(a+cm)\,\varphi_1(t)+(b+mn)\,\varphi_2(t)]\,dt &= 0\\ \int_0^{2\pi}[(a+cm)\,\varphi_1(t)+(b-mn)\,\varphi_2(t)]\,dt &= 0\end{aligned}\right\} \qquad (30.11)$$

Thus, we have exhausted all possible cases of a system of two equations when the matrices U_1 and U_2 satisfy conditions (5.2) and (5.3).

31. Questions Involving the Boundedness and Periodicity of Solutions of a System of Two Linear Differential Equations With the Aid of a Special Exponential Substitution Obtained by Lappo-Danilevskiy

Let us now express the conditions for boundedness of solutions of the system of two equations (29.1) in terms of the elements of the matrix A that appears in formula (29.2).

When we study the question of the existence of bounded and periodic solutions of period 2π, we may assume that the matrix $Z(t)$ in formula (29.2) is of period 2π. In so doing, we allow the matrix A to be complex. On the basis of formulas (1.2) and (1.3), we draw the following conclusion:

If

$$A = S\begin{Vmatrix}\lambda_1 & 0\\ 0 & \lambda_2\end{Vmatrix}S^{-1}, \qquad (31.1)$$

then

$$V = e^{2\pi A} = S\begin{Vmatrix}e^{2\pi\lambda_1} & 0\\ 0 & e^{2\pi\lambda_2}\end{Vmatrix}S^{-1},$$

*Much more detailed systems, shown in Sects. 3, 4, and 32 (as well as other systems) are studied in the works by P. B. Golokvoschus [50-55].

and if

$$A = S \begin{Vmatrix} \lambda & 0 \\ 1 & \lambda \end{Vmatrix} S^{-1}, \tag{31.2}$$

then

$$V = e^{2\pi A} = S \begin{Vmatrix} e^{2\pi\lambda} & 0 \\ 2\pi\, e^{2\pi\lambda} & e^{2\pi\lambda} \end{Vmatrix} S^{-1}.$$

From this we see that, if

$$R(\lambda_1) < 0, \tag{31.3}$$

where $R(\lambda)$ denotes the real part of λ, then the characteristic number μ_1 of the matrix V will be less in absolute value than unity; consequently, there is a one-parameter family of solutions possessing the property (29.15).

In the case in which $R(\lambda_2) < 0$, all the solutions of the system (29.1) possess the property (29.15). If $R(\lambda) < 0$ in (31.2), then all solutions of the system (29.1) possess the property (29.15). If $\lambda_1 = ki$ in (31.1), where k is an integer, then the characteristic number μ_1 of the matrix V will be equal to unity: $\mu_1 = e^{2k\pi i} = 1$.

However, it should be pointed out that these methods of finding the matrix A in terms of the parameters that appear in the matrix $P(t)$ are such that the number k can always be made equal to 0 (or, in fact, to an arbitrary integer); that is, it is always possible to reduce the problem to the case in which $\lambda_1 = 0$.

In this case, the system (29.1) has a one-parameter family of periodic solutions of period 2π. All solutions of (29.1) can be periodic with period 2π only when $\lambda_1 = \lambda_2 = 0$ and this characteristic number of the matrix A corresponds to simple elementary divisors, that is, only if

$$A = 0 \tag{31.4}$$

or

$$\lambda_1 = k_1 i, \ \lambda_2 = k_2 i, \tag{31.4$_1$}$$

where k_1 and k_2 are integers.

If the matrix A proves to be real, we obviously can only have $-k_1 = k_2 = k$. If the matrix A has a multiple characteristic number $\lambda = 0$, but is of the form

$$A = S \begin{Vmatrix} 0 & 0 \\ 1 & 0 \end{Vmatrix} S^{-1}, \tag{31.5}$$

there is only a one-parameter family of periodic solutions; the remaining solutions will not be bounded because

$$V^n = e^{2n\pi A} = S \begin{Vmatrix} 1 & 0 \\ 2\pi n & 1 \end{Vmatrix} S^{-1},$$

where n is an integer.

Let us suppose now that the characteristic numbers of the matrix A are

$$\lambda_1 = \lambda i, \quad \lambda_2 = -\lambda i, \tag{31.6}$$

where λ is a real positive nonintegral number. Obviously, this case corresponds to the conditions (29.33) and (29.40). If λ is a rational number, then all solutions will be periodic with period $T = 2k\pi$, where k is the denominator of the number λ. On the other hand, if λ is an irrational number all the solutions will be bounded and oscillatory.

As can be seen from what has been said earlier (see Sect. 8), the situation is possible in which

$$\lambda_1 = \lambda_2 = i/2 \tag{31.7}$$

(with the matrix A complex) or

$$\lambda_1 = i/2, \ \lambda_2 = -(i/2). \tag{31.8}$$

or finally, in general,

$$\lambda_1 = \frac{2n+1}{2} i, \ \lambda_2 = \frac{2n_1 - 1}{2} i \quad (n, \ n_1 \text{ integers}). \tag{31.8$_1$}$$

Then, all solutions of the system (29.1) will be periodic with period 4π. We note that, in this case,

$$\sigma(A) = \frac{1}{2\pi} \int_0^{2\pi} \sigma(P(t))\, dt, \tag{31.9}$$

if we wish to have the matrix A real ($n = -n_1$).

A necessary and sufficient condition for finding a solution that is periodic with period 2π under the condition that the matrix A is real is expressed by the equations

$$\left. \begin{aligned} \sigma(A) = 0, \text{ i.e.,} \int_0^{2\pi} \sigma(P(t))\, dt = 0 \\ D(A) = n^2 \quad (n - \text{an integer} \geqslant 1) \end{aligned} \right\}, \tag{31.10}$$

when we have two linearly independent periodic solutions or by

$$D(A) = 0, \ \sigma(A) \text{ — arbitrary,} \tag{31.10$_1$}$$

when we have a single periodic solution*.

We recall that the general expression of the matrix A for the system (28.1), where $P(t)$ is defined by (28.4), is given by formula (28.15), which becomes (28.18) when

$$\int_0^{2\pi} P(t)\,dt = 2\pi\sigma(b_0) = 0.$$

Consequently, in the case (28.18), the characteristic equation of the matrix A is of the form

$$\lambda^2 - \frac{m^2}{4}(\sigma^2(V) - 4) = 0, \tag{31.10$_2$}$$

where

$$m = \frac{\ln\left(\frac{\sigma(V)}{2} + \sqrt{\frac{\sigma^2(V)}{4} - 1}\right)}{2\pi\sqrt{\frac{\sigma^2(V)}{4} - 1}}.$$

Thus, we have

$$\lambda_1 = \frac{\ln\left(\frac{\sigma(V)}{2} + \sqrt{\frac{\sigma^2(V)}{4} - 1}\right)}{2\pi}, \quad \lambda_2 = -\frac{\ln\left(\frac{\sigma(V)}{2} + \sqrt{\frac{\sigma^2(V)}{2} - 1}\right)}{2\pi}.$$

On the basis of (31.10), the condition for periodicity of the solution may be written

$$\ln^2\left(\frac{\sigma(V)}{2} + \sqrt{\frac{\sigma^2(V)}{4} - 1}\right) = -4\pi^2 n^2,$$

$$\ln\left(\frac{\sigma(V)}{2} + \sqrt{\frac{\sigma^2(V)}{4} - 1}\right) = \pm i\,2\pi n.$$

As before, we obtain the condition for periodicity (29.48) of the solution (29.47).

On the basis of (28.13) and the reasoning followed in connection with formula (28.25), we have

*If (31.4) is satisfied, then, as we have noted, there are two linearly independent periodic solutions with period 2π.

$$D(A) = -D(W) = -D(H). \qquad (31.10_3)$$

Therefore, condition (31.10_1) for the existence of a periodic solution may be written in the form

$$D(H) = 0, \qquad (31.10_4)$$

where H is defined by the series (9.24).

However, we need to keep in mind the fact that the series (9.24) converges for small values of T_p. Therefore, on the basis of (31.10_4), it is convenient to find the relationship between the parameters of the equation, a relationship that ensures existence of a periodic solution only for small values of the parameters, for example, for small values of the matrices T_p. We note, however, that, in (31.10_4), we can sometimes obtain a series of infinitesimals of increasing orders even when some of the elements of the matrices T_p (or even some of the matrices T_p themselves) are not small. We shall see this from some examples. The convergence of such series in infinitesimals of increasing orders (that is, when not all the matrices T_p are sufficiently small) does not follow from Lappo-Danilveskiy's theorems but from the theorems proven in the present book (Sect. 29). Furthermore, a relationship between the parameters that ensure existence of a periodic solution can also be found from Eq. (29.48), in which the series representing V converges for all finite values of the matrices T_p:

$$V = +\sum_{\nu=1}^{\infty} \sum_{p_1 \dots p_\nu = -m-1}^{m-1} T_{p_1} \dots T_{p_\nu} \sum_{\mu=0}^{\nu}{}^{*} \alpha^{(0)}_{p_1 \dots p_\mu} \sum_{\varkappa=0}^{\nu-\mu}{}^{*} \alpha_{p_{\mu+1} \dots p_\nu} (2\pi i)^{\varkappa} .$$

As was noted above (following formula (28.21)), the imaginary terms in this equation cancel since V is real. Of course, instead of this form of V, we could have taken its representation in the form (6.1), considering it as

$$V = X(2\pi) = \sum_{k=0}^{\infty} X_k(2\pi)$$

for the system (28.19).

Let us consider Mathieu's equation

$$\frac{d^2y}{dt^2} + (a - 2q\cos 2t)\, y = 0, \qquad (31.11)$$

where a and q are constants. This equation is equivalent to the system

$$\frac{dX}{dt} = X \begin{Vmatrix} 0 & 1 \\ 2q\cos 2t - a & 0 \end{Vmatrix} = X\left[\begin{Vmatrix} 0 & 1 \\ -a & 0 \end{Vmatrix} + \begin{Vmatrix} 0 & 0 \\ 2q & 0 \end{Vmatrix} \cos 2t\right] \quad (31.12)$$

Here, the coefficient matrix is of period π. We introduce the new independent variable $\tau = 2t$:

$$\frac{dX}{d\tau} = X\left[\frac{1}{2}\begin{Vmatrix} 0 & 1 \\ -a & 0 \end{Vmatrix} + \begin{Vmatrix} 0 & 0 \\ q & 0 \end{Vmatrix} \cos\tau\right]. \quad (31.13)$$

Consequently, this system is such that, in accordance with (28.4), we have in this case

$$\left.\begin{aligned} b_0 &= \frac{1}{2}\begin{Vmatrix} 0 & 1 \\ -a & 0 \end{Vmatrix}, \quad b_1 = \begin{Vmatrix} 0 & 0 \\ q & 0 \end{Vmatrix} \\ P_0 = \frac{1}{2}\begin{Vmatrix} 0 & 1 \\ -a & 0 \end{Vmatrix}, \quad P_1 &= \frac{1}{2}\begin{Vmatrix} 0 & 0 \\ q & 0 \end{Vmatrix}, \quad P_{-1} = \frac{1}{2}\begin{Vmatrix} 0 & 0 \\ q & 0 \end{Vmatrix} \end{aligned}\right\}. \quad (31.14)$$

If we write (31.13) in the form (28.6), we obtain

$$\frac{dX}{dz} = X\left[T_{-2}z^{-2} + T_{-1}z^{-1} + T_0\right]. \quad (31.15)$$

$$T_{-2} = \frac{-i}{2}\begin{Vmatrix} 0 & 0 \\ q & 0 \end{Vmatrix}, \quad T_{-1} = -\frac{i}{2}\begin{Vmatrix} 0 & 1 \\ -a & 0 \end{Vmatrix}, \quad T_0 = -\frac{i}{2}\begin{Vmatrix} 0 & 0 \\ q & 0 \end{Vmatrix}. \quad (31.16)$$

In accordance with (31.10_3), we have $D(A) = -D(H)$ with H given by formula (9.24)

$$H = \sum_{\nu=1}^{\infty} \sum_{p_1 \ldots p_\nu = -s}^{l} T_{p_1} \ldots T_{p_\nu} \delta^{(0)}_{p_1 + \ldots + p_\nu + \nu} \alpha^{(1)}_{p_1 \ldots p_\nu}, \quad (9.24)$$

where $\delta^{(0)}_m$ is the Kronecker delta

$$\delta^{(0)}_m = \begin{cases} 0 & m \neq 0 \\ 1 & m = 0, \end{cases} \quad (31.17)$$

where the $\alpha^{(1)}_{p_1 \ldots p_\nu}$ are defined by the formulas in Sect. 7, and where $p_1, \ldots, p_\nu$ in formula (9.24) assume the values -2, -1, and 0.

On the basis of formuls (31.16),

$$T_0^2 = T_{-2}^2 = T_0 T_{-2} = T_{-2} T_0 = \|0\|. \quad (31.18)$$

It follows from this that all products of the matrices T_0, T_{-1}, T_{-2}, where T_0 and T_{-2} occur next to each other or one of these is squared, are equal to 0. We find that the sum of the terms containing the product $T_{p_1}T_{p_2}\ldots T_{p_5}T_{p_6}$ for $p_1+\ldots+p_6+6=0$ is equal to 0. Keeping (31.18) in mind as regards the remaining products, substituting the values of the coefficients $\alpha^{(l)}_{p_1\ldots p_\nu}$, and leaving the products $T_{p_1}\ldots T_{p_\nu}$ in the sum (9.24) only for $\nu = 1, 2, \ldots, 7$, we obtain

$$H = T_{-1} + T_{-2}T_{-1}T_0 + T_0T_{-1}T_{-2} + 2T_{-1}T_{-2}T_{-1}T_0 -$$
$$- 2T_{-1}T_0T_{-1}T_{-2} - T_{-2}T_{-1}T_{-1}T_0 + T_0T_{-1}T_{-1}T_{-2} +$$
$$+ 3T_{-1}T_{-1}T_{-2}T_{-1}T_0 + 3T_{-1}T_{-1}T_0T_{-1}T_{-2} - 3T_{-1}T_{-2}T_{-1}T_{-1}T_0 +$$
$$+ T_{-2}T_{-1}T_{-1}T_{-1}T_0 + T_0T_{-1}T_{-1}T_{-1}T_{-2} - 3T_{-1}T_0T_{-1}T_{-1}T_{-2} +$$
$$+ 3T_0T_{-1}T_{-2}T_{-1}T_0T_{-1}T_{-2} + \frac{1}{4}T_0T_{-1}T_0T_{-1}T_{-2}T_{-1}T_{-2} +$$
$$+ 3T_0T_{-1}T_{-2}T_{-1}T_{-2}T_{-1}T_0 + 3T_{-2}T_{-1}T_0T_{-1}T_0T_{-1}T_{-2} +$$
$$+ \frac{1}{4}T_{-2}T_{-1}T_{-2}T_{-1}T_0T_{-1}T_0 + 3T_{-2}T_{-1}T_0T_{-1}T_{-2}T_{-1}T_0 +$$
$$+ 5T_{-1}T_{-1}T_{-1}T_{-1}T_{-2}T_{-1}T_0 + 10T_{-1}T_{-1}T_{-2}T_{-1}T_{-1}T_{-1}T_0 +$$
$$+ T_{-2}T_{-1}T_{-1}T_{-1}T_{-1}T_{-1}T_0 + 5T_{-1}T_{-1}T_{-1}T_{-1}T_0T_{-1}T_{-2} +$$
$$+ 10T_{-1}T_{-1}T_0T_{-1}T_{-1}T_{-1}T_{-2} + T_0T_{-1}T_{-1}T_{-1}T_{-1}T_{-1}T_{-2}.$$

If we evaluate this sum on the basis of (31.16), we obtain

$$H = \begin{Vmatrix} 0 & -\frac{i}{2} \\ \frac{i}{2}\left(a + \frac{q^2}{2} + \frac{aq^2}{2} + \frac{25q^4}{128} + \frac{a^2q^2}{2}\right) & 0 \end{Vmatrix}$$

Therefore,

$$D(H) = \frac{1}{4}\left(a + \frac{q^2}{2} + \frac{aq^2}{2} + \frac{25}{128}q^4 + \frac{a^2q^2}{2}\right).$$

From $D(H) = 0$, we have

$$q^2a^2 + (2 + q^2)\,a + q^2 + \frac{25}{64}q^4 = 0\,,$$

$$aq^2 = -\frac{2 + q^2}{2} \pm \sqrt{1 + q^2 + \frac{q^4}{4} - q^6 - \frac{25}{64}q^8}\,.$$

$$a_1 = -\frac{q^2}{2} + \frac{7}{128} q^4 + O(q^6), \quad a_2 = -\frac{2+q^2}{q^2} + $$
$$+ \frac{q^2}{2} - \frac{7q^4}{128} + O(q^6). \tag{31.19}$$

Here, $O(q^6)$ denotes an infinitesimal of order q^6 as $q \to 0$. Thus,* in this case, a_1 is an approximate value of a root of the equation $D(H) = 0$. If we substitute the value $a = a_1(q) = -\frac{q^2}{2} + + \frac{7}{128} q^4$ into the general representation of the quantity A defined by (28.18), we obtain** an approximate solution of the system (31.12) in the form (28.2).

These solutions differ only slightly from the corresponding periodic solutions over a large interval of variations of t.

To find a periodic solution of the system (31.13) with period 4π, let us apply the method presented in Sect. 10, treating the system (31.13) as a system of the form (10.1). Let us also set $a = 1 - 2\alpha$ and let us write the system (31.13) in the form

$$\frac{dX}{dt} = X\left[\frac{1}{2}\left\|\begin{matrix} 0 & 1 \\ -1 & 0 \end{matrix}\right\| + \left\|\begin{matrix} 0 & 0 \\ \alpha + q\cos t & 0 \end{matrix}\right\| \varepsilon\right], \tag{31.20}$$

that is,

$$P_0 = \frac{1}{2}\left\|\begin{matrix} 0 & 1 \\ -1 & 0 \end{matrix}\right\| \text{ and } P_1 = \left\|\begin{matrix} 0 & 0 \\ \alpha + q\cos t & 0 \end{matrix}\right\|, \tag{31.21}$$
$$P_k(t) = \|0\|, \ k \geqslant 2.$$

Let us seek a periodic solution of period 4π such that

$$X = X(t, q) \longrightarrow e^{P_0 t} \quad \text{as} \quad q \longrightarrow 0.$$

We set (see (10.16))

---

*There is no justification for assuming that a_2 is an approximate value of a since, for small q, a_2 is great and it is not clear whether the sum of the discarded portion of the series $D(H)=0$ is small in comparison with a_2.

**If we set $a = a_1$ in (13.13), we can obtain A and N in (28.2) both by use of the formulas of Sect. 11 and from Lappo-Danilevskiy's formulas determining the solution of the system (31.15) in the form (7.11) (namely, formulas (7.13), and (7.51$_1$), or (9.24) and (9.24$_1$)). Here, we only need to set $z = \exp it$ in accordance with (28.5). The solution in the row corresponding to the zero characteristic number of the matrix A will be an approximate value of a periodic solution.

and

$$\left.\begin{aligned} A_0 = 0,\ Z_0 &= e^{\frac{1}{2}\begin{Vmatrix} 0 & 1 \\ -1 & 0 \end{Vmatrix} t} \\ A = \sum_{k=1}^{\infty} A_k \lambda^k,\ Z &= \sum_{k=0}^{\infty} Z_k(t) \lambda^k . \end{aligned}\right\} \qquad (31.23)$$

Since the characteristic numbers of the matrix

$$P_0 = \frac{1}{2}\begin{Vmatrix} 0 & 1 \\ -1 & 0 \end{Vmatrix}$$

are $\lambda_1 = \frac{i}{2}$, $\lambda_2 = -\frac{i}{2}$, we have, in accordance with formula (1.14),

$$Z_0 = e^{P_0 t} = \begin{Vmatrix} \cos\frac{t}{2} & \sin\frac{t}{2} \\ -\sin\frac{t}{2} & \cos\frac{t}{2} \end{Vmatrix} \qquad (31.23_1)$$

$$Z_0^{-1} = e^{-P_0 t} = \begin{Vmatrix} \cos\frac{t}{2} & -\sin\frac{t}{2} \\ \sin\frac{t}{2} & \cos\frac{t}{2} \end{Vmatrix} \qquad (31.24)$$

According to formula (11.9),

$$Z_1 = \int_0^t [Z_0 P_1 Z_0^{-1} - A_1]\, dt\, Z_0. \qquad (31.25)$$

On the basis of (31.21) and (31.24), we find

$$Z_0 P_1 Z_0^{-1} = \begin{Vmatrix} \frac{\alpha}{2}\sin t + \frac{q}{4}\sin 2t, & \frac{q-2\alpha}{4} + \frac{\alpha - q}{2}\cos t + \frac{q\cos 2t}{4} \\ \frac{2\alpha + q}{4} + \frac{\alpha+q}{2}\cos t + \frac{q\cos 2t}{4}, & \frac{-\alpha\sin t}{2} - \frac{q}{4}\sin 2t \end{Vmatrix}$$

For Z_1 to be periodic with period 4π, we must set

$$A_1 = \begin{Vmatrix} 0 & \dfrac{q-2\alpha}{4} \\ \dfrac{2\alpha+q}{4} & 0 \end{Vmatrix} \qquad (31.25_1)$$

as is clear from (31.25). With such a choice of A_1, we have

$$Z_1 = \begin{Vmatrix} z_{11} & z_{12} \\ z_{21} & z_{22} \end{Vmatrix} \begin{Vmatrix} \cos\dfrac{t}{2} & \sin\dfrac{t}{2} \\ -\sin\dfrac{t}{2} & \cos\dfrac{t}{2} \end{Vmatrix} \qquad (31.26)$$

where

$$z_{11} = \frac{\alpha}{2} + \frac{q}{2} - \frac{\alpha}{2}\cos t - \frac{q}{8}\cos 2t, \quad z_{12} = \frac{\alpha - q}{2}\sin t +$$

$$+ \frac{q}{8}\sin 2t, \quad z_{21} = \frac{\alpha+q}{2}\sin t + \frac{q}{8}\sin 2t,$$

$$z_{22} = -\frac{\alpha}{2} - \frac{q}{8} + \frac{\alpha}{2}\cos t + \frac{q}{8}\cos 2t.$$

The first approximation* of the equation

$$D(A_{\varepsilon=1}) = 0$$

is

$$D(A_1) = \frac{q^2 - 4\alpha^2}{16} = 0.$$

Therefore, we have

$$2\alpha_1 = q, \; 2\alpha_2 = -q. \qquad (31.27)$$

Consequently, we obtain an approximate value of a in the system (31.13) at which it has a periodic solution, with period 4π, in the form

$$a_1 = 1 + q, \; a_2 = 1 - q. \qquad (31.28)$$

For $a_1 = 1 + q$ we obtain approximately a fundamental system of solutions of equations (31.12) in the form**

*We set $\varepsilon = 1$ and assume q and a small.

**The first row of X yields an approximate value of a periodic solution of period 4π.

$$X = e^{\left\| \begin{matrix} 0 & 0 \\ \frac{q}{2} & 0 \end{matrix} \right\| t} [Z_0(t) + Z_1(t)], \tag{31.29}$$

where Z_0 and Z_1 are given by formulas (31.23_1) and (32.26), in which we need to set $2\alpha = q$.

It should be noted that the representation (31.29) is in general valid only for small values of q. To obtain an approximate value of the solutions for $a = 1 + q$ when q is large, we need to use the general representation of A given by formula (9.1). Then, we obtain $Z(t)$ from the equation $Z(t) = X(t)e^{-At}$.

To find the following approximate value of a, we can find A_2 and Z_2 from formulas (11.9). But we can also proceed in a different way. Specifically, in accordance with formula (12.13), instead of writing the system (31.20), we can write the system

$$\frac{dX}{dt} = X[P_0(t) + P_1(t)\varepsilon], \tag{31.30}$$

where $P_0(t)$ is such that the corresponding integral matrix of the system

$$\frac{dY}{dt} = YP_0(t) \tag{31.31}$$

will be of the form

$$Y = e^{A_1 t} Z_1(t), \tag{31.32}$$

where A_1 and $Z_1(t)$ are found from formulas (31.25_1) and (31.26).

The corresponding value of $P_0(t)$ is easily found from the equation

$$A_1 Z_1 + \frac{dZ_1}{dt} = Z_1 P_0, \tag{31.33}$$

which is obtained by substituting the expression (31.32) into (31.31). In accordance with (12.13), we take the matrix $P_1(t)$ in formula (31.30) in the form

$$P_1(t) = \left\| \begin{matrix} 0 & \frac{1}{2} \\ -\frac{a}{2} + q\cos\tau & 0 \end{matrix} \right\| - P_0(t). \tag{31.34}$$

Now,* we can seek A and $Z(t)$ in the form

$$A = \sum_{k=0}^{\infty} A_k \lambda^k, \quad Z = \sum_{k=0}^{\infty} Z_k \lambda^k. \tag{31.35}$$

where

$$A_0 = \begin{Vmatrix} 0 & \frac{q - 2\alpha}{4} \\ \frac{2\alpha + q}{4} & 0 \end{Vmatrix}$$

and Z_0 is given by the expression (31.23_1).

32. Periodic Solutions of a System of Two Equations When Condition (3.6) is Satisfied

Consider again the second-order system

$$\frac{dX}{dt} = XP(t) \tag{32.1}$$

assuming that (4.6) holds. Then, we have (4.11) and

$$X = \exp \int_0^t P(t)\, dt. \tag{32.2}$$

Since the functions $\varphi_1(t)$ and $\varphi_2(t)$are periodic with period 2π, we have

$$\int_0^{2\pi} \varphi_k(t)\, dt = a_k t + \psi_k(t),$$

where $a_k = \frac{1}{2\pi} \int_0^{2\pi} \varphi_k(t)\, dt$ and $\psi_k(t)$are periodic functions with period 2π. This enables us to write (32.2) in the form

$$X(t) = \exp At \cdot \exp Z(t),$$

where A is a constant matrix

$$A = \begin{Vmatrix} a_1 + b_1 a_2 & a_2 \\ b_2 a_2 & a_1 \end{Vmatrix},$$

*We note that here, P_0 as defined by Eq. (31.33) will be nonzero for $\alpha = q = 0$ but that $P_1(t)$ as defined by Eq. (31.34) vanishes for $\alpha = q = 0$.

and $Z(t)$ is a periodic matrix

$$Z(t) = \begin{Vmatrix} \psi_1(t) + b_1\psi_2(t) & \psi_2(t) \\ b_2\psi_2(t) & \psi_1(t) \end{Vmatrix}$$

with period 2π. The condition for the existence of a periodic solution (31.10_1) now takes the form

$$a_1^2 + b_1 a_1 a_2 - b_2 a_2^2 = 0. \tag{32.3}$$

This condition is equivalent to the two conditions (30.7) since multiplication of equation (30.7) leads us to (32.3). Conditions (31.10) yield the equations

$$2a_1 + b_1 a_2 = 0, \ a_1^2 + b_1 a_1 a_2 - a_2^2 b_2 = n^2,$$

which coincide with (30.7_1).

In particular, for $a_1 = a_2 = 0$, the system has a periodic solution with period 2π*.

We can also easily establish conditions (30.9)-(30.11) by using conditions (31.10)**.

33. Lyapunov's Equation $\ddot{x} + p(t)x = 0$

Let us stop to consider separately the equation

$$\frac{d^2x}{dt^2} + p(t)x = 0, \tag{33.1}$$

where $p(t) = p(t+1)$ is continuous function. We are concerned with the existence of bounded solutions of this equation. Equation (33.1) is equivalent to the system

$$\frac{dx_1}{dt} = x_2, \quad \frac{dx_2}{dt} = -px_1. \tag{33.2}$$

In connection with (33.2), let us also look at the system

$$\frac{dx_1}{dt} = x_2, \quad \frac{dx_2}{dt} = \varepsilon px_1, \tag{33.3}$$

corresponding to the equation

$$\frac{d^2x}{dt^2} - \varepsilon p(t)x = 0. \tag{33.4}$$

*We noted in Sect. 28 that Lyapunov studied a system that, in the case of two equations, is a particular case of the system (29.1) under the assumption that condition (3.6) is satisfied. A. P. Gremyachenskiy [56] considered this system of $2n$ equations of Lyapunov and exhibited a case in which the matrix m has a zero characteristic number.

**In Sect. 4, we noted that Fedorov [23] exhibited a more general case than system (4.1), one in which $X(t)$ is obtained in closed form. This enables us to solve in an easy manner the question of the existence of bounded and periodic solutions.

Suppose that $x = f(t)$ and $x = \varphi(t)$ are two linearly independent solutions of Eq. (33.4) satisfying initial conditions $f(0) = 1$, $f'(0) = 0$ and $\varphi(0) = 0$, $\varphi'(0) = 1$. If we determine these solutions by Lyapunov's method, we obtain

$$f(t) = 1 + \varepsilon f_1(t) + \varepsilon^2 f_2(t) + \dots, \quad \varphi(t) = t + \varepsilon\varphi_1(t) + \varepsilon^2\varphi_2(t) + \dots, \tag{33.5}$$

where

$$f_n(t) = \int_0^t dt \int_0^t p f_{n-1}(t)\, dt, \quad \varphi_n(t) = \int_0^t dt \int^t p\, \varphi_{n-1}(t)\, dt,$$

$$f_0(t) = 1, \quad \varphi_0(t) = t. \tag{33.6}$$

For $\varepsilon = -1$, the system of functions (33.5) yields two linearly independent solutions of Eq. (33.1). The integral matrix of the system (33.3) is

$$X = \begin{Vmatrix} f(t) & f'(t) \\ \varphi(t) & \varphi'(t) \end{Vmatrix} \tag{33.7}$$

and the integral substitution is

$$V = \begin{Vmatrix} f(1) & f'(1) \\ \varphi(1) & \varphi'(1) \end{Vmatrix}. \tag{33.8}$$

On the basis of formula (29.7), the characteristic numbers ρ_1 and ρ_2 of the matrix (33.8) can be found from the equation

$$\rho^2 - (f(1) + \varphi'(1))\rho + 1 = 0, \quad \rho_1\rho_2 = 1. \tag{33.9}$$

Here, $\sigma(V) = f(1) + \varphi'(1)$.

Two cases are possible:

I. The roots ρ_1 and ρ_2 are real and distinct. Then, one of them is greater in absolute value than unity and the other less than unity.

II. The roots ρ_1 and ρ_2 are complex or equal to unity. Then, $|\rho_1| = |\rho_2| = 1$.

Let us look at case I. We have a one-parameter family of solutions that approach zero as $t \to \infty$. According to formulas (29.33)-(29.39), this will be the case when

$$[f(1) + \varphi'(1)]^2 - 4 > 0. \tag{33.10}$$

From (33.9), we find ρ_1 and ρ_2:

$$2\rho_1 = f(1) + \varphi'(1) - \sqrt{[f(1) + \varphi'(1)]^2 - 4},$$
$$2\rho_2 = f(1) + \varphi'(1) + \sqrt{[f(1) + \varphi'(1)]^2 - 4}. \tag{33.11}$$

On the basis of (33.5), we can write this in the form

$$2\rho_1 = \sum_{k=0}^{\infty} \varepsilon^k \psi_k(1) - \left[\sum_{k=1}^{\infty} \varepsilon^k \psi_k(1) \left(\sum_{k=1}^{\infty} \varepsilon^k \psi_k(1) + 4\right)\right]^{1/2},$$
$$2\rho_2 = \sum_{k=0}^{\infty} \varepsilon^k \psi_k(1) + \left[\sum_{k=1}^{\infty} \varepsilon^k \psi_k(1) \left(\sum_{k=1}^{\infty} \varepsilon^k \psi_k(1) + 4\right)\right]^{1/2}, \tag{33.12}$$

$$\psi_k(t) = f_k(t) + \varphi_k'(t), \quad \psi_0(t) = 2. \tag{33.13}$$

From (33.6), we have, for $n = 1$,

$$\psi_1(t) = \int_0^t dt \int_0^t p\,dt + \int_0^t tp\,dt = t\int_0^t p\,dt \tag{33.14}$$

and, consequently,

$$\psi_1(1) = \int_0^1 p\,dt. \tag{33.15}$$

If $\psi_1(1) \neq 0$, then, for small values of ε, the roots ρ_1 and ρ_2 can be represented in the form of series of positive powers of the quantity $\eta = \varepsilon^{1/2}$. On the other hand, if $\psi_1(1) = 0$ and $\psi_2(1) \neq 0$, then these roots can be represented in series of positive powers* of ε.

On the basis of formulas (33.6), we have $(-1)^k \psi_k(1) > 0$ for $p(t) \leqslant 0$. But then inequality (33.10) is satisfied and ρ_1 and ρ_2 are real and distinct for Eq. (33.1) and $\rho_1 \rho_2 = 1$.

We have obtained the well-known result of Lyapunov.

When condition (33.10) is satisfied, Eq. (33.4) has two linearly independent solutions

$$x_1 = \exp(-\alpha t) \cdot \varphi_1(t), \quad x_2 = \exp(\alpha t) \cdot \varphi_2(t), \tag{33.16}$$

where $\alpha = \ln \rho_2 > 0$ and $\varphi_k(t+1) = \varphi_k(t)$, $k = 1, 2$.

The set of solutions $x(t)$ of Eq. (33.4) possessing the property that $x(t) \to 0$ as $t \to \infty$, is obviously given by the formula

---

*The series will be of the form $\rho = 1 + \sum_{k=1}^{\infty} \rho_k \tau^k$, where $\tau = \varepsilon$ or $\tau = \varepsilon^{1/2}$.

$$x = c\exp(-\alpha t)\cdot\varphi_1(t), \qquad (33.17)$$

where c is an arbitrary constant. Let us find the set of initial values $x(0)$ and $x'(0)$ of these equations. Obviously, these initial values are related by

$$x'(0) = \left[-\alpha + \frac{\varphi_1'(0)}{\varphi_1(0)}\right] x(0). \qquad (33.18)$$

Without loss of generality, we can assume $\varphi_1(0) = 1$. Therefore, formula (33.18) can be rewritten

$$x'(0) = [-\alpha + \varphi_1'(0)]\, x(0), \quad \varphi_1(0) = 1. \qquad (33.19)$$

Keeping (33.16) in mind, we can write the integral matrix X of the system (33.3) as follows:

$$X = \exp([-\alpha,\ \alpha]\, t)\cdot Z(t); \qquad (33.20)$$

where the matrix $Z(t) = Z(t+1)$,

$$Z(0) = \begin{Vmatrix} 1 & z_{12}^0 \\ z_{21}^0 & 1 \end{Vmatrix}, \qquad (33.21)$$

and the numbers z_{12}^0 and z_{21}^0 are constants to be determined; $[-\alpha, \alpha]$ is a diagonal matrix. In matrix form, the system (33.3) is written

$$\frac{dX}{dt} = X \begin{Vmatrix} 0 & \varepsilon p \\ 1 & 0 \end{Vmatrix}. \qquad (33.22)$$

To find the initial values $x(0)$ and $x'(0)$ of the bounded solutions, we must, as is clear from (33.19), find $\varphi_1'(0)$.

We can find the matrix (33.21) or the matrix (33.20) as follows: We find the integral matrix X of Eq. (33.22) under the condition that $X(0) = I$, in the form (8.8) or (10.3):

$$X = \exp At\cdot Z_1(t), \quad Z_1(0) = I. \qquad (33.23)$$

Here, A and Z_1 can be represented by the series (10.11) and (10.13) or by formulas (8.6) and (8.7) [with 2π replaced by unity].

Let us now find the canonical representation of the matrix A:

$$A = S[-\alpha,\ \alpha]\, S^{-1}.$$

We can then rewrite (33.23) in the form

$$X = S\exp([-\alpha,\ \alpha]\,t)\cdot S^{-1}Z_1(t). \tag{33.24}$$

The matrix

$$X = \exp([-\alpha,\ \alpha]\,t)\cdot Z(t), \quad Z(t) = S^{-1}Z_1(t) \tag{33.25}$$

will also be an integral matrix of (33.20), and the matrix (33.21) can be written in the form

$$Z(0) = \left\| \begin{matrix} 1 & z_{12}^0 \\ z_{21}^0 & 1 \end{matrix} \right\| = S^{-1}. \tag{33.26}$$

If we use formulas (8.6) and (8.7), then, in (33.23) we have

$$A = \ln X(1), \tag{33.27}$$

$$Z_1(t) = \exp\{[-\ln X(1)]\,t\}\cdot X(t), \tag{33.28}$$

and $X(1)$ is given by the series (6.14) for $t = 1$

$$X(t) = \sum_{k=0}^{\infty} X_k(t)\,\varepsilon^k, \tag{33.29}$$

$$X_k(t) = \int_0^t X_{k-1}(t)\,P_1(t)\,X_0^{-1}(t)\,dt\,X_0(t), \tag{33.30}$$

$$P_1(t) = \left\| \begin{matrix} 0 & p \\ 0 & 0 \end{matrix} \right\|, \quad X_0 = \left\| \begin{matrix} 1 & 0 \\ t & 1 \end{matrix} \right\|, \quad X_0^{-1} = \left\| \begin{matrix} 1 & 0 \\ -t & 1 \end{matrix} \right\|, \tag{33.31}$$

$$X_k(t) = \int_0^t X_{k-1}(t) \left\| \begin{matrix} -tp & p \\ 0 & 0 \end{matrix} \right\| dt \left\| \begin{matrix} 1 & 0 \\ t & 1 \end{matrix} \right\|. \tag{33.32}$$

The series (33.29) converges for all finite values of ε and the general representation of the matrix (33.27) can be obtained from formula (28.18), where we need to set

$$\sigma(V) = \sigma(X(1)) = f(1) + \varphi'(1) = \psi(1)$$

and replace 2π with unity:

$$A = \frac{\ln\left(\frac{\psi(1)}{2} + \sqrt{\frac{\psi^2(1)}{4} - 1}\right)}{\sqrt{\frac{\psi^2(1)}{4} - 1}}\left[X(1) - \frac{\psi(1)}{2}\right]. \tag{33.33}$$

Obviously, $\varphi_1(t)$ in (33.16) is equal to the elements z_{11} of the matrix Z in (33.20) or (33.25).

We note that $\varphi_1(t)$ could also have been found as follows: If we make the substitution $x(t) = \exp(-\alpha t)\cdot\varphi_1(t)$, in accordance with (33.16), where

$$\alpha = \ln\rho_2 = \frac{\ln[\psi(1) + \sqrt{\psi^2(1) - 4}]}{2}, \tag{33.34}$$

in (33.4) and divide by $\exp(-\alpha t)$, we obtain the following equation for determining $\varphi_1(t)$ [here, we take $\varphi_1(t) = \varphi(t)$]:

$$\frac{d^2\varphi}{dt^2} - 2\alpha\frac{d\varphi}{dt} + (\alpha^2 - \varepsilon p)\varphi = 0. \tag{33.35}$$

We noted right after formula (33.15) the conditions under which ρ_2 (and hence α) can be represented as a series in positive powers of ε or $\varepsilon^{1/2}$.

Consider the case in which

$$\rho_2 = 1 + \sum_{k=1}^{\infty}\rho_k^{(2)}\tau_k, \quad \tau = \varepsilon^{1/2}.$$

Then, if we substitute the series

$$\alpha = \sum_{k=1}^{\infty}\alpha_k\tau^k, \quad \varphi = 1 + \sum_{k=1}^{\infty}\varphi_k\tau^k, \quad \tau^2 = \varepsilon \tag{33.36}$$

into (33.35) and equate coefficients of like powers of τ, we obtain equations from which we can find all the φ_k and α_k, where the φ_k are subjected to the periodicity condition $\varphi_k(t) = \varphi_k(t+1)$. In so doing, we establish the values of α_k, which can also be found easily, directly from (33.34).

Formula (33.34) provides an analytic continuation of the series (33.36) for α to all values of ε since, for $\varepsilon = -1$, we obtain α for Eq. (33.1).

The analytic continuation of the series (33.36) for φ is provided by the value of z_{11} in (33.25), where the matrix $Z_1(t)$ is given by formula (33.28), in which $X(1)$ is given by the series (33.29). This series converges for all finite values of ε. We point out in addition that, in (33.28),

$$\exp[-\ln X(1)\cdot t] = \frac{\rho_2\exp(-\ln\rho_1\cdot t) - \rho_1\exp(-\ln\rho_2\cdot t)}{\rho_2 - \rho_1} + \frac{\exp(-\ln\rho_2\cdot t) - \exp(-\ln\rho_1\cdot t)}{\rho_2 - \rho_1}X(1),$$

where ρ_1 and ρ_2 are given by formulas (33.11) and $\rho_1 \rho_2 = 1$. We have thus obtained

Theorem 33.1. *In the case (33.10), the set of initial values* $x(0)$ *and* $x'(0)$ *of the solutions* $x(t)$ *of Eq. (33.4)* [*or equation (33.1)*] *possessing the property that* $x(t) \to 0$ *as* $t \to \infty$, *is given by Eq. (33.19), where* α *is given by formula (33.34) and* $\varphi_1(t)$ *is the element* z_{11} *of the matrix Z in formula (33.25).*

We have observed that α and φ can be determined from Eq. (33.35) for small values of ε. Specifically, it is clear from formula (33.34) just how small the values of ε need to be since, if the series for α converges, it follows, as can be seen from (33.25), that the series for $Z(t)$ also converges.

34. (33.1) The Case in Which Equation (33.9) Has Roots $|\rho_1| = |\rho_2| = 1$. The Finding of Periodic Solutions.

We have considered the case in which the roots ρ_1 and ρ_2 of Eq. (33.9) are real and distinct. Now, assuming $p \geqslant 0$, we shall find conditions under which ρ_1 and ρ_2 will be complex or equal to unity. In this case, $|\rho_1| = |\rho_2| = 1$ and all solutions of Eq. (33.4) or of the system (33.3) are bounded and oscillatory (if we exclude the case in which $\rho_1 = \rho_2 = 1$ and a nonprime elementary divisor of the matrix (33.8) corresponds to this root).

Let us suppose that $\varepsilon = -1$; that is, let us study Eq. (33.1).

Lyapunov found an infinite number of inequalities [57] the satisfaction of any one of which ensures boundedness of all solutions of Eq. (33.1). These conditions exhaust all cases of boundedness of the solutions of Eq. (33.1) except for certain periodic solutions (cf. corollary to Theorem 34.2). Lyapunov first showed [26] that, for

$$\int_0^1 p\,dt < 4 \quad \text{or} \quad \omega\int_0^\omega p(t)\,dt \leqslant 4 \quad \text{if } p(t+\omega) = p(t) \tag{34.1}$$

we have

$$|\rho_1| = |\rho_2| = 1. \tag{34.2}$$

Then [57], he found all the remaining conditions under which (34.2) is satisfied.

Let us elaborate on this question, using the article* [58] (which rests on the results and ideas of Lyapunov's studies [26]) and also Lyapunov's article [57].

---

*This work was completed in October, 1942, at a time when the author had no access to mathematical literature (except for possession of the book [26]). It was written on the

Since $p \geqslant 0$, it follows from (33.6) that $f_k(t)$ and $\varphi_k'(t)$ are positive. Therefore (see (33.13)), $\psi_k(t) > 0$ for $t > 0$.

If we set $\varepsilon = -1$ in (33.12), we obtain

$$2\rho_1 = \sum_{k=0}^{\infty} (-1)^k \psi_k(1) - \left[\sum_{k=1}^{\infty} (-1)^k \psi_k(1) \times \left(\sum_{k=1}^{\infty} (-1)^k \psi_k(1) + 4\right)\right]^{1/2}$$

$$2\rho_2 = \sum_{k=0}^{\infty} (-1)^k \psi_k(1) + \left[\sum_{k=1}^{\infty} (-1)^k \psi_k(1) \times \left(\sum_{k=1}^{\infty} (-1)^k \psi_k(1) + 4\right)\right]^{1/2}. \tag{34.3}$$

We see that, if

$$J = \sum_{k=1}^{\infty} (-1)^k \psi_k(1) \left(\sum_{k=1}^{\infty} (-1)^k \psi_k(1) + 4\right) > 0, \tag{34.4}$$

then ρ_1 and ρ_2 are real and distinct (and $\rho_1\rho_2 = 1$). On the other hand, if

$$J < 0, \tag{34.5}$$

then ρ_1 and ρ_2 are complex (and $|\rho_1| = |\rho_2| = 1$).

Let us suppose that

$$\psi_k(1) - \psi_{k+1}(1) \geqslant 0 \quad (k = 1, 2, \ldots). \tag{34.6}$$

Then,

$$\sum_{k=1}^{\infty} (-1)^k \psi_k(1) < 0, \tag{34.7}$$

since this is an alternating series (with terms decreasing in absolute value) and the first term is negative. If, in addition,

$$\sum_{k=1}^{\infty} (-1)^k \psi_k(1) + 4 > 0, \tag{34.8}$$

we have (34.5); that is, $|\rho_1| = |\rho_2| = 1$, and all solutions of Eq. (33.1) are bounded and oscillatory. When

---

recommendation of Academician V. I. Smirnov with the purpose of providing a generalization of condition (34.1). The author was unaware of [57] and other writings in that direction. During those days (October-November, 1942), the article [14] was completed. This last article, which included the article [58] was defended by the author as a doctoral dissertation in July 1943 at the university of Kazan.

$$\sum_{k=1}^{\infty}(-1)^k \psi_k(1)+4<0 \tag{34.9}$$

(34.4) is satisfied and not all the solutions of Eq. (33.1) are bounded.

Inequality (34.8) will be satisfied if

$$-\psi_1(1)+4>0 \quad \text{or} \quad \int_0^1 dt \int_0^t p dt + \int_0^1 tpdt \leqslant 4, \tag{34.10}$$

since the sum of the discarded terms in (34.8) can, by virtue of (34.6), only intensify inequality (34.10).

We note now that inequality (34.10) is equivalent to Lyapunov's inequality (34.1). Integrating by parts, we obtain

$$\int_0^1 tpdt = \int_0^1 pdt - \int_0^1 dt \int_0^t pdt,$$

after which it is clear that inequality (34.10) is simply inequality (34.1). Lyapunov showed that, for all t and $p \geqslant 0$, the inequality [26, Chapt. III, No. 48, formula (15)]

$$t\,\psi_{n-1}(t)\int_0^t pdt - 2n\,\psi_n(t)>0, \tag{34.11}$$

holds. For $t=1$, this formula yields

$$\psi_{n-1}(1)\int_0^1 pdt - 2n\,\psi_n(1)>0. \tag{34.12}$$

Therefore, for $n \geqslant 2$, we have (34.6) in the strict-inequality form

$$\psi_{n-1}(1)-\psi_n(1)>0, \tag{34.6$_1$}$$

if (34.1) is satisfied.

Thus, (34.1) yields (34.6), (34.7) and (34.8). Therefore, all solutions of Eq. (33.1) are bounded.

However, inequalities (34.6) may be satisfied when (34.1) is not satisfied. If, in addition,

$$-\psi_1(1)+\psi_2(1)+4 \leqslant 0, \tag{34.13}$$

we have (34.9). Consequently, when conditions (34.6) and (34.13) are satisfied, not all solutions of equation (33.1) are bounded.

If (34.13) is not satisfied, but if

$$-\psi_1(1)+\psi_2(1)-\psi_3(1)+4\geqslant 0, \tag{34.14}$$

then we have (34.8) and all solutions of Eq. (33.1) are bounded.

In general, as can be seen from (33.12), we have

Lemma 34.1. *Suppose that*

$$\psi_k(1)-\psi_{k+1}(1)\geqslant 0,\ k\geqslant 2m+1. \tag{34.15}$$

Then, for

$$\sum_{k=1}^{2m}(-1)^k\psi_k(1)\leqslant 0,\quad \sum_{k=1}^{2m+1}(-1)^k\psi_k(1)+4\geqslant 0 \tag{34.16}$$

we have $|\rho_1|=|\rho_2|=1$; *that is, all solutions of Eq. (33.1) are bounded but, for*

$$4+\sum_{k=1}^{2m}(-1)^k\psi_k(1)\leqslant 0, \tag{34.17}$$

and also for

$$\sum_{k=1}^{2m+1}(-1)^k\psi_k(1)\geqslant 0 \tag{34.18}$$

not all solutions of Eq. (33.1) are bounded.

For the moment, we exclude the case in which either

$$\sum_{k=1}^{\infty}(-1)^k\psi_k(1)=0\quad (\text{i.e., } \rho_1=\rho_2=1)$$

or

$$\sum_{k=1}^{\infty}(-1)^k\psi_k(1)+4=0\ (\text{i.e., } \rho_1=\rho_2=-1).$$

If we have (34.16), then, on the basis of (34.15),

$$\sum_{k=1}^{\infty}(-1)^k\psi_k(1)<0,\quad \sum_{k=1}^{\infty}(-1)^k\psi_k(1)+4>0. \tag{34.19}$$

From this it follows (on the basis of (34.3)) that $|\rho_1| = |\rho_2| = 1$.

If (34.17) is satisfied, then, on the basis of (34.15),

$$4 + \sum_{k=1}^{\infty} (-1)^k \psi_k(1) < 0 \tag{34.20}$$

and a fortiori,

$$\sum_{k=1}^{\infty} (-1)^k \psi_k(1) < 0.$$

Then, ρ_1 and ρ_2 are obviously real.

If (34.18) is satisfied, then, a fortiori

$$\sum_{k=1}^{\infty} (-1)^k \psi_k(1) > 0, \quad 4 + \sum_{k=1}^{\infty} (-1)^k \psi_k(1) > 0$$

and, consequently, ρ_1 and ρ_2 are real.

Remark 34.1. Lyapunov showed [57] by a complicated line of reasoning that

$$\frac{\psi_{n+1}(1)}{\psi_n(1)} < \frac{\psi_n(1)}{\psi_{n-1}(1)} \quad \text{or} \quad \frac{\psi_{n-1}(1)}{\psi_n(1)} < \frac{\psi_n(1)}{\psi_{n+1}(1)}, \tag{34.21}$$

from which it follows that, if

$$\psi_{2m+1}(1) - \psi_{2m+2}(1) > 0, \tag{34.22}$$

then

$$\psi_k(1) - \psi_{k+1}(1) > 0, \quad k \geqslant 2m+1. \tag{34.23}$$

Thus, inequalities (34.15) are satisfied if (34.22) is satisfied.

Lemma 34.2. (Lyapunov). *Suppose that one of the inequalities (34.16), (34.17), or (34.18) is satisfied. Then,*

$$\psi_{2m+1}(1) - \psi_{2m+2}(1) \geqslant 0. \tag{34.24}$$

Proof: If (34.24) is not satisfied, then

$$\psi_{2m+1}(1) < \psi_{2m+2}(1). \tag{34.25}$$

But then, on the basis of (34.21), we have

$$\psi_1(1) < \psi_2(1) < \ldots < \psi_{2m+1}(1) < \psi_{2m+2}(1). \tag{34.26}$$

This contradicts inequalities (34.17) and (34.18) and the first of inequalities (34.16).

Let us show that (34.26) contradicts the second of inequalities (34.16) also. On the basis of (34.26), we obtain from the second of inequalities (34.16)

$$-\psi_1(1)+4>0, \tag{34.26$_1$}$$

since

$$\sum_{k=2}^{2m+1}(-1)^k\psi_k(1)<0.$$

But we have shown that (34.26) implies (34.24) [inequality (34.10) implies (34.6) when (34.12) is satisfied], and this means that (34.25) is not satisfied. This completes the proof of the lemma.

Theorem 34.1. (Lyapunov). *If (34.16) is satisfied, then all solutions of Eq. (33.1) are bounded. If (34.17) or (34.18) is satisfied, not all solutions of Eq. (33.1) are bounded.*

Proof: Any one of the three inequalities (34.16), (34.17), (34.18) implies (34.24). Consequently, on the basis of Remark 34.1 and inequality (34.15), the conclusion of this theorem follows.

We have shown that satisfaction of any one of the inequalities (34.16), (34.17), (34.18) implies satisfaction of inequalities (34.15). However, inequality (34.15) can be satisfied when none of these three inequalities are satisfied.

Let us give some other sufficient conditions under which (34.15) can be satisfied.

Remark 34.2. When

$$\int_0^1 p\,dt \leqslant 2(2m+2), \tag{34.27}$$

inequalities (34.15) are satisfied. This follows from (34.12) with $n \geqslant 2m+2$

Remark 34.3. By a complicated line of reasoning, Lyapunov proved, instead of (34.15), the inequality [57, formula (26)]

$$\psi_n(1)<\int_0^1 p\,dt\,\frac{\psi_{n-1}(1)}{2n^2}, \tag{34.28}$$

from which it follows that inequalities (34.15) are satisfied whenever

$$\int_0^1 p\,dt \leqslant 2(2m+2)^2. \tag{34.29}$$

Remark 34.4. Whenever [58]

$$f_{n-1}(t) - f_n(t) \geqslant 0, \quad \varphi'_{n-1}(t) - \varphi'_n(t) \geqslant 0, \quad 0 \leqslant t \leqslant 1 \tag{34.30}$$

we have

$$\psi_k(1) - \psi_{k+1}(1) \geqslant 0 \quad \text{for } k \geqslant n-1. \tag{34.31}$$

Proof: On the basis of (33.6), we obtain from (34.30)

$$f_k(t) - f_{k-1}(t) \geqslant 0, \quad \varphi'_k(t) - \varphi'_{k+1}(t) \geqslant 0, \quad k \geqslant n-1,$$

from which it follows that

$$\psi_k(t) - \psi_{k+1}(t) = \int_0^t \int_0^t p(f_{k-1} - f_k)\, dt\, dt + \int_0^t p(\varphi_{k-1} - \varphi_k)\, dt \geqslant 0$$

for $k \geqslant n+1$.

Remark 34.4 is contained in Remark 34.1, but it is much more easily proven.

Theorem 34.2. *Suppose that the inequalities*

$$\psi_{m-1}(1) - \psi_m(1) \geqslant 0, \; m \geqslant n \tag{34.32}$$

are satisfied and that, for every m, either

$$\sum_{k=1}^{2m} (-1)^k \psi_k(1) > 0, \quad \sum_{k=1}^{2m+1} (-1)^k \psi_k(1) < 0 \tag{34.33}$$

or

$$4 + \sum_{k=1}^{2m} (-1)^k \psi_k(1) > 0, \quad \sum_{k=1}^{2m+1} (-1)^k \psi_k(1) + 4 < 0. \tag{34.34}$$

Then,

$$\sum_{k=1}^{\infty} (-1)^k \psi_k(1) = 0, \quad \rho_1 = \rho_2 = 1 \tag{34.35}$$

in the first case and

$$\sum_{k=1}^{\infty} (-1)^k \psi_k(1) + 4 = 0, \quad \rho_1 = \rho_2 = -1 \tag{34.36}$$

in the second.

We note that the quantitites in the first half of inequalities (34.33) and (34.34) decrease [by virtue of (34.32)] with increasing m and that those in the second increase.

Corollary. *If (34.35) is satisfied and*

$$\varphi(1) = f'(1) = 0, \tag{34.37}$$

then, by virtue of (33.8), the general solution of Eq. (33.1) will be periodic with period $\omega = 1$. *If (34.35) is satisfied but (34.37) is not, we have a one-parameter periodic solution, but the general solution will not be periodic (or bounded). If (34.36) and (34.37) are satisfied, then the general solution of Eq. (33.1) is periodic with period* $\omega = 2$. *On the other hand, if*

$$\varphi^2(1) + f'^2(1) \neq 0, \tag{34.38}$$

we have a one-parameter solution with period $\omega = 2$, *but the general solution will not be periodic.*

Suppose that (34.35) is satisfied and that

$$\varphi(1) \neq 0. \tag{34.39}$$

Then, we have a one-parameter periodic solution to Eq. (33.1) with period $\omega = 1$:

$$x = cx_1(t), \tag{34.40}$$

where c is an arbitrary constant and $x_1(t)$ is a periodic solution of Eq. (33.1) with period $\omega = 1$.

Let us find the initial values of $x_1(t)$ and the entire set of initial values of the periodic solutions (34.40).

The general solution of Eq. (33.1) is of the form

$$x(t) = c_1 f(t) + c_2 \varphi(t). \tag{34.41}$$

Suppose that

$$x(t+1) = x(t). \tag{34.42}$$

Then,

$$x(0) = c_1 = c_1 f(1) + c_2 \varphi(1),$$
$$x'(0) = c_2 = c_1 f'(1) + c_2 \varphi'(1).$$

From this, we have

$$\left.\begin{aligned} c_1[f(1) - 1] + c_2\varphi(1) = 0 \\ c_1 f'(1) + c_2[\varphi'(1) - 1] = 0 \end{aligned}\right\}. \tag{34.43}$$

The determinant of this system is

$$\Delta = f(1)\varphi'(1) - \varphi'(1) - f(1) - \varphi(1)f'(1) + 1 = 0,$$

since, in accordance with (33.8), (33.9) and (34.35),

$$f(1)\varphi'(1) - \varphi(1)f'(1) = 1 \text{ and } f(1) + \varphi'(1) = 2.$$

Therefore, c_1 and c_2 can be found from (34.43). On the basis of (34.39),

$$c_2 = c_1 \frac{1 - f(1)}{\varphi(1)}.$$

Therefore, we write (34.41) in the form

$$x(t) = c_1 \left[f(t) + \frac{1 - f(1)}{\varphi(1)} \varphi(t) \right]. \qquad (34.44)$$

Obviously, the solution

$$x_1(t) = f(t) + \frac{1 - f(1)}{\varphi(1)} \varphi(t) \qquad (34.45)$$

has initial conditions

$$x_1(0) = 1, \quad x_1'(0) = \frac{1 - f(1)}{\varphi(1)}. \qquad (34.46)$$

Consequently, periodic solutions $x(t)$ *of (33.1) in the case (34.35) have initial conditions*

$$x(0) = c, \quad x'(0) = c \frac{1 - f(1)}{\varphi(1)}, \qquad (34.47)$$

where c *is an arbitrary constant.* In other words, these initial values are given by

$$x'(0) = x(0) \frac{1 - f(1)}{\varphi(1)}. \qquad (34.48)$$

If (34.35) is satisfied and if

$$f'(1) \neq 0, \qquad (34.49)$$

then, instead of (34.47) and (34.48), we have

$$x'(0) = c, \quad x(0) = c\frac{1-\varphi'(1)}{f'(1)} \tag{34.50}$$

$$x(0) = x'(0)\,\frac{1-\varphi'(1)}{f'(1)} \tag{34.51}$$

and, instead of (34.44),

$$x(t) = c\left[\frac{1-\varphi'(t)}{f'(1)}\,f(t) + \varphi(t)\right]. \tag{34.51$_1$}$$

If it turns out that $f(1) = 1$ or that $\varphi'(1) = 1$, we shall have respectively $x_1(t) = f(t)$ or $x_1(t) = \varphi(t)$ and, instead of (34.48) or (34.51), we shall have $x(0) = c$ and $x'(0) = 0$ or $x(0) = 0$ and $x'(0) = c$.

Remark 34.5. Obviously, the conditions under which a periodic solution of (34.35) or (34.36) exists and under which the general solution of (34.37) is periodic are not connected with the condition $p(t) \geqslant 0$. If conditions (34.35) and (34.37) are satisfied, then, on the basis of (33.9), we have $\varphi'(1) = f(1) = 1$ and, if conditions (34.36) and (34.37) are satisfied, we have $f(1) = \varphi'(1) = -1$.

35. Regions of Values of the Parameters Appearing in Equation (33.1) in Which There Are Bounded and Periodic Solutions

Consider the equation

$$\frac{d^2x}{dt^2} + p(t)\,x = 0 \tag{35.1}$$

(Eq. (33.1) repeated). Suppose that the function $p(t)$ is a nonnegative periodic function with period $\omega = 1$. If $p(t)$ contains a parameter ε, then Theorem 34.1 enables us to obtain those regions of values of ε in which the general solution of Eq. (35.1) is bounded and those in which it is unbounded. Theorem 34.2 enables us to find those values of ε (from Eqs. (34.35)) at which there is a periodic solution with period $\omega = 1$ (from (34.35)) or $\omega = 2$ (from (34.36)). The corollary to Theorem 34.2 gave conditions under which the general solution is periodic.

If ε satisfies Eqs. (34.35) and if

$$\varphi(1) = f'(1) = 0,$$

then the general solution is periodic with period $\omega = 1$. But if ε satisfies Eqs. (34.36) and if

$$\varphi(1) = f'(1) = 0,$$

then the general solution is periodic with period $\omega = 2$. It may happen that $p(t)$ contains parameters ε and μ. Then, from (34.35) and (34.36) , we also find the functions $\mu = \mu(\varepsilon)$ for which Eq. (33.1) has a periodic solution. If $p(t)$ is an entire function of ε and μ, the function

$$\Phi(\varepsilon, \mu) = \sum_{k=1}^{\infty} (-1)^k \psi_k(1)$$

will also be an entire function. It will then follow [32, Theorem 12, p. 47] that the function $\mu = \mu(\varepsilon)$ can have only algebraic singularities. It was shown in [32] how to find the region of convergence of the series

$$\mu = \mu(\varepsilon) = \sum_{k=0}^{\infty} a_k \varepsilon^k.$$

Suppose now that $p(t)$ is expressed in terms of parameters ε, μ, and λ, and that it is an entire function of these parameters. Then, the functions (see Sect. 6)

$$\sum_{k=1}^{\infty} (-1)^k \psi_k(1), \quad \varphi(1) \text{ and } f'(1)$$

will also be entire functions of these parameters.

How can we find values of the parameters ε, μ, and λ for which Eq. (33.1) has a periodic solution?

We can find the set of these values from (34.35) (then, there will be a periodic solution with period $\omega = 1$) or (34.36) (there will be a a periodic solution with period $\omega = 2$). To find those values of ε, μ, and λ for which the general solution of Eq. (33.1) will be periodic, we first find the functions $\mu = \mu(\varepsilon)$ and $\lambda = \lambda(\varepsilon)$ from the equations

$$\varphi(1) = 0 \quad f'(1) = 0. \tag{34.37}$$

If we substitute these functions into Eqs. (34.35) or (34.36), respectively, we obtain an equation from which we can, generally speaking, find the values of $\varepsilon_1, \varepsilon_2, \ldots$ (and hence $\mu_1, \mu_2, \ldots, \lambda_1, \lambda_2, \ldots$) at which the general solution of (33.1) is periodic.

We note also that, in satisfying conditions (34.37) and (34.35) or (34.36), we are in effect (by virtue of (33.9)) satisfying the equations

$$\varphi(1) = f'(1) = 0, \quad f(1) = \varphi'(1) = 1$$

or

$$\varphi(1) = f'(1) = 0, \quad f(1) = \varphi'(1) = -1.$$

Suppose, for example, that

$$p(t) = \varepsilon p_1(t) + \mu p_2(t).$$

Then, (34.35) will be of the form

$$\sum_{k=1}^{\infty} (-1)^k \psi_k(1) = -\psi_1(1) + \psi_2(1) - \ldots = 0,$$

where (see (33.14))

$$\psi_1(1) = f_1(1) + \varphi_1'(1) = \int_0^1 dt \int_0^t p(t)\,dt + \int_0^1 tp\,dt =$$

$$= \int_0^1 p\,dt = \varepsilon \int_0^1 p_1(t)\,dt + \mu \int_0^1 p_2(t)\,dt,$$

and the $\psi_k(1)$ (for $(k > 1)$ will be infinitesimals of order k for small values of ε and μ (which is obvious from formulas (33.6) and (33.13)).

On the basis of (34.35), we see that, if

$$\int_0^1 p_2(t)\,dt \neq 0,$$

there exists a function

$$\mu = \alpha_1 \varepsilon + \alpha_2 \varepsilon^2 + \ldots,$$

$$\alpha_1 = -\int_0^1 p_1(t)\,dt \Big/ \int_0^1 p_2(t)\,dt,$$

that is holomorphic in a neighborhood of $\varepsilon = 0$ and for which Eq. (35.1) has a periodic solution with period $\omega = 1$.

On the basis of the results obtained in Sect. 6 of [32], it is usually easy to ascertain whether, under all other assumptions regarding $\int_0^1 p_1 dt$ and $\int_0^1 p_2 dt$, a function $\mu = \mu(\varepsilon)$ exists that approaches 0 as $\varepsilon \to 0$ and for which Eq. (35.1) has a periodic solution.

For a periodic solution to exist, it is necessary and sufficient that a real function $\eta = \eta(\varepsilon)$ exist, defined by the equation

$$\sum_{k=1}^{\infty}(-1)^k \psi_k(1) = 0$$

that approaches zero as $\varepsilon \to 0$. Since the function

$$\sum_{k=1}^{\infty}(-1)^k \psi^k(1)$$

is an entire function with respect to ε and η, the function $\eta = \eta(\varepsilon)$ (which $\to 0$ as $\varepsilon \to 0$), if it exists, can, under analytic continuation, have only algebraic singularities. It is shown in [32, Theorem 12] how one may find the radius of convergence of the series

$$\eta = \sum_{k=1}^{\infty} \eta_k \varepsilon^k.$$

However, we see that Eq. (35.1) cannot have a periodic solution with period $\omega = 2$ for small values of ε and η since Eq. (34.36) is not satisfied for small values of ε and η.

If we assume that

$$p(t) = \varepsilon p_1(t) + \eta p_2(t) \geqslant 0$$

and

$$\int_0^1 p_1(t)\,dt > 0, \quad \int_0^1 p_2(t)\,dt > 0,$$

in (35.1), then, in general, (35.1) will not have a periodic solution for small values of ε and η since the condition $p(t) \geqslant 0$ contradicts the equation

$$\varepsilon \int_0^1 p_1(t)\,dt + \mu \int_0^1 p_2(t)\,dt + O_2(\varepsilon, \eta) = 0.$$

Actually, this follows from the more general hypothesis. Specifically, suppose (see (34.22)) that

$$-\psi_1(1) + \psi_2(1) < 0. \tag{35.2}$$

Then (see Remark 34.1),

$$-\psi_{2n-1}(1)+\psi_{2n}(1)<0, \quad n\geqslant 1 \tag{35.2$_1$}$$

and, hence, the equation

$$\sum_{k=1}^{\infty}(-1)^k\psi_k(1)=0 \tag{34.35}$$

is impossible. But if the $\psi_1(1)$ are infinitesimals of order k for small values of ε and μ, then, for sufficiently small ε and μ, (35.2) will be satisfied. It follows from this that a periodic solution with period $\omega=1$ does not exist. But Eq. (34.36) is also impossible for small ε and η.

Remark 35.1. We have seen that if the condition

$$[f(1)+\varphi'(1)]^2-4=0,$$

is satisfied, then Eq. (33.1) does not have a solution that is periodic with period $\omega=1$ or $\omega=2$. However, among the bounded solutions that do not approach zero (which can be found, for example, with the aid of Theorem (34.1)), there may still be periodic solutions with period $\omega=n$ or $\omega=2n$, where n is a positive integer. These periodic solutions exist if and only if

$$[f(n)+\varphi'(n)]^2-4=0. \tag{35.3}$$

If

$$f(n)+\varphi'(n)=\sum_{k=0}^{\infty}(-1)^k\psi_k(n)=2, \tag{35.4}$$

there is a periodic solution with period $\omega=n$. On the other hand, if

$$f(n)+\varphi'(n)=\sum_{k=0}^{\infty}(-1)^k\psi_k(n)=-2, \tag{35.5}$$

a periodic solution with period $\omega=2n$ will exist. For the general solution to be periodic with period n or $2n$, it is necessary and sufficient that, in addition to (35.3), the condition

$$f'(n)=\varphi(n)=0 \tag{35.6}$$

be satisfied.

Just as in the cases in which $n = 1$ or $n = 2$, it is easy to find the relation between the parameters appearing in the expression for $p(t)$ that ensures the existence of a periodic solution with period $\omega = n$ (on the basis of (35.4)) or $\omega = 2n$ (on the basis of (35.5)). In accordance with (34.45), it is easy to find this periodic solution:

$$x(t) = f(t) + \frac{1 - f(n)}{\varphi(n)} \varphi(t); \tag{35.7}$$

if $\varphi(n) \neq 0$. Or, in accordance with (34.50$_1$), we can find it from the formula

$$x(t) = \frac{1 - \varphi'(n)}{f'(n)} f(t) + \varphi(t), \tag{35.8}$$

if $\varphi(n) = 0$ but $f'(n) \neq 0$. Here, we need to set $\mu = \mu(\varepsilon)$ as found in (35.4), in (35.7) and (35.8). Or, in other words, the solution (35.7) is periodic by virtue of Eq. (35.4). The initial values of the periodic solution (35.7) are

$$x(0) = 1, \quad \dot{x}(0) = \frac{1 - f(n)}{\varphi(n)} . \tag{35.9}$$

We have shown that Eq. (35.1) can have periodic solutions with period $\omega = 1, 2, \ldots$. The question then arises as to whether it can have periodic solutions with period ω, where ω is not an integer. We shall shortly prove

Remark (35.2). With no loss of generality as regards this question, we may assume that Eq. (35.1) does not have a periodic solution with rational period $\omega = \frac{m}{n} < 1$, where m and n are integers without a common factor.

Lemma 35.1. *Equation (35.1), where $p(t)$ can have only integral periods n, cannot have a periodic solution with period $\omega \neq n$.*

Proof: If $x(t)$ is a periodic solution with period ω, then $\ddot{x}(t + \omega) = \ddot{x}(t)$. Therefore from (35.1), we have

$$[p(t + \omega) - p(t)]\, x(t) = 0,$$

from which the assertion of the lemma follows.

If $p(t)$ has period $\omega_1 = 1$ and rational period $\omega_2 = \frac{m}{n} < 1$, where m and n are positive integers without common factor, then $p(t)$ is of period $\omega_3 = \frac{1}{n}$. This follows from the fact that [61] integers k and l exist such that $kn + lm = 1$. If $\frac{1}{n}$ and $\frac{1}{n+1}$ are periods, then $\frac{1}{n(n+1)}$ is also a period. If $p(t)$ has periods

$$\frac{1}{2}, \frac{1}{3}, \frac{1}{4}, \ldots, \frac{1}{n}, \frac{1}{n+1}, \ldots$$

then $p(t)$ is constant.

From this and from what was said above, we have

Lemma 35.2. *If $p(t)$ is a nonconstant periodic function with rational periods, there exists a smallest period, $\omega = \frac{1}{n}$, where n is a positive integer, such that all periods can be obtained from the formula $\omega = \frac{k}{n}$, where k is an integer.*

We may assume that the smallest period is $\omega = 1$. Then, all periods can be obtained from the formula $\omega = n$, where n ranges over the integers. This proves Remark 35.2.

In Sect. 36, we shall show that Eq. (35.1) cannot have periodic solutions with irrational periods either.

Now, let us look at the question of the radius of convergence of the series representing a periodic solution of Eq. (35.1).

Suppose that, from (35.4) and Theorem 7 [or the results obtained in connection with Eq. (6.40)] of the book [32] (see Sect. 47 of the present book), we have a relation between μ and ε

$$\mu = \sum_{k=0}^{\infty} \mu_k \varepsilon^k, \quad \mu_k \tag{35.10}$$

where the μ_k are real and $|\varepsilon| \leqslant r$, under which (35.1) has a periodic solution (but not all solutions of this equation will be periodic).

The radius of convergence of the series (35.10) is determined in [32].

We note also that it is always possible to assume μ represented in the form of a series (35.10) [in positive powers of ε] since we can always represent ε in the form

$$\varepsilon = \sum_{k=0}^{\infty} \varepsilon_k \eta^k.$$

If substitution of the expression for μ given by (35.10) into $p(\varepsilon, \mu, t)$ gives us

$$p(\varepsilon, \mu, t) = \sum_{k=0}^{\infty} p_k(t) \varepsilon^k, \tag{35.11}$$

then the solutions of Eq. (35.1) can be represented in the form of series of positive powers of ε. The series (35.11) will, in general, converge in the region in which the series (35.10) converges. Therefore, the series representing the solutions of Eq. (35.1) also converge in the region of convergence of the series (35.10) if the initial values of these solutions are independent of ε (see Theorem 6.1). For example, in this region, the solutions $f(t)$ and $\varphi(t)$ given by formulas (33.5) can be represented by such series. But the region of convergence of the series representing a periodic solution of (35.7) can also be determined by means of a series representing $\dot{x}(0)$ in accordance with (35.9). This region of convergence of a series (representing a solution of (35.7)) is determined by the inequality

$$|\varepsilon| < R, \tag{35.12}$$

where R is the smallest absolute value of the nonzero roots ε^* of the equation

$$\varphi(n, \varepsilon) = 0. \tag{35.13}$$

But if (35.13) holds and $f'(n, \varepsilon^*) \neq 0$, we obtain a periodic solution in accordance with formula (35.8) and the region of convergence of the series representing the periodic solution will be

$$|\varepsilon| < R_1, \tag{35.14}$$

where R_1 is the smallest absolute value of the roots ε_* of the equation

$$f'(n, \varepsilon) = 0. \tag{35.15}$$

However, if ε_* is a root of Eq. (35.13), then the radius of convergence will again be lengthened. If, in addition,

$$f'(n, \varepsilon_*) = 0 \quad \text{and} \quad \varphi(n, \varepsilon_*) = 0, \tag{35.15$_1$}$$

then, for $\varepsilon = \varepsilon_*$, all solutions of Eq. (35.1) will be periodic with period $\omega = n$, including the solutions $f(t)$ and $\varphi(t)$ given by formulas (33.5), for which the series in positive powers of ε converge in the region of convergence of the series (35.10).

We have obtained the following result: If Eq. (35.1) has a one-parameter periodic solution with period $\omega = n$, then the basic periodic solution of (35.7) or (35.8) can be represented as a series in positive powers of ε that converges in the region in which the series (35.11) converges. On the other hand, all solutions of Eq. (35.1) are periodic, then the solutions $f(t)$ and $\varphi(t)$ will also be periodic and representable in the form of series that converge in the region of convergence of the series (35.11). Thus, we have proven

Theorem 35.1. *Periodic solutions of Eq. (35.1) can be represented as series in positive powers of* ε *that converge in the region in which the series (35.11) converges.*

The set of equations (35.7) and (35.4) provides the general representation (for all values of ε and μ that are admissible for given $p(t, \varepsilon, \mu)$) of a one-parameter solution with respect to ε and μ. From (35.7), we can also obtain an expansion of this solution in a series of positive powers of ε.

However, let us show how we can obtain a periodic solution (35.7) in the form of a series of positive powers of ε directly, without using the representation (35.7). Let us suppose that we have proven the existence of a solution (35.10) of Eq. (35.4). In so doing, we have proven that there is a periodic solution of Eq. (35.1) with period $\omega = n$. Let us suppose now that, on the basis of (35.10),

$$p(\varepsilon, \mu, t) = \sum_{k=1}^{\infty} p_k(t, \mu_1, \ldots, \mu_k)\, \varepsilon^k. \tag{35.11$_1$}$$

Let us seek a periodic solution of Eq. (35.1) with period $\omega = n$ in the form

$$x = \sum_{k=0}^{\infty} x_k(t)\, \varepsilon^k. \tag{35.16}$$

The initial conditions of the solution (35.7) [and hence, of (35.16)] will be

$$x(0) = 1, \quad \dot{x}(0) = \frac{1 - f(n)}{\varphi(n)}\,. \tag{35.17}$$

If we substitute (35.16) into (35.1), we obtain

$$\sum_{k=0}^{\infty} \ddot{x}_k(t)\, \varepsilon^k + \sum_{k=1}^{\infty} p_k(\mu_1, \ldots, \mu_m, t)\, \varepsilon^k \sum_{k=0}^{\infty} x_k(t)\, \varepsilon^k = 0.$$

If we equate the coefficients of like powers of ε, we obtain

$$\ddot{x}_0 = 0, \quad \ddot{x}_1 + p_1(t, \mu_1) = 0, \tag{35.18}$$

$$\ddot{x}_k + \sum_{\nu=0}^{k-1} p_{k-\nu} x_\nu = 0. \tag{35.19}$$

On the basis of (35.17), we take $x_0 = 1$. From (35.18), we obtain

$$\dot{x}_1(t) = c_1 - \int_0^t p_1(t, \mu_1)\, dt, \qquad (35.20)$$

where c_1 is an arbitrary constant. Since this function is periodic with period $\omega = n$, we need to choose μ_1 from the equation

$$\int_0^n p_1(t, \mu_1)\, dt = 0. \qquad (35.21)$$

Obviously, the constant c_1 is the coefficient of the first power of ε in the expansion of $\dot{x}(0)$ given by Eq. (35.17):

$$\dot{x}(0) = \frac{1 - f(n)}{\varphi(n)} = \sum_{k=1}^{\infty} c_k \varepsilon^k. \qquad (35.22)$$

From (35.20), we obtain

$$x_1(t) = \int_0^t \left(c_1 - \int_0^t p_1(t, \mu_1)\, dt \right) dt. \qquad (35.23)$$

Therefore, we find c_1 in the form

$$c_1 = \frac{1}{n} \int_0^n \int_0^t p_1(t, \mu_1)\, dt\, dt. \qquad (35.24)$$

Similarly, we find all the other μ_k and c_k (for $k = 2, 3, \ldots$) from the equations

$$\int_0^n \sum_{\nu=0}^{k-1} p_{k-\nu}(t, \mu_1, \ldots, \mu_{k-\nu})\, dt = 0 \quad (k = 2, 3, \ldots) \qquad (35.25)$$

and

$$c_k = \frac{1}{n} \int_0^n \int_0^t \sum_{\nu=0}^{k-1} p_{k-\nu}(t, \mu_1, \ldots, \mu_{k-\nu})\, dt\, dt. \qquad (35.26)$$

We have proven the existence of a periodic solution (35.16) under the assumption that the solution (35.10) of Eq. (35.4) exists.

Therefore, we can find $\mu_1, \mu_2, \ldots$ from Eqs. (35.21) and (35.35). In accordance with Theorem 35.1, the series (35.16) converges at least throughout the region in which the series (35.11) converges.

Consider now a system of n linear differential equations [87]

$$\frac{dX}{dt} = XP(t, \mu, \varepsilon), \tag{35.27}$$

where X is an nth-order integral matrix and $P(t, \mu, \varepsilon,)$ is an nth-order matrix that is continuous and periodic with period 2π with respect to t and that can be represented in the form of a series

$$P(t, \mu, \varepsilon) = \sum_{k=0,\ l=0}^{\infty} P_{kl}(t)\mu^k\varepsilon^l, \quad P_{kl}(t+2\pi) = P_{kl}(t), \tag{35.28}$$

that converges in the region

$$|\mu| < R, \ |\varepsilon| < R, \ -\infty < t < \infty. \tag{35.29}$$

Consider the integral matrix

$$X(t, \mu, \varepsilon)|_{t=0} = \mathrm{I}, \tag{35.30}$$

which can be represented as series of the forms

$$X(t, \mu, \varepsilon) = \mathrm{I} + \sum_{k=1}^{\infty} X_k(t, \mu, \varepsilon), \ X_k(0, \mu, \varepsilon) = 0 \tag{35.31}$$

or

$$X(t, \mu, \varepsilon) = X_0(t) + \sum_{k,l=1}^{\infty} X_{kl}(t)\mu^k\varepsilon^l, \ X_0(0) = \mathrm{I}, \ X_{kl}(0) = 0, \tag{35.32}$$

these series converging uniformly in the region $|\mu| < R$, $|\varepsilon| < R$, $a < t < a$, where a is an arbitrary positive number.

Let us find a function

$$\mu = \mu(\varepsilon) = \sum_{k=0}^{\infty} \mu_k\varepsilon^k \tag{35.33}$$

such that the system (35.27) has a periodic solution with period $\omega = 2\pi n$. We need to seek this function from the equation

$$\Delta(\mu, \varepsilon) = (-1)^n D(X(2\pi n, \mu, \varepsilon)\text{-}\mathrm{I}\lambda) = 0, \ \lambda = 1, \tag{35.34}$$

since one of the characteristic numbers of the matrix $X(2\pi n, \mu, \varepsilon)$ will be equal to unity when this equation is satisfied and this ensures the existence of a periodic solution of the system (35.27). We assume that Eq. (35.34) determines the function (35.33), where the series (35.33) converges in the region*

$$|\varepsilon| < \delta. \tag{35.35}$$

Suppose that, for such $\mu = \mu(\varepsilon)$, the system (35.27) has a ν-parameter family of periodic solutions. If we substitute (35.33) into (35.27), we obtain

$$\frac{dX}{dt} = XP(t, \varepsilon) = \sum_{k=0}^{\infty} P_k(t)\,\varepsilon^k \tag{35.36}$$

and this series, generally speaking, converges at least in the region (35.35). Suppose that

$$x_l(t) = x_l(t, \alpha_1, \ldots, \alpha_\nu, \varepsilon) = \sum_{k=0}^{\infty} a_k^{(l)}(t, \alpha_1, \ldots, \alpha_\nu)\,\varepsilon^k \quad (l = 1, \ldots, n) \tag{35.37}$$

is a ν-parameter family of periodic solutions the existence of which we have assumed. Let us suppose that the parameters $\alpha_1, \ldots, \alpha_\nu$ are independent of ε. Then,

$$x_l(t) = \sum_{k=1}^{n} c_k x_{kl}(t, \varepsilon) \quad (l = 1, \ldots, n). \tag{35.38}$$

Here, $c_1, \ldots, c_n$ are constants and the $x_{kl}(t, \varepsilon)$ are the elements of the integral matrix $X(t, \varepsilon)$ (where $X(0, \varepsilon) = I$)of the system (35.36), which can be represented in the form of series

$$x_{kl}(t, \varepsilon) = \sum_{p=0}^{\infty} a_p^{(kl)}(t)\,\varepsilon^p, \tag{35.39}$$

that converge in the region (35.35).

---

*This region is found in accordance with Sects. 8 and 9 of [32]. See also Sect. 47 of the present book. If Eq. (35.34) defines a function

$$\mu = \sum_{k=0}^{\infty} \mu_k \tau^k, \quad \tau = \varepsilon^{\frac{1}{p}},$$

where p is a positive integer, then, instead of (35.36), we obtain a series in powers of τ and our subsequent reasoning is the same.

We can find* the solutions of (35.37) by substituting (35.38) into the equations

$$x_l(2\pi n) - x_l(0) = 0 \quad (l = 1, \ldots, n). \tag{35.40}$$

Since, by assumption, we have a ν-parameter family of periodic solutions of (35.37), the rank m of the matrix

$$\Delta(\varepsilon) = X(2\pi n, \varepsilon) - I, \tag{35.41}$$

corresponding to the coefficient matrix of the system (35.40) will be equal to ν, that is, $m = \nu$.

Consider all νth-order minors $\Delta_k(\varepsilon)$ (for $k = 1, 2, \ldots, q$) of the matrix (35.41). Suppose that $\varepsilon_1, \ldots, \varepsilon_q$ are the roots of smallest absolute value of the equations $\Delta_k(\varepsilon) = 0$ (for $k = 1, \ldots, q$). The radius of convergence of the series representing the $x_l(t)$ (for $l = 1, \ldots, n$) is not less than $r = \max\{|\varepsilon_1|, \ldots, |\varepsilon_q|\}$ since we can choose as basic (in solving the system (35.40)) any one of the minors $\Delta_k(\varepsilon)$. Suppose that $r = |\varepsilon_q|$. However, if ε_ν is not a root of one of the minors $\Delta_1(\varepsilon), \ldots, \Delta_q(\varepsilon)$, then $\varepsilon = \varepsilon_q$ will not be a singular point of the series representing a periodic solution of (35.38). On the other hand, if ε_q is a zero of all minors $\Delta_k(\varepsilon)$ (for $k = 1, \ldots, q$), then the rank m of the determinant (35.34) will be less than ν, which contradicts the assumption. Consequently, the radius of convergence ρ of the series representing periodic solutions of (35.38) is less than r. Thus, we have proven

Theorem 35.2. *The series (35.37) representing periodic solutions of the system (35.27) with period $\omega = 2\pi n$ converge (at least) in the region (35.35) of convergence of the series (35.36).*

In connection with the existence of periodic solutions of the system (35.27) with periods not equal to $2\pi n$ and methods of finding them, we point out the following facts:

It follows from Lemma 35.2 that, by means of a transformation of the independent variable, it is possible to arrange for the matrix P in the system (35.27) to have periods only of the form $\omega = 2\pi n$, where n is an integer. Furthermore, the following two facts follow immediately from the results obtained in Sect. 36: (1) if the system (35.27) is second-order, it cannot have periodic solutions with period different from the periods of the matrix P (cf. the reasoning following formula (36.2), where A can now be periodic with period $2\pi n$ and where $a = 2\pi b$); (2) if the system (35.27) is mth-order, it

---

*That is, we find $c_1, \ldots, c_n$ from Eqs. (35.40) such that (35.38) will be a periodic solution. Here $x_l(t)$ is found as the ratio of series in positive powers of ε, that converge in the region (35.35). The denominators of these series consist of a νth-order minor of the matrix (35.41).

can have periodic solutions with period different from the periods of the matrix P and even with period incommensurable with 2π. Existence tests and methods of finding such periods are given in the following section.

36. Periodic Solutions of a Linear Homogeneous System of Differential Equations [94]

We have found necessary and sufficient conditions for the existence of periodic solutions of Eq. (35.1) with period $\omega = n$ and methods for constructing them. However, the question arises: have we found all periodic solutions? We know [60] that a nonlinear system can have a periodic solution with period that is incommensurable with the period of the right-hand members (as functions of t). We shall now show that this is impossible for a linear system of two differential equations.

Theorem 36.1. *Let*

$$\frac{dx}{dt} = xP(t), \quad P(t+\omega) = P(t) \neq \text{const}, \tag{36.1}$$

be a system of two differential equations, where x is a two-dimensional vector and $P(t)$ is a second-order matrix the elements $p_{kl}(t)$ of which possess the property that $p_{kl}(t_\nu) \longrightarrow p_{kl}(T)$ as $t_\nu \to T$ by some mode of approach. Here, T is arbitrary and $p_{kl}(t)$ is continuous at the points t_ν. Then, the system (36.1) has no periodic solution with period a that is incommensurable with ω.

Remark 36.1. Let $\varphi(t)$ be a function such that, for every T, there exists a sequence $t_\nu \longrightarrow T$ such that $\varphi(t_\nu) \longrightarrow \varphi(T)$ as $t_\nu \longrightarrow T$ and suppose that $\varphi(t)$ is continuous at the points t_ν. Then, if $\varphi(t)$ has two incommensurable periods a and b, it is constant.*

Proof. We have $\varphi(t + an + bm) = \varphi(t)$, where m and n are integers. Let τ denote an arbitrary number. Then [61], $na + bm \to \tau$ as $|m| \longrightarrow \infty$ and $|n| \longrightarrow \infty$ in some manner. From this it follows that $\varphi(t + \tau) = \varphi(t)$; that is, $\varphi(t)$ is a constant. Suppose that (36.1) is a single equation with a single unknown function. Then,

$$x = \exp \int_0^t P(t)\,dt$$

and x cannot have a period a different from ω. Let us now suppose that (36.1) is a system of two equations. Then, if $x = (x_1, x_2)$ has a

*It follows from this on the basis of Remark 35.2 that Eq. (35.1) has no periodic solutions with period incommensurable with the period of the function $p(t)$.

period a that is incommensurable with ω, we obtained from (36.1) [since $x(t+a)=x(t)$ and $x(t+a)=x(t)$]

$$x(t)[P(t+a)-P(t)]=x(t)L(t,a)=0. \tag{36.2}$$

Therefore,

$$\sum_{\nu=1}^{2} x_\nu(t)\,q_\nu^{(k)}(t)=0 \quad (k=1,2), \tag{36.3}$$

where

$$q_\nu^{(k)}(t)=p_{\nu k}(t+a)-p_{\nu k}(t),$$

that is, $q_\nu^{(k)}(t)$ are periodic functions with period ω. Since the matrix $P(t)$ is nonconstant, it follows in accordance with Remark 36.1 that one of the quantities $q_\nu^{(k)}(t)\not\equiv 0$. But then, we obtain from (36.3), for example, $x_2(t)=Ax_1(t)$, where A is a constant since there are two incommensurable periods (ω and a). Therefore, we have

$$\dot{x}_1=[p_{11}(t)+Ap_{21}(t)]\,x_1.$$

Consequently, x_1 cannot have a period distinct from ω. This completes the proof of Theorem 36.1. This theorem is not valid for a system of more than two equations.

Example. The system

$$\left.\begin{aligned} \dot{x}_1&=-p_1(t)x_1-[1+p_1(t)]x_2+p_1(t)x_3\\ \dot{x}_2&=[1-p_2(t)]x_1-p_2(t)x_2+p_2(t)x_3\\ \dot{x}_3&=[1-p_3(t)]x_1-[1+p_3(t)]x_2+p_3(t)x_3 \end{aligned}\right\} \tag{36.4}$$

has a two-parameter family of periodic solutions

$$x_1=A\sin t+B\cos t,\quad x_2=-A\cos t+B\sin t,$$
$$x_3=(B-A)\cos t+(B+A)\sin t,$$

where $p_1(t)$, $p_2(t)$ and $p_3(t)$ are arbitrary functions and A and B are arbitrary constants. From this we see that, just as in the general case of nonlinear systems [60], a linear system can have periodic solutions even when the coefficient matrix $P(t)$ is not periodic. This is also valid for a system of two linear homogeneous equations. We can find periodic solutions with period incommensurable with the period of the matrix $P(t)$, or in the case in which the matrix

$P(t)$ is nonperiodic. We then obtain the conditions under which there are no periodic solutions with period incommensurable with the period of the matrix $P(t)$. Specifically, we find the period a from the equation

$$D(L(t,\ a))=0, \tag{36.5}$$

where D is the symbol for a determinant. If there is no number a incommensurable with ω that satisfies this equation, there is no periodic solution $x(t)$ with period incommensurable with ω. Suppose that Eq. (36.5) has a root incommensurable with ω. Let us substitute this value a into Eq. (36.2). Suppose that the system (36.1) is a system of n equations. Then, (36.2) will be a system of n linear homogeneous algebraic equations with unknowns $x_1, x_2, \ldots, x_n$.

Let us suppose that the rank of the matrix $L(t, a)$ is equal to $n-1$. Then, $x_k = a_k x_1$ (for $k = 2, 3, \ldots, n$), where the a_k are constants. We see from this that the system (36.1) cannot have a periodic solution with period a incommensurable with ω.

Suppose now that the rank of the matrix $L(t, a)$ is equal to $n-2$. Then, from Eqs. (36.2), we obtain

$$x_k = a_k(t)x_1 + b_k(t)x_2 \quad (k=3,\ 4,\ \ldots,\ n), \tag{36.6}$$

where the $a_k(t)$ and $b_k(t)$ are periodic solutions with period ω. Let us suppose that among the coefficients a_k and b_k there is one, let us say, $b_3(t)$, that is constant. Then, we have

$$x_3(t+a)-x_3(t)=[a_3(t+a)-a_3(t)]\,x_1+[b_3(t+a)-b_3(t)]\,x_2=0.$$

In accordance with Remark 36.1, we have $b_3(t+a)-b_3(t)\not\equiv 0$. Therefore, we have $x_2 = Ax_1$, where A is a constant. Consequently, from (36.6), we obtain $x_k(t)=A_k x_1$ (for $k = 2, \ldots, n$). We again obtain $x = a(t)x_1$, where $a(t)$ is a periodic function with period ω. Therefore, x_1 (and, consequently, $x(t)$) cannot have a period incommensurable with ω.

Suppose now that all the coefficients a_k and b_k in Eqs. (36.6) are constants. Using these equations, we obtain the system of equations

$$\dot{x}_1 = a(t)x_1 + b(t)x_2\,, \quad \dot{x}_2 = c(t)x_1 + d(t)x_2\,, \tag{36.7}$$

where the coefficient matrix $P(t)$ is periodic with period ω. If this matrix $P(t)$ is nonconstant, then, according to Theorem 36.1, the system (36.7) cannot have a periodic solution (x_1, x_2) with period a incommensurable with ω. But this matrix $P(t)$ may also be constant.

If $P(t)$ is a constant matrix, then the system (36.7) can have a periodic solution with period a incommensurable with ω. Suppose that such a solution (x_1, x_2) is found from the system (36.7). On the basis of (36.6), we obtain solutions $x_1, \ldots, x_n$ that are periodic with period a. If these $x_1, \ldots, x_n$ satisfy the system (36.1), we also obtain a periodic solution $x(t)$ of the system (36.1) with period a incommensurable with ω.

We consider those cases in which the rank of the matrix $L(t, a)$ is equal to $k \leqslant n-3$ in the same way. Here, we first of all obtain a system of $n-k$ linear differential equations the coefficient matrix of which is of period ω.

Suppose that the system (36.1) is of the form

$$\dot{x}_k = \sum_{\nu=1}^{n} p_{\nu k}(t) x_\nu, \quad p_{\nu k}(t) = a_{\nu k} p_k(t) + b_{\nu k} \quad (k = 1, \ldots, n), \qquad (36.1_1)$$

where the $a_{\nu k}$ and the $b_{\nu k}$ are real constants. Then, Eqs. (36.2) will be of the form

$$\sum_{\nu=1}^{n} a_{\nu k}(p_k(t+a) - p_k(t)) x_\nu = 0, \quad k = 1, \ldots, n .$$

If a is not the period of the functions $p_k(t)$ (for example, if the $p_k(t)$ are periodic functions with period ω incommensurable with a), then, in accordance with Remark (36.1), we have

$$p_k(t+a) - p_k(t) \neq 0$$

and these equations are of the form

$$\sum_{\nu=1}^{n} a_{k\nu} x_\nu = 0. \qquad (36.2_1)$$

If the determinant $D(\|a_{\nu k}\|) \neq 0$, then the system (36.1_1) has no periodic solution with period a. (This is true both when the coefficient matrix of the system (36.1_1) is periodic with period ω incommensurable with a and when this matrix is nonperiodic and $p_k(t+a) - p_k(t) \not\equiv 0$.)

Let us now suppose that

$$D(\|a_{\nu k}\|) = 0 \qquad (36.8)$$

and that the rank of the matrix $\|a_{\nu k}\|$ is equal to $n-m$. Then, from (36.2_1), we have

$$x_\nu = \sum_{l=1}^{m} c_{\nu l} x_l, \qquad c_{\nu l} \text{ — constant}, \quad \nu = m+1, \ldots, n. \qquad (36.9)$$

If we substitute the values given by (36.9) into the first m of equations (36.1_1), we obtain

$$\dot{x}_k = \sum_{\nu=1}^{m} [p_{\nu k}(t) + p_{m+1,k}(t)\, c_{m+1,\nu} + \ldots + p_{n,k}(t)\, c_{n,\nu}]\, x_\nu$$

or, remembering the values of $p_{\nu k}(t)$ in Eqs. (36.1_1),

$$\dot{x}_k = \sum_{\nu=1}^{m} [(a_{\nu k} + a_{m+1,k}\, c_{m+1,\nu} + \ldots + a_{n,k}\, c_{n,\nu})\, p_k(t) + \\ + b_{\nu k} + b_{m+1,k}\, c_{m+1,\nu} + \ldots + b_{n,k}\, c_{n,\nu}]\, x_\nu. \tag{36.10}$$

Here, it may happen that

$$a_{\nu k} + a_{m+1,k} c_{m+1,\nu} + \ldots + a_{n,k} c_{n,\nu} = 0, \tag{36.11}$$

where $k = 1, \ldots, m$ and $\nu = 1, \ldots, m$. Then, Eqs. (36.10) take the form

$$\dot{x}_k = \sum_{\nu=1}^{m} (b_{\nu k} + b_{m+1,k}\, c_{m+1,\nu} + \ldots + b_{n,k} c_{n,\nu})\, x_\nu\,. \tag{36.12}$$

This system with real constant coefficients can have distinct two-parameter* solutions (several at once) with period a incommensurable with ω. If we have found a periodic solution $(x_1, \ldots, x_m)$ of this system, then we shall also find from (36.9) $x_{m+1}, \ldots, x_n$ that are periodic. If these values found for $x_1, \ldots, x_n$ satisfy Eqs. (36.1_1), then (36.1_1) has a periodic solution with period a incommensurable with ω. Let us suppose that Eqs. (36.11) are not satisfied. Then, Eqs. (36.10) have variable coefficients.

Thus, we have arrived at a system of the form (36.1_1) with unknowns $x_1, \ldots, x_m$. Again, we need to look at this system. Finally, either we shall obtain a system with constant coefficients or we shall arrive at a single equation with a single unknown function or we shall arrive at two equations with two unknown functions, and the question will be answered.

Thus, we can subject the parameters of the system (36.1_1) to conditions that will ensure that this system has a periodic solution with prestated period a independent of the period of the functions $p_k(t)$.

---

*In Sect. 42 we shall find necessary and sufficient conditions for the existence of purely imaginary roots of the characteristic polynomial. These conditions ensure the existence of periodic solutions.

37. An Equation of the Form (33.1) With Variable-Sign Function *p(t)*

Thus, thanks to the profound investigations of Lyapunov, the questions regarding the existence of bounded solutions of Eq. (33.1) have been entirely settled from a theoretical standpoint.

Beginning with Zhukovskiy [62], many authors have found sufficient conditions for boundedness of the general solution of Eq. (33.1) (both for constant-sign and for variable-sign $p(t)$), using different devices. Examples of such studies are [63–65]. Several surveys of these investigations appear in the articles [66–68]. We shall not stop for this.

Lyapunov also considered the case in which $p(t)$ is a variable-sign function. He exhibited various transformations that transform Eq. (33.1) with variable-sign $p(t)$ into an equation of the same form with constant sign $p(t)$ ([26], p. 332). Let us show how he did this.

Consider the Eq. (33.1)

$$\ddot{x} + p(t)x = 0, \quad p(t + \omega) = p(t). \tag{37.1}$$

We introduce a new unknown function y defined by

$$x = wy \tag{37.2}$$

and a new independent variable τ defined by

$$\tau = \int_0^t \frac{dt}{w^2}. \tag{37.3}$$

Here, w is a real periodic function with period ω that does not vanish and that has continuous derivatives

$$\dot{w} = \frac{dw}{dt}, \quad \ddot{w} = \frac{d^2w}{dt^2}.$$

We obtain

$$\frac{d^2y}{d\tau^2} + q(\tau)y = 0, \tag{37.4}$$

where

$$q_1(\tau) = q(t) = w^3[\ddot{w} + p(t)w] \tag{37.5}$$

is a periodic function with period

$$a = \int_0^{\omega} \frac{dt}{w^2} \tag{37.5$_1$}$$

that may prove to be sign-constant.

Suppose that $w > 0$. If

$$w + pw \leqslant 0, \tag{37.6}$$

then $q \leqslant 0$ and, consequently,* the general solution of Eq. (37.4) (and with it, (37.1)) will be unbounded.

Lyapunov realizes the case (37.6) in the following manner:

Let k denote any real number such that $k\omega/2\pi$ is not an integer. Then, the function

$$w(t) = 1 - \frac{1}{2k \sin \frac{k\omega}{2}} \int_0^{\omega} \cos k\left(s - \frac{\omega}{2}\right) p(s+t)\, ds \tag{37.7}$$

which is periodic with period ω, is a solution of the equation

$$\ddot{w} + k^2 w = k^2 - p(t). \tag{37.8}$$

Suppose that k satisfies the condition

$$k^2 - p \geqslant 0, \ w - 1 \geqslant 0. \tag{37.9}$$

Then, by virtue of (37.8),

$$\ddot{w} + pw = -(w-1)(k^2 - p). \tag{37.10}$$

Therefore, the condition (37.6) is satisfied.

Of course, it may turn out that, on the basis of (37.7),

$$q(t) \geqslant 0. \tag{37.11}$$

Then, we need to use Theorem 34.1 to solve the problem.

With the aid of this device, Lyapunov studied the differential equation

$$\frac{d^2x}{dt^2} - \lambda^2 (1 - \varepsilon \sin^n t) x = 0, \tag{37.12}$$

where $\omega = 2\pi$, $\varepsilon > 0$, and n is a positive integer. For this equation,

*Cf. the reasoning following formula (33.15).

formula (37.7) yields

$$w = 1 + \frac{\lambda^2}{k^2} - \frac{\lambda^2 \varepsilon}{2k \sin k\pi} \int_0^{2\pi} \cos k(\tau - \pi) \sin^n(\tau + t)\, d\tau. \quad (37.13)$$

Condition (37.9) will be satisfied if

$$k^2 + \lambda^2 - \lambda^2 \varepsilon > 0 \quad (37.14)$$

and

$$J(t) = \frac{k\varepsilon}{2 \sin k\pi} \int_0^{2\pi} \cos k(\tau - \pi) \sin^n(\tau + t)\, dt \leqslant 1. \quad (37.15)$$

Lyapunov noted that, for even n and negative ε,

$$p = -\lambda^2(1 - \varepsilon \sin^n t) < 0,$$

that is, the general solution is unbounded and, for odd n, the sign of ε does not affect the answer to the question (since the left member of inequality (33.10) contains only even powers of ε). Therefore, we may assume that $\varepsilon > 0$.

By using different devices, Lyapunov studied many particular cases of Eq. (37.12).

We note that the integral in (37.15) can be calculated. If we find the maximum $J(t) = M$ from the condition that $J'(t) = 0$, then, for

$$M \leqslant 1 \quad (37.16)$$

we have (37.15).

Let us define

$$J_1(t) = \int_0^{2\pi} \cos k(\tau - \pi) \cdot \sin^n(\tau + t)\, d\tau. \quad (37.17)$$

It is easy to see that the equation

$$J_1'(t) = 0 \quad (37.18)$$

leads to the equation

$$\int_0^{2\pi} \sin k(\tau - \pi) \sin^n(\tau + t)\, d\tau = 0. \quad (37.19)$$

Thus, to show that condition (37.15) is satisfied, we need to show that

$$J(t) = \frac{k\varepsilon}{2\sin k\pi} J_1(t) \leqslant 1 \tag{37.20}$$

on the basis of (37.19).

Let us consider in greater detail the case in which $n = 2$. From (37.17), we have

$$\begin{gathered} J_1(t) = \int_0^{2\pi} \cos k(\tau - \pi)\cdot\sin^2(\tau + t)\,d\tau = \\ = \sin k\pi\cdot\left\{\frac{1}{k} - \frac{k}{k^2-4}\cos 2t\right\},\quad k^2 \neq 4. \end{gathered} \tag{37.21}$$

In accordance with (37.20), we obtain

$$J(t) = \frac{k\varepsilon}{2}\left(\frac{1}{k} - \frac{k}{k^2-4}\cos 2t\right), \tag{37.22}$$

from which we get

$$J'(t) = \frac{\varepsilon k^2}{k^2-4}\sin 2t = 0.$$

Therefore, two extreme values of $J(t)$ are

$$J^{(1)} = \frac{2\varepsilon}{4-k^2},\quad J^{(2)} = \varepsilon\frac{2-k^2}{4-k^2}.$$

Thus, if (37.14) holds, if $J^{(1)} \leqslant 1$, and if $J^{(2)} \leqslant 1$, then conditions (37.9) will also be satisfied; that is,

$$q(t) \leqslant 0. \tag{37.23}$$

But, for $k^2 < 4$, we have $J^{(2)} < J^{(1)}$ and, for $k^2 > 4$, we have $J^{(1)} < J^{(2)}$. Therefore, for condition (37.23) to be satisfied, it is necessary that

$$\frac{2\varepsilon}{4-k^2} < 1,\ \lambda^2(\varepsilon - 1) < k^2,\quad \text{if}\quad k^2 < 4 \tag{37.24}$$

and

$$\varepsilon\frac{2-k^2}{4-k^2} < 1,\ \lambda^2(\varepsilon - 1) < k^2,\quad \text{if}\quad k^2 > 4. \tag{37.25}$$

Consequently, if we have [from (37.24)]

$$\lambda^2(\varepsilon - 1) < 4, \quad (2 + \lambda^2)(\varepsilon - 1) < 2,$$

then the general solution of Eq. (37.12) will not be bounded for $n = 2$. The first and third of Eqs. (37.25) are impossible.

If

$$1 < \varepsilon \frac{2 - k^2}{4 - k^2} \quad \text{and} \quad k^2 < 4,$$

then

$$1 < J^{(2)} < J^{(1)}.$$

In this case, $w - 1 < 0$. It is easy to exhibit* in addition inequalities that can be satisfied for k, λ, and ε such that $w > 0$. Then, we shall have (37.11).

Lyapunov noted that in determining the solution of Eq. (37.8) from formula (37.7) and requiring that $w - 1$ be nonnegative, we are in effect considering the case

$$\int_0^\omega p \, dt < 0, \tag{37.26}$$

since it follows from (37.8) that

$$\int_0^\omega p \, dt = -k^2 \int_0^\omega (w - 1) \, dt.$$

Therefore, for the case in which

$$\int_0^\omega p \, dt > 0, \tag{37.27}$$

Lyapunov exhibited a different w obtained from the first by replacing k^2 with $-k^2$. This second w sometimes satisfies the inequality

---

*If we substitute the values of t from the equation $w' = 0$ into w, we obtain

$$w^{(1)} = 1 + \frac{\lambda^2}{k^2}\left[1 + \frac{2\varepsilon}{k^2 - 4}\right],$$

$$w^{(2)} = 1 + \frac{\lambda^2}{k^2}\left[1 - \frac{\varepsilon(k^2 - 2)}{k^2 - 4}\right].$$

Now $w^{(1)} > 0$ and $w^{(2)} > 0$ are necessary conditions for $w > 0$.

$$w + pw \geqslant 0, \tag{37.28}$$

which yields $q(t) \geqslant 0$.

Let k denote a nonzero real number. Then the equation

$$\ddot{w} - k^2 w = -k^2 - p, \tag{37.29}$$

obtained from (37.8) by replacing k^2 with $-k^2$ has the periodic solution

$$w = 1 + \frac{1}{2k} \int_0^\omega \frac{e^{-k\tau} + e^{-k(\omega-\tau)}}{1 - e^{-k\omega}} p(\tau + t)\, d\tau. \tag{37.30}$$

Here, we have from (37.29)

$$\ddot{w} + pw = (k^2 + p)(w - 1). \tag{37.31}$$

For $k^2 + p \geqslant 0$ and $w - 1 > 0$, we obtain (37.28) from (37.31). Consequently, $q(t) \geqslant 0$. Lyapunov also noted that such a transformation in the case of $p(t) > 0$ for every nonzero k leads to the case in which $q(t) \geqslant 0$.

*However, it may happen that, for some k, one of the tests for boundedness of the general solution of Eq. (37.4) is satisfied in accordance with Theorem 34.1 and yet none of these are satisfied for Eq. (37.1).**

If one of these tests is satisfied for Eq. (37.1), then there exists a k such that this test will also be satisfied for (37.4) since (37.1) is obtained from Eq. (37.4) by taking the limit as $k^2 \to \infty$.

As an example, Lyapunov considered the equation

$$\frac{d^2x}{dt^2} + \lambda^2(1 - \varepsilon \sin t)x = 0 \tag{37.32}$$

and found sufficient conditions for boundedness of the general solution with the aid of such a transformation. He also considered the case

$$\int_0^\omega p\,dt = 0, \tag{37.33}$$

---

*This is in accordance with Remark 35.1, where it was noted that among the bounded solutions of Eq. (37.1) there may be a periodic solution with period 2ω or greater. If (37.1) has a periodic solution with period ω or 2ω, then, as we have seen, none of the tests for boundedness of the general system is satisfied. However, Eq. (37.4), obtained from the transformation (37.2), where w is given by formula (37.30) may also fail to have a periodic solution with period ω or 2ω.

assuming that

$$p(2\alpha - t) + p(t) = 0 \tag{37.34}$$

and that $p(t)$ changes sign only at points of the form $\alpha + n\omega/2$, where n is an integer and α a real constant. That $p(t)$ must necessarily change sign at the points $\alpha + n\omega/2$ is obvious from (37.34). To see this, when we substitute $t = \alpha + n\omega/2 + \beta$ into (37.34), we obtain

$$p\left(\alpha - n\frac{\omega}{2} - \beta\right) = -p\left(\alpha + n\frac{\omega}{2} + \beta\right) =$$
$$= -p\left(\alpha + n\omega - n\frac{\omega}{2} + \beta\right) = -p\left(\alpha - n\frac{\omega}{2} + \beta\right)$$

where β is an arbitrarily small number.

It follows from (37.34) that Eq. (37.33) is satisfied. On the basis of (37.33), the equation

$$\ddot{w} = -p \tag{37.35}$$

which is obtained from (37.29) for $k = 0$, admits periodic solutions that differ from each other by constant values.

For w, Lyapunov took a periodic solution whose value is 1 at $t = \alpha$. Assuming also (without loss of generality) that $p \geqslant 0$ in the interval $t = \alpha$, $t = \alpha + \omega/2$, he showed that w attains its maximum at the point β defined by

$$\int_{\alpha}^{\alpha+\omega} tpdt + \omega \int_{\alpha}^{\beta} pdt = 0. \tag{37.36}$$

Assuming that

$$\int_{\alpha}^{\beta} (t - \alpha)\, pdt < 1, \tag{37.36$_1$}$$

Lyapunov showed that the chosen function w does not vanish and that $q(t) \geqslant 0$ in Eq. (37.4). As an example, he studied the equation

$$\frac{d^2x}{dt^2} + \mu \sin t \cdot x = 0, \ \mu^2 < 1, \tag{37.37}$$

for which we can easily find

$$w = 1 + \mu \sin t, \ \omega = 2\pi, \ \alpha = 0$$

and q (in Eq. (37.4)) in the form

$$q = \mu^2(1 + \mu \sin t)^3 \sin^2 t.$$

The period of q in Eq. (37.4) is found from the formula (37.5$_1$):

$$a = \int_0^{2\pi} \frac{dt}{(1 + \mu \sin t)^2} = \frac{2\pi}{(1 - \mu^2)^{3/2}}$$

A necessary condition for the general solution to be bounded is* that $|\mu| \leqslant 0.39$ .... Lyapunov also noted that, in the case in which $\int_0^{\omega} pdt > 0$ we may set

$$w = e^{-\int v dt}, \quad x = ye^{-\int v dt}, \quad \tau = \int_0^t e^{2\int v dt}\, dt,$$

where

$$v' = p - B, \; B = \frac{1}{\omega}\int_0^{\omega} pdt.$$

Then, Eq. (37.1) is reduced to (37.4), in which

$$q(\tau) = (B + v^2)\, e^{-4\int v dt} > 0$$

with period

$$\tau = T = \int_0^{2\pi} e^{2\int v\, dt} dt.$$

By means of such a transformation, he found sufficient conditions for boundedness of the general solution of the equation

$$\frac{d^2x}{dt^2} + (\lambda^2 + \mu \sin t)\, x = 0, \qquad (37.38)$$

for which we may take $v' = \mu \sin t$, $v = -\mu \cos t$. We then obtain in (37.4)

$$q(\tau) = (\lambda^2 + \mu^2 \cos^2 t)\, e^{4\mu \sin t} > 0$$

---

*We obtain this result on the basis of the test $\omega \int_0^{\omega} pdt \leqslant 4$ for Eq. (37.4). However, as Lyapunov noted, if we assume that $\mu > 0$, we can obtain $\mu < 0$ by using Zhukovskiy's method.

with period

$$T = \int_0^{2\pi} e^{-2\mu \sin t}\, dt.$$

Here, the test (34.1), which in present notation is $T \int_0^T q(\tau)\, d\tau \leqslant 4$, yields

$$T \int_0^{2\pi} q e^{-2\mu \sin t}\, dt < 4. \qquad (37.39)$$

where

$$T = \int_0^{2\pi} e^{-2\mu \sin t}\, dt = 2\int_0^{\pi/2} (e^{2\mu \sin t} + e^{-2\mu \sin t})\, dt.$$

If we set

$$2 \int_0^{\pi/2} (e^{2\mu \sin t} + e^{-2\mu \sin t}) \cos^2 t dt = \tau_1,$$

we obtain

$$\int_0^{2\pi} q e^{-2\mu \sin t}\, dt = T \lambda^2 + \tau_1 \mu^2$$

and (37.39) becomes

$$T^2\lambda^2 + T \tau_1 \mu^2 < 4.$$

We shall not go into a detailed exposition of this equation of Lyapunov. In certain cases, he has been able to strengthen the methods described by choosing w in a different manner. We shall not go into this matter but refer the reader to Lyapunov's book [26, p. 333].

38. Starzhinskiy's Transformation [69]

We shall now show how Starzhinskiy proposed to study the case in which $P(t)$ changes sign. He transformed an arbitrary system of two linear homogeneous differential equations

$$\frac{dX}{dt} = XP(t), \quad P(t+\omega) = P(t), \tag{38.1}$$

where $P(t)$ is a second-order matrix, into Eq. (33.1) with $p(t) \geqslant 0$. He introduced the new unknown matrix

$$Y = X \exp \frac{2k\pi}{\omega} Jt, \quad J = \begin{Vmatrix} 0 & 1 \\ -1 & 0 \end{Vmatrix}, \tag{38.2}$$

$$\frac{dY}{dt} = YQ, \tag{38.3}$$

$$Q = \frac{2k\pi}{\omega} J + \exp\left(-\frac{2k\pi}{\omega} Jt\right) P \exp\left(\frac{2k\pi}{\omega} Jt\right). \tag{38.4}$$

In expanded form, the system (38.3) is written $\left(Q = \begin{Vmatrix} q_{11} & q_{21} \\ q_{12} & q_{22} \end{Vmatrix}\right)$:

$$\frac{dy_1}{dt} = q_{11}y_1 + q_{12}y_2, \quad \frac{dy_2}{dt} = q_{21}y_1 + q_{22}y_2, \tag{38.5}$$

where

$$\left.\begin{aligned} q_{11} &= \cos^2\tau \cdot p_{11} - \sin\tau \cdot \cos\tau \cdot p_{21} - \sin\tau \cdot \cos\tau \cdot p_{12} + \\ &\quad + \sin^2\tau\, p_{22} \\ q_{12} &= -\frac{2k\pi}{\omega} + \cos^2\tau \cdot p_{21} + \sin\tau \cdot \cos\tau \cdot p_{11} - \\ &\quad - \cos\tau \cdot \sin\tau \cdot p_{22} - \sin^2\tau \cdot p_{12} \\ q_{21} &= \frac{2k\pi}{\omega} + \sin\tau \cdot \cos\tau \cdot p_{11} - \sin^2\tau \cdot p_{21} + \cos^2\tau \cdot p_{12} - \\ &\quad - \sin\tau \cdot \cos\tau \cdot p_{22} \\ q_{22} &= \sin\tau \cdot \cos\tau \cdot p_{21} + \sin^2\tau \cdot p_{11} + \cos^2\tau \cdot p_{22} + \\ &\quad + \sin\tau \cdot \cos\tau \cdot p_{12} \end{aligned}\right\}. \tag{38.6}$$

and

$$\tau = \frac{2k\pi}{\omega} t.$$

For sufficiently large integral k, the elements q_{12} and q_{21} (which are periodic with period ω) are arbitrarily large for all t and

$$q_{12} < 0, \quad q_{21} > 0. \tag{38.7}$$

The functions q_{11} and q_{22} are periodic with period ω and they are uniformly bounded with respect to k. The unknown y_1 satisfies the equation

$$\ddot{y}_1 - (q_{11} + q_{22} + \dot{q}_{12}/q_{12})\,\dot{y}_1 + (q_{11}q_{22} - q_{12}q_{21} - \dot{q}_{11} + q_{11}\cdot\dot{q}_{12}/q_{12})\,y_1 = 0. \quad (38.8)$$

Here, we use the notation $dz/dt = \dot{z}$.

Furthermore, by making the substitution

$$y_1 = z\exp\left[\frac{1}{2}\int (q_{11} + q_{22} + \dot{q}_{12}/q_{12})\,dt\right], \quad (38.9)$$

Starzhinskiy shifted from (38.8) to the equation

$$\ddot{z} + [-q_{12}q_{21} + q_{11}q_{22} - \dot{q}_{11} + q_{11}\dot{q}_{12}/q_{12} - \frac{1}{4}(q_{11} + q_{12} + \dot{q}_{12}/q_{12})^2 + $$
$$+ \frac{1}{2}(\dot{q}_{11} + \dot{q}_{22} + \ddot{q}_{12}/q_{12} - \dot{q}_{12}^2/q_{12}^2)]\,z = 0$$

or

$$\ddot{z} + q(t)\,z = 0, \quad (38.10)$$

$$q(t) = -q_{12}q_{21} + q_{11}q_{22} - \dot{q}_{11} + q_{11}\dot{q}_{12}/q_{12} -$$
$$-\frac{1}{4}(q_{11} + q_{22} + \dot{q}_{12}/q_{12})^2 + \quad (38.10_1)$$
$$+\frac{1}{2}(\dot{q}_{11} + \dot{q}_{22} + \ddot{q}_{12}/q_{12} - \dot{q}_{12}^2/q_{12}^2).$$

If the first and second derivatives of the elements of the matrix $P(t)$ are bounded, then the coefficient $q(t)$ is periodic with period ω and is positive for all values of t; that is, Eq. (38.10) is an equation of the type (33.1) with $p(t) \geqslant 0$. For sufficiently large k, we can get $q(t)$ arbitrarily large. Specifically, this function is of the form

$$q(t) = \frac{4\pi^2 k^2}{\omega^2} + kq_1(t, k) + q_0(t, k). \quad (38.11)$$

Here, $q_1(t, k)$ and $q_0(t, k)$ are periodic functions with period ω,

$$|q_\nu(t, k)| < M, \quad \nu = 0, 1$$

and the constant M is independent of k.

There are several remarks that may be made in connection with this.

Remark 38.1. Let us suppose that we have shown by use of one of Lyapunov's tests that the general solution of Eq. (38.10) is bounded. Then, as we can see from (38.2) and (38.9), the system (38.1) has only one characteristic number and it coincides with the characteristic number of the function

$$Q = \exp\left[-\frac{1}{2}\int (q_{11} + q_{22} + \dot{q}_{12}/q_{12})\, dt\right] \tag{38.12}$$

But since the integrand in this expression is periodic with period ω, the characteristic number of the system (38.1) will be

$$v = -\frac{1}{2\omega}\int_0^\omega (q_{11} + q_{22} + \dot{q}_{12}/q_{12})\, dt. \tag{38.13}$$

For the general solution of the system (38.1) to be bounded, it is necessary and sufficient that $v = 0$. If the general solution of Eq. (38.10) is unbounded, the question of the boundedness of the system (38.1) is also answered by the characteristic number (38.12). Let us find the characteristics numbers v_1 and v_2 of Eq. (38.10) and then find the characteristic numbers $v_1 + v$ and $v_2 + v$ of (38.8). Remembering that the characteristic numbers of the system (38.1) do not depend on k, we can obtain them too from the numbers $v_1 + v$ and $v_2 + v$.

Remark 38.2. Starzhinskiy's transformation converts an arbitrary system (38.1) with period coefficients into a canonical system with periodic coefficients since the canonical system*

$$\dot{x} = y, \quad \dot{y} = -qx \tag{38.14}$$

corresponds to Eq. (38.10).

Remark 38.3. If we take a large value of k in Eq. (38.10), then inequalities (34.16), (34.17), or (34.18), which ensure a solution of the problem on the basis of Theorem 34.1, will contain a large number of terms and will therefore be difficult to verify. For this reason, we should choose for the number k in (38.6) the smallest of the numbers that ensure (in 38.6) that $q(t) \geqslant 0$.

39. Transformation of an Arbitrary System of Two Equations into a Canonical System

Consider a system of two linear homogeneous differential equations

$$\frac{dY}{dt} = YP \tag{39.1}$$

---

*The general form of a canonical system of two equations is as follows:

$$\dot{x} = -bx - cy, \quad \dot{y} = ax + by$$

or, in matrix form,

$$\dot{X} = X\begin{Vmatrix} -b & a \\ -c & b \end{Vmatrix}.$$

with periodic second-order matrix $P(t+\omega) = P(t)$. Let us make the substitution

$$X = YZ, \tag{39.2}$$

where Z and Z^{-1} are both continuous for $|t|<\infty$. To determine the matrix X, we obtain the equation

$$\dot{X} = XQ, \quad Q = Z^{-1}(PZ + \dot{Z}), \tag{39.3}$$

$$\dot{Z} = ZQ - PZ. \tag{39.4}$$

Let us choose the matrix Z in such a way that the system (39.3) will be a canonical system, that is, so that

$$Q = \begin{Vmatrix} -b & a \\ -c & b \end{Vmatrix}, \tag{39.5}$$

where a, b and c are arbitrary functions. We shall, in addition, try to arrange for a, b and c to be bounded and periodic with period ω. Let us denote the elements of the matrix Z and z_{kl} and those of the matrix P by p_{kl}. Then, we can write Eq. (39.4) in expanded form as follows:

$$\left.\begin{aligned} \dot{z}_{11} &= -z_{11}(b + p_{11}) - z_{12}c - z_{21}p_{12} \\ \dot{z}_{12} &= z_{12}(b - p_{11}) + z_{11}a - z_{22}p_{12} \\ \dot{z}_{21} &= -z_{21}(b + p_{22}) - z_{11}p_{21} - z_{22}c \\ \dot{z}_{22} &= z_{22}(b - p_{22}) - z_{12}p_{21} + z_{21}a \end{aligned}\right\} \tag{39.6}$$

These equations need to be satisfied in an arbitrary manner provided only the matrices Z and Z^{-1} are continuous in the region $|t|<\infty$ and the functions a, b, and c are bounded and periodic with period ω.

Let us show that the solution of (39.6) is determined algebraically when we set up a relationship between z_{11}, z_{22}, z_{12} *and* z_{21}.

Suppose that we are given the relation

$$z_{22} = \varphi(z_{11}, z_{12}, z_{21}, t). \tag{39.7}$$

Then, from the system (39.6), we have

$$\dot{z}_{22} = (b - p_{22})\varphi(z_{11}, z_{12}, z_{21}, t) - p_{21}z_{12} + az_{21}, \tag{39.8}$$

$$\dot{z}_{11} = -z_{11}(b + p_{11}) - z_{12}c - z_{21}p_{12}, \tag{39.9}$$

$$\dot{z}_{12} = z_{12}(b - p_{11}) + z_{11}a - p_{12}\varphi(z_{11}, z_{12}, z_{21}, t), \tag{39.10}$$

$$\dot{z}_{21} = -z_{21}(b + p_{22}) - z_{11}p_{21} - \varphi(z_{11}, z_{12}, z_{21}, t)c. \tag{39.11}$$

On the other hand, from (39.7), we have

$$\begin{aligned} \dot{z}_{22} = &-\varphi'_{z_{11}}(z_{11}, z_{12}, z_{21}, t)[z_{11}(b + p_{11}) + z_{12}c + z_{21}p_{12}] + \\ &+\varphi'_{z_{12}}(z_{11}, z_{12}, z_{21}, t)[z_{12}(b - p_{11}) + z_{11}a - p_{12}\varphi(z_{11}, z_{12}, z_{21}, t)] - \\ &-\varphi'_{z_{21}}(z_{11}, z_{12}, z_{21}, t)[z_{21}(b + p_{22}) + z_{11}p_{21} + \varphi(z_{11}, z_{12}, z_{21}, t)c] + \\ &+\varphi'_t(z_{11}, z_{12}, z_{21}, t). \end{aligned} \tag{39.12}$$

By equating the right-hand members of Eqs. (39.8) and (39.12), we obtain the equation

$$\psi_1(z_{11}, z_{12}, z_{21}, t) = 0. \tag{39.13}$$

Let us suppose that, from this,

$$z_{11} = \psi_1(z_{12}, z_{21}, t). \tag{39.14}$$

Then, from (39.7), we obtain

$$z_{22} = \psi_2(z_{12}, z_{21}, t). \tag{39.15}$$

If we substitute the values of z_{11} from (39.14) into the right-hand members of (39.9), (39.10) and (39.11), we obtain

$$\dot{z}_{11} = -\psi_1(z_{12}, z_{21}, t)(b + p_{11}) - z_{12}c - z_{21}p_{12}, \tag{39.16}$$

$$\begin{aligned} \dot{z}_{12} = &z_{12}(b - p_{11}) + \psi_1(z_{12}, z_{21}, t)a - \\ &-p_{12}\varphi[\psi_1(z_{12}, z_{21}, t), z_{12}, z_{21}, t], \end{aligned} \tag{39.17}$$

$$\begin{aligned} \dot{z}_{21} = &-z_{21}(b + p_{22}) - \psi_1(z_{12}, z_{21}, t)p_{21} - \\ &-\varphi[\psi_1(z_{12}, z_{21}, t), z_{12}, z_{21}, t]c. \end{aligned} \tag{39.18}$$

Similarly, from (39.14), we obtain

$$\begin{aligned} \dot{z}_{11} = &\psi'_{1_{z_{12}}}[z_{12}(b - p_{11}) + \psi_1(z_{12}, z_{21}, t)a - \\ &-\varphi(\psi_1(z_{12}, z_{21}, t), z_{12}, z_{21} t)p_{12}] - \\ &-\psi'_{1_{z_{21}}}[z_{21}(b + p_{22}) + \psi_1(z_{12}, z_{21}, t)p_{21} + \\ &+\varphi(\psi_1(z_{12}, z_{21}, t), z_{12}, z_{21}, t)c] + \\ &+\psi'_{1_t}(z_{12}, z_{21}, t). \end{aligned} \tag{39.19}$$

If we equate the right-hand members of Eqs. (39.16) and (39.19), we obtain the relation

$$\psi_2(z_{12}, z_{21}, t) = 0. \tag{39.20}$$

Let us suppose that, for this, we have

$$z_{21} = \psi_2(z_{12}, t). \tag{39.21}$$

If we substitute this value of z_{21} into the right-hand member of (39.17), we obtain

$$z_{12} = \psi_3(z_{12}, t). \tag{39.22}$$

On the basis of this same equation, we obtain from (39.18)

$$z_{21} = \psi_4(z_{12}, t). \tag{39.23}$$

From (39.21), we obtain

$$\dot{z}_{21} = \psi'_{2_{z_{12}}}(z_{12}, t)\,\dot{z}_{12} + \psi'_{2_t}(z_{12}, t) = \psi'_{2_{z_{12}}}(z_{12}, t)\,\psi_3(z_{12}, t) + \psi'_{2_t}(z_{12}, t). \tag{39.24}$$

By equating the right-hand members of (39.23) and (39.24), we obtain

$$\psi_4(z_{12}, t) = 0. \tag{39.25}$$

Let us suppose that, for this, we obtain

$$z_{12} = \varphi_1(t). \tag{39.26}$$

Then, from (39.21), we obtain

$$z_{21} = \varphi_2(t). \tag{39.27}$$

Equation (39.20) is also satisfied on the basis of (39.21). With the values (39.26) and (39.27), the right-hand members of (39.16) and (39.19) coincide. Therefore, the values of z_{11} defined by (39.16) and (39.19) also coincide. We obtain the value of z_{11} on the basis of (39.16), (39.27) and (39.14). Thus, Eq. (39.13) is also satisfied. But then, the right-hand members of (39.8) and (39.12) coincide. From this it follows that the values of z_{22} defined by Eqs. (39.8) and (39.12) coincide. But we obtain the value of z_{22} from (39.7) (from which (39.12) follows).

We have obtained explicit expressions for z_{11}, z_{22}, z_{12} and z_{21} with the aid of algebraic operations* in terms of the undetermined

*That is, from algebraic equations.

functions a, b and c and their derivatives. Let us suppose that the values found for z_{11}, z_{22}, z_{12} and z_{21} satisfy the first three equations of the system (39.6). Then, the fourth equation of this system will be satisfied since z_{22}, as found from (39.7) satisfies (39.12) and also (39.8), from which the fourth equation in the system (39.6) follows for the values found for z_{11}, z_{22}, z_{12} and z_{21}.

Using the values found for z_{11}, z_{22}, z_{12} and z_{21} to satisfy the first three equations of the system (39.6), we obtain three equations from which we then find the functions a, b and c. Then Eqs. (39.10) and (39.11) and also Eqs. (39.17) and (39.18) will be satisfied.

We shall not stop to consider the various cases that can be encountered in this procedure. For example, it may happen that the relation (39.13) does not contain z_{11}. Then, we immediately have a relation of the type (39.20). Subsequent reasoning in this case differs only slightly from the case considered. Since the z_{kl} are found algebraically, they will be periodic functions when a, b, c and p_{kl} are periodic. We can choose a, b and c arbitrarily. Then, the z_{kl} will be determined as the solutions of the system (39.6), that is, not algebraically.

Let us now consider certain special cases of the function φ in (39.7) that allow us to get explicit expressions for z_{kl}, a, b and c easily.

40. The Case in which (39.7) is of the Form $z_{22} = 0$

Suppose that if in (39.7),

$$z_{22} = 0. \tag{40.1}$$

Then, Eqs. (39.6) take the form

$$\begin{gathered}\dot{z}_{11} = -z_{11}(b + p_{11}) - z_{12}c - z_{21}p_{12}, \quad \dot{z}_{12} = z_{12}(b - p_{11}) + z_{11}a, \\ \dot{z}_{21} = -z_{21}(b + p_{22}) - z_{11}p_{21}, \quad 0 = az_{21} - z_{12}p_{21}.\end{gathered} \tag{40.2}$$

Consequently,

$$z_{21} = \frac{p_{21}z_{12}}{a} \tag{40.3}$$

and

$$\dot{z}_{11} = -z_{11}(b + p_{11}) - z_{12}c - \frac{p_{12}p_{21}}{a} z_{12}, \tag{40.4}$$

$$\dot{z}_{12} = z_{12}(b - p_{11}) + z_{11}a, \tag{40.5}$$

$$\dot{z}_{21} = -z_{12}\frac{b + p_{22}}{a}p_{21} - p_{21}z_{11}. \tag{40.6}$$

On the basis of (40.5), we obtain from (40.3)

$$\dot{z}_{21} = \left[\frac{\dot{p}_{21}}{a} - \frac{p_{21}\dot{a}}{a^2} + p_{21}\frac{b - p_{11}}{a}\right]z_{12} + p_{21}z_{11}. \tag{40.7}$$

Equating the right-hand members of Eqs. (40.6) and (40.7), we obtain

$$z_{11} = \frac{1}{2}\left[\frac{\dot{a}}{a^2} - \frac{2b}{a} - \frac{p_{22}}{a} + \frac{p_{11}}{a} - \frac{\dot{p}_{21}}{ap_{21}}\right]z_{12} \tag{40.8}$$

which, if we define

$$M = \frac{1}{2}\left[\frac{\dot{a}}{a^2} - \frac{2b}{a} - \frac{p_{22}}{a} + \frac{p_{11}}{a} - \frac{\dot{p}_{21}}{ap_{21}}\right], \tag{40.9}$$

becomes

$$z_{11} = Mz_{12}. \tag{40.10}$$

Then, on the basis of (40.5), we obtain

$$\dot{z}_{11} = \dot{M}z_{12} + M\left[z_{12}(b - p_{11}) + aMz_{12}\right].$$

If we equate the right-hand members of this equation and Eq. (40.4) and divide by z_{12}, we obtain

$$\dot{M} + M2b + M^2a = -\frac{ac + p_{12}p_{21}}{a}. \tag{40.11}$$

On the basis of (40.10), Eqs. (40.5) and (40.6) take the forms

$$\dot{z}_{12} = (b - p_{11} + aM)\,z_{12}, \tag{40.12}$$

$$\dot{z}_{21} = -\left(p_{21}M + \frac{b + p_{22}}{a}p_{21}\right)z_{12}. \tag{40.13}$$

We must now satisfy Eqs. (40.11), (40.12) and (40.13). This can be done in several ways.

In (40.11), let us set

$$M=0, \quad ac + p_{12}p_{21} = 0. \tag{40.14}$$

From $M=0$, we easily find

$$a = Ap_{21} \exp \int_0^t (2b + p_{22} - p_{11})\, dt, \tag{40.15}$$

where A is an arbitrary constant. Then, from (40.12), we find

$$z_{12} = B \exp \int_0^t (b - p_{11})\, dt. \tag{40.16}$$

From (40.13), we find on the basis of (40.3)

$$z_{21} = K \exp \left[-\int_0^t (b + p_{22})\, dt\right], \tag{40.17}$$

where B and K are constants. From (40.10), we have

$$z_{11} = 0. \tag{40.18}$$

From (40.15) and the second of Eqs. (40.14), we obtain

$$c = -\frac{p_{12}}{A} \exp\left[-\int_0^t (2b + p_{22} - p_{11})\, dt\right]. \tag{40.19}$$

We have obtained the matrix Z of the transformation (39.2) and the elements a and c of the matrix (39.5) of the canonical system (39.3). The function b is still to be determined. For the matrix Q in Eq. (39.5) of the canonical system (39.3) to be periodic, we need only set

$$b = \frac{1}{2\omega} \int_0^\omega (p_{11} - p_{22})\, dt. \tag{40.20}$$

On the basis of (40.3), we still have $K = B/A$. Now, the matrix Z and its inverse Z^{-1}, which are determined by Eqs. (40.16), (40.17), (40.1) and (40.18), will be continuous in the interval $|t| < \infty$.

Example. Consider the noncanonical system

$$\frac{dY}{dt} = Y \begin{Vmatrix} p & 0 \\ 1 & p \end{Vmatrix}$$

where p is a constant. On the basis of (40.16), (40.17), (40.18) and (40.1), we obtain by setting $B = K = 1$

$$Z = \begin{Vmatrix} 0 & e^{-pt} \\ e^{-pt} & 0 \end{Vmatrix}, \quad Z^{-1} = \begin{Vmatrix} 0 & e^{pt} \\ e^{pt} & 0 \end{Vmatrix}$$

and, on the basis of (40.15), (40.19) and (40.20),

$$Q = \begin{Vmatrix} 0 & 1 \\ 0 & 0 \end{Vmatrix}.$$

Consequently, the system (39.3) is now put in the form

$$\frac{dX}{dt} = X \begin{Vmatrix} 0 & 1 \\ 0 & 0 \end{Vmatrix}.$$

Then, on the basis of (39.2),

$$X = Ce^{\begin{Vmatrix} 0 & 1 \\ 0 & 0 \end{Vmatrix} t} = YZ,$$

where C is an arbitrary constant matrix. But, obviously,

$$Y = e^{\begin{Vmatrix} p & 0 \\ 1 & p \end{Vmatrix} t}$$

Therefore

$$C = \begin{Vmatrix} 0 & 1 \\ 1 & 0 \end{Vmatrix}.$$

This yields

$$Y = XZ^{-1} = \begin{Vmatrix} 0 & 1 \\ 1 & 0 \end{Vmatrix} e^{\begin{Vmatrix} 0 & 1 \\ 0 & 0 \end{Vmatrix} t} \begin{Vmatrix} 0 & e^{pt} \\ e^{pt} & 0 \end{Vmatrix}.$$

Suppose now that, in (40.9),

$$a = 1, \quad b = 0. \tag{40.21}$$

Then,

$$M = \frac{1}{2}\left[p_{11} \quad p_{22} - \frac{\dot{p}_{21}}{p_{21}}\right].$$

$$\dot{M} = \frac{1}{2}\left(\dot{p}_{11} \quad \dot{p}_{22} \quad \frac{\ddot{p}_{21}}{p_{21}} + \frac{\dot{p}_{21}^2}{p_{21}^2}\right) \tag{40.22}$$

and, from (40.11),

$$c = -p_{21}p_{12} - \dot{M} - M^2. \tag{40.23}$$

Equations (40.12) and (40.13) become

$$\dot{z}_{12} = -\frac{1}{2}(p_{11} + p_{22} + \dot{p}_{21}/p_{21})z_{12}, \tag{40.24}$$

$$\dot{z}_{21} = -\frac{1}{2}(p_{11} + p_{22} - \dot{p}_{21}/p_{21})z_{21}. \tag{40.25}$$

Therefore,

$$z_{12} = \frac{1}{\sqrt{p_{21}}}\exp\left[-\frac{1}{2}\int_0^t (p_{11} + p_{22})\,dt\right], \tag{40.26}$$

$$z_{21}^{-1} = \sqrt{p_{21}}\exp\left[\frac{-1}{2}\int_0^t (p_{11} + p_{22})\,dt\right]. \tag{40.27}$$

The quantity z_{11} is determined from formula (40.10) and $z_{22} = 0$. The matrices Z and Z^{-1} will be continuous if $p_{21} \neq 0$. The canonical system (39.3) will be of the form

$$\frac{dX}{dt} = X\begin{Vmatrix} 0 & 1 \\ -c & 0 \end{Vmatrix}, \tag{40.28}$$

where c is determined from formula (40.23). The coefficients of the system (40.28) will be periodic with period ω if the coefficients of the system (39.1) are periodic with period ω.

The system (40.28) is equivalent to the equation

$$\ddot{x} + cx = 0. \tag{40.29}$$

We saw above that this equation canbe reduced to the case in which $c > 0$ by Lyapunov's or Starzhinskiy's method. It can also be done by the method shown in Sect. 39.

41. The Transformation of n Linear Equations Into a Canonical System

Suppose that the system (39.1) is an nth-order system. If the system (39.3) is canonical, then [34]

$$Q = H\begin{Vmatrix} 0 & -I \\ I & 0 \end{Vmatrix}, \quad h_{ik} = h_{ki}, \tag{41.1}$$

where the h_{ik} are the elements of the matrix H.

We leave the question open as to whether Z can be found in closed form in such a way that the system (39.3) will be canonical with periodic bounded matrix Q.

We note that Arzhanykh's work [70] contains a method for transforming a given system (which may be nonlinear) into a canonical system.

42. Necessary and Sufficient Conditions for a Polynomial to Have Roots Located on the Unit Circle

Consider a polynomial with real coefficients [90]

$$P(x) = x^n + a_1 x^{n-1} + a_2 x^{n-2} + \dots + a_{n-1} x + a_n. \tag{42.1}$$

We shall give a method for determining the number of roots of $P(x)$ that are located on the unit circle. We introduce y defined by

$$2y = x + x^{-1}, \tag{42.2}$$

$$x = y + \sqrt{y^2 - 1}, \qquad x = y - \sqrt{y^2 - 1}. \tag{42.3}$$

Let us substitute the first of these values of x into (42.1). We obtain

$$P(x) = Q(y) = P_1^{(n)}(y) + \sqrt{y^2 - 1}\, P_2^{(n-1)}(y). \tag{42.4}$$

Here, $P_1^{(n)}(y)$ and $P_2^{(n-1)}(y)$ are polynomials of degrees n and $n-1$, respectively. Since the coefficients of the polynomial (42.1) are real, to every root $x_1 = \exp i\varphi$ there corresponds a root $x_2 = \exp(-i\varphi)$. To these two roots there corresponds a single real value y in Eq. (42.2). The absolute value of this $y = \cos\varphi$ will be less than unity if $y \neq \pm 1$. Let us suppose that $y \neq \pm 1$ and that its value is such that both values of x, given by Eqs. (42.3) will be roots of the polynomial (42.1). Then,

$$P_1^{(n)}(y) + \sqrt{y^2 - 1}\, P_2^{(n-1)}(y) = 0, \quad P_1^{(n)}(y) - \sqrt{y^2 - 1}\, P_2^{(n-1)}(y) = 0.$$

Consequently,

$$P_1^{(n)}(y) = 0, \quad P_2^{(n-1)}(y) = 0. \tag{42.5}$$

If $x = \pm 1$, then $y = \pm 1$ and $P^{(n)}(\pm 1) = 0$.

Let us denote by $N(y)$ the polynomial that is the greatest common divisor of the polynomials (42.5). We have proven

Theorem 42.1. *If* $x = \exp i\varphi$ *is a root of the equation*

$$P(x) = 0 \tag{42.6}$$

with real $\varphi \neq k\pi$ *(for integral k), then the corresponding value of y is a real root of Eq. (42.5) or of the equation*

$$N(y) = 0, \tag{42.7}$$

or

$$[P^{(n)}(y)]^2 + [P^{(n-1)}(y)]^2 = 0 \tag{42.8}$$

with $|y| < 1$. *Conversely, every real root y of* Eq. *(42.7) or (42.8) such that* $|y| < 1$ *yields two conjugate roots of Eq. (42.6) located on the unit circle.*

Remark 42.1. If Eq. (42.7) has a real root y such that $|y| > 1$, then the polynomial (42.1) has two roots (42.3): one with $|x| < 1$, the other with $|x| > 1$. If there is no polynomial $N(y)$ (or if Eq. (42.8) has no real root), then there are no values of y that provide two roots (42.3) of the polynomial (42.1). The number of real roots y of Eq. (42.7) (or (42.8)) such that $|y| < 1$ is, as we know, easily found [35].

Suppose that the degree of the polynomial (42.1) is even: $n = 2m$. Then, there are no roots $x = \pm 1$ (their possibility is easily excluded) and the remaining roots are located on the unit circle in the form of pairs of complex conjugates: $x_1 = \cos\varphi + i\sin\varphi$, $x_2 = \cos\varphi - i\sin\varphi$. Consequently, the polynomial (42.1) is a product of pairs of factors:

$$(x - x_1)(x - x_2) = 2x\left[(x + x^{-1})\frac{1}{2} - \cos\varphi\right].$$

From this it follows that Eq. (42.1) is of the form

$$x^m Q_m(y) = 0, \quad 2y = x + x^{-1}, \quad x = y + \sqrt{y^2 - 1}, \tag{42.9}$$

where $Q_m(y)$ is an mth-degree polynomial with real roots y that are less than unity in absolute value and Eq. (42.1) is reciprocal. It is easy to find the polynomial $Q_m(y)$. This proves

Theorem 42.2. *For all roots of Eq. (42.1) or even degree* $n = 2m$ *to be equal to unity in absolute value (but not* ± 1), *it is necessary and sufficient that (42.1) be reciprocal and that the roots of the equation* $Q_m(y) = 0$ *be real with* $|y| < 1$.

Instead of (42.9), let us obtain an equation all the roots of which lie in the left half-plane and within the unit circle. With this in mind, we rewrite (42.9) as follows:

$$Q_m(y) = Q_1(y^2) + yQ_2(y^2) = 0. \tag{42.10}$$

If $m = 2k$, then $Q_1(z)$ and $Q_2(z)$ are polynomials of degree k and $k-1$ respectively. If $m = 2k+1$, then both are of degree k. From (42.10) we obtain

$$L(z) = Q_1^2(-z) + zQ_2^2(-z) = 0,\ z = -y^2. \tag{42.11}$$

The roots of this mth-degree polynomial $L(z)$ are real, negative, and of absolute value less than unity. Every root of Eq. (42.11) such that $|z| < 1$ provides (on the basis of the equation $y = i\sqrt{z}$ and Eqs. (42.3)) two roots of Eq. (42.6) that are located on the unit circle. With the aid of methods that we are familiar with from algebra [35], we can easily find in this way the number of roots of the polynomial (42.1) that are located on the unit circle.

For other methods of solving this problem, see [71]. If we show that the polynomial (42.1) does not have roots on the unit circle, then the number* of roots N that are located inside the unit circle** can, as we know, be found from the formula

$$N = \frac{1}{2\pi}\int_0^{2\pi} \frac{P'(e^{i\varphi})e^{i\varphi}\,d\varphi}{P(e^{i\varphi})}. \tag{42.12}$$

This number is a nonnegative integer, and which integer it is, is easily found by an approximate calculation.

43. Investigation of the Roots of the Polynomial (42.1) as Functions of a Parameter Appearing in the Coefficients a_k [90]

Suppose that the coefficients of the polynomial $P(x, \varepsilon)$ shown in (42.1) are functions of a parameter ε that are analytic in a neighborhood of the point $\varepsilon = 0$. Suppose that, for $\varepsilon = 0$, we have m distinct pairs of complex conjugate roots situated on the unit circle:

$$x_1^{(k)} = \exp i\varphi_k,\ x_2^{(k)} = \exp(-i\varphi_k) \quad (k = 1, \ldots, m), \tag{43.1}$$

where $\varphi_k \neq \nu\pi$ (where ν is an integer). Corresponding to these

---

*If the polynomial (42.1) is reciprocal, then, as we know, the number of roots within the circle is the same as the number outside it.

**For other methods, see the book by I. S. Arzhanykh [70].

pairs of roots there are m common distinct real roots $y = y_k$, where $|y_k| < 1$ (for $k = 1, \ldots, m$) of the equations*

$$P^{(n)}(y, \varepsilon) = 0, \quad P^{(n-1)}(y, \varepsilon) = 0 \quad \text{for} \quad \varepsilon = 0 \tag{43.2}$$

or

$$L(y) = [P^{(n)}(y, 0)]^2 + [P^{(n-1)}(y, 0)]^2 = 0. \tag{43.3}$$

The question arises as to the distribution of the roots of the equation

$$P(x, \varepsilon) = 0 \tag{43.4}$$

for small values of ε. Since the coefficients of the equations

$$P^{(n)}(y, \varepsilon) = 0, \quad P^{(n-1)}(y, \varepsilon) = 0 \tag{43.5}$$

or

$$L(y, \varepsilon) = [P^{(n)}(y, \varepsilon)]^2 + [P^{(n-1)}(y, \varepsilon)]^2 = 0 \tag{43.6}$$

will in this case obviously be analytic also in a neighborhood of the point $\varepsilon = 0$ (with radius of convergence at least as great as that of the coefficients of the polynomial (43.4), Eq. (43.5) or (43.6) yields m distinct holomorphic roots

$$y = y_\nu(\varepsilon) = y_\nu + \sum_{k=1}^{\infty} \alpha_\nu^{(k)} \varepsilon^k \quad (\nu = 1, \ldots, m) \tag{43.7}$$

in a neighborhood of the point $\varepsilon = 0$. For small values of ε, these roots will be real and distinct and $|y_\nu(\varepsilon)| < 1$ if $P(x, \varepsilon)$ is reciprocal. This is obvious from (42.9). If follows from this that the corresponding pairs of roots of Eq. (43.4) will remain on the unit circle for small values of ε. This proves

Theorem 43.1. *If $P(x, \varepsilon)$ is reciprocal and if $P(x, 0)$ has m distinct pairs of solutions (43.1), then for all sufficiently small real values of x, Eq. (43.4) also* has *m distinct conjugate pairs of solutions located on the unit circle.*

Suppose now that, for $\varepsilon = 0$, we have a p-multiple real root y_0 of Eq. (43.6) such that $|y_0| < 1$. Then, the following cases may arise:

I. There exist p distinct real (for real ε) functions

$$y = \left(y_0 + \sum_{l=n}^{\infty} a_l^{(\nu)} \varepsilon^l\right)\varepsilon \quad (\nu = 1, \ldots, p), \tag{43.8}$$

---

*These equations are the same as (42.5) except that the coefficients $a_k(\varepsilon)$ contain the parameter ε.

that satisfy Eq. (43.6). Corresponding to these functions are p pairs of complex conjugate roots of Eq. (43.4).

II. There exist functions $y = y_\nu(\varepsilon)$ (for $\nu = 1, \ldots, p$) satisfying Eq. (43.6) that possess the property that $y_\nu(\varepsilon) \to y_0$ as $\varepsilon \to 0$ and that are real only when $\varepsilon > 0$ or only when $\varepsilon < 0$. Then, we have p conjugate pairs of roots of Eq. (43.4) located on the unit circle for small (in absolute value) positive or negative values of ε, respectively. These roots $y_\nu(\varepsilon)$ can be represented by series of positive powers of the quantities $\varepsilon^{1/q}$, where q is a positive integer, that converge for small values of ε.

III. There exist functions $y = y_\nu(\varepsilon)$ (for $\nu = 1, \ldots, m < p$) that are real for real values of ε throughout some neighborhood of $\varepsilon = 0$ and that can be represented by convergent series in positive powers of $\varepsilon^{1/q}$, where q is a positive integer. The regions of convergence of these series have been determined. All these conclusions are obtained on the basis of [32].

Let us now look at the case in which $x = 1$ is a root of Eq. (43.4) for $\varepsilon = 0$. In this case, as can be seen from (42.4), we also have, for $\varepsilon = 0$,

$$P^{(n)}(1, 0) = 0. \tag{43.9}$$

In accordance with [32, Sect. 6], we shall have a solution of the first of Eqs. (43.5) in one of the following forms:

$$y = 1 + \sum_{k=1}^{\infty} \alpha_k \varepsilon^{k/q} \tag{43.10}$$

where q is a positive integer, or

$$y = 1 + \sum_{k=1}^{\infty} \alpha_k (-\varepsilon)^{k/q}, \tag{43.11}$$

or

$$y = 1 + \varepsilon \sum_{k=1}^{\infty} \alpha_k \varepsilon^{k/q}, \tag{43.12}$$

or

$$y = 1 + \varepsilon \sum_{k=1}^{\infty} \alpha_k (-\varepsilon)^{k/q}. \tag{43.13}$$

Here, the α_k are real and the series converge for small values of ε.

We may obtain one of the series (43.10), (43.11), (43.12), or (43.14) or several such series. These series are real either for $|\varepsilon| < \varepsilon_0$ or only for small positive $\varepsilon > 0$ or only for $\varepsilon < 0$.

But to answer the question as to whether the corresponding roots of Eq. (43.4) that assume the value $x = 1$ for $\varepsilon = 0$ remain on the unit circle for small values of ε, we need to consider the following fact: If the solution found for the first of Eqs. (43.5) is not a solution of the second of Eqs. (43.5), it does not generate solutions of Eq. (43.4).

Let us suppose now that the solution found satisfies both of Eqs. (43.5), that is, that it is a solution of Eq. (43.6). For it to generate roots of Eq. (43.4) that are located on the unit circle, it is necessary and sufficient that it be real and that its absolute value be less than unity. Suppose, for example, that we have (43.10). Then, if q is an odd number, y remains real for $|\varepsilon| < \varepsilon_0$. But if q is an even number, then y will be real only when $\varepsilon > 0$. Here, if we have $\alpha_1 < 0$, it is obvious that, for small $\varepsilon > 0$, the function y will be real and $|y| < 1$. This gives us two conjugate roots of Eq. (43.4) that are located on the unit circle for small values of ε. The number of such pairs of roots of Eq. (43.4) is equal to the number of real roots of (43.6) such that $|y| < 1$.

If we have (43.11), we repeat the same line of reasoning for $\varepsilon < 0$. We again follow this line of reasoning if we have (43.12). Here, the deciding factor for the existence of a real y such that $|y| < 1$ is the sign of α_1 and the region $\varepsilon > 0$ or $\varepsilon < 0$. If, for example, q is even and $\alpha_1 > 0$, then y, as defined by the series (43.12), will not be real even when $|y| < 1$. To see this, if $\varepsilon > 0$, then $y = y(\varepsilon)$ is real but $|y| > 1$ since $\varepsilon\alpha_k > 0$, but if $\varepsilon < 0$, then $y = y(\varepsilon)$ is not real. On the other hand, if $y = y(\varepsilon)$ is real and $|y| > 1$ and if y satisfies the equation* (not necessarily both of Eqs. (43.5))

$$P(x, \varepsilon) = Q(y, \varepsilon) = P^{(n)}(y, \varepsilon) + \sqrt{y^2 - 1}\, P^{(n-1)}(y, \varepsilon) = 0,$$

then, since $x = y + \sqrt{y^2 - 1}$, the corresponding x will be greater than 1 in absolute value. If Eq. (43.4) has roots $x = x(\varepsilon)$ on the unit circle for small (in absolute value) positive or negative ε and if $x = 1$ for $\varepsilon = 0$, then, in accordance with Theorem (42.1), there exists a real root of Eq. (43.6) such that $|y| < 1$. We obtain this root in the form of the series shown above.

We note also that when we examine Eq. (42.9), which corresponds to a polynomial of even degree $n = 2m$, we can also consider the case in which $P(x, \varepsilon)$ is continuous with respect to ε. We need only use the methods expounded in Sects. 2-5 of [32].

---

*This equation is obtained by making the substitution $x = y + \sqrt{y^2 - 1}$ into (43.4).

44. Questions Regarding the Stability and Boundedness of Solutions of Linear Systems of Differential Equations with Periodic Coefficients on the Basis of the Methods of Section 43 [93]

Consider the canonical linear system of differential equations

$$\frac{dX}{dt} = XP(t, \varepsilon), \quad P(t, \varepsilon) = \sum_{k=0}^{\infty} P_k(t)\varepsilon^k, \tag{44.1}$$

where the series converges in the region $|\varepsilon| < r$, where the $P_k(t)$ are continuous nth-order matrices that are periodic with period 2π, and where X is the integral matrix. We have seen (cf. Sect. 6) that the integral matrix X can be represented in the form

$$X(t, \varepsilon) = \sum_{k=0}^{\infty} X_k(t)\varepsilon^k, \quad X(0, \varepsilon) = I, \tag{44.2}$$

where the $X_k(t)$ are continuous matrix functions of t and the series converges in the region $|\varepsilon| < r$. This integral matrix possesses the property

$$X(t + 2\pi, \varepsilon) = X(2\pi, \varepsilon) X(t, \varepsilon), \tag{44.3}$$

where

$$X(2\pi, \varepsilon) = \sum_{k=0}^{\infty} X_k(2\pi)\varepsilon^k. \tag{44.4}$$

The question as to when the matrix (44.2) possesses the property that $X(t, \varepsilon) \longrightarrow \|0\|$ as $t \longrightarrow \infty$ or when it is bounded is solved as follows: If all the characteristic numbers of the matrix (44.4) are less than unity in absolute value, then $X(t, \varepsilon) \rightarrow \|0\|$ as $t \rightarrow \infty$. However, if all the characteristic numbers of the matrix (44.4) are equal to unity in absolute value and if the elementary divisors are simple, then the matrix (44.2) does not possess the property that $X(t, \varepsilon) \rightarrow \|0\|$ as $t \rightarrow \infty$ but it is bounded and oscillatory. Since we have assumed the system (44.1) to be canonical, it follows from a theorem of Lyapunov [26] that the characteristic equation

$$P(x, \varepsilon) = 0 \tag{44.5}$$

of the matrix (44.4) is reciprocal. Therefore, whenever the matrix (44.4) has a characteristic number equal to ρ, there is also a characteristic number equal to ρ^{-1}. From this it follows that the matrix (44.2) cannot possess the property that $X(t, \varepsilon) \to \|0\|$ as $t \to \infty$.

Let us find the conditions under which the matrix (44.2) will be bounded (without approaching the zero matrix as $t \to \infty$) for sufficiently small values of the parameter ε. If the matrix $X(2\pi, 0)$ defined by the series (44.4) has a characteristic number ρ such that $|\rho| < 1$, then there exists (in view of the fact that, even for $\varepsilon = 0$, the system (44.1) is canonical) a characteristic number ρ such that $|\rho| > 1$. Then, it is obvious that, for all sufficiently small ε, there are characteristic numbers ρ such that $|\rho| > 1$. Therefore, the matrix (44.2) is unbounded.

Let us suppose now that the absolute value of every characteristic number of the matrix $X(2\pi, 0)$ is equal to unity, that is, that all the characteristic numbers lie on the unit circle. The characteristic numbers x of the matrix (44.4) are roots of the nth-degree polynomial (44.5), where the coefficients of all powers of x are holomorphic functions of ε in a neighborhood of $\varepsilon = 0$. These series converge for $|\varepsilon| < r$. For $\varepsilon = 0$, (44.5) becomes the characteristic equation of the matrix $X(2\pi, 0)$. Consequently, all roots of Eq. (44.5) lie on the unit circle for $\varepsilon = 0$.

In Sect. 43 it was shown how one could prove that, for all sufficiently small values of ε, all the roots of Eq. (44.5) are distinct (and hence that all elementary divisors of the matrix (44.4) are simple), and that they are located on the unit circle. For example, this will be the case when all characteristic numbers of the matrix $X(2\pi, 0)$ are simple and located on the unit circle. It will also be the case whenever all roots of Eq. (43.6) are, for sufficiently small ε (possibly only for $\varepsilon > 0$ or $\varepsilon < 0$), real, simple, and less than unity in absolute value. (In this case, the matrix $X(2\pi\ 0)$ may have non-simple elementary divisors.) Let us suppose that the system (44.1) of even order $n = 2m$ is not canonical. Then, for the integral matrix (44.2) to be bounded for small values of ε without approaching the zero matrix as $t \to \infty$, it is necessary that the characteristic numbers of the matrix $X(2\pi, 0)$ lie on the unit circle. If they are of the form (43.1) and are distinct, then, by Theorem 43.1, they are distinct and located on the unit circle for all sufficiently small ε. For the characteristic numbers of the matrix $X(2\pi, 0)$ to lie on the unit circle, it is necessary that the characteristic equation of the matrix $X(2\pi, 0)$ be reciprocal (Theorem 42.2). If it is reciprocal and if Eq. (42.10) has m (where $n = 2m$) distinct real roots y of absolute value less than 1 for (44.5), then all the characteristic numbers of the matrix $X(2\pi, \varepsilon)$ lie on the unit circle for all sufficiently small ε.

We may even say that the characteristic numbers of the matrix $X(2\pi, \varepsilon)$ will in fact remain on the unit circle for all real $|\varepsilon| < \varepsilon_0$ such that $D(\varepsilon) \neq 0$ and $Q_m(\pm 1, \varepsilon) \neq 0$ (cf. Eq. (42.11)), where $D(\varepsilon)$ is the discriminant of Eq. (42.10). For such values of ε, the roots of Eq. (42.10) will all remain distinct and less than unity in absolute value. These singular values ε_0, which are all close together, must also satisfy the equation $\Delta(\varepsilon_0) = 0$, where $\Delta(\varepsilon)$ is the discriminant of the characteristic Eq. (44.5). This proves

Theorem 44.1. *For the integral matrix (44.2) of the system (44.1) (which is noncanonical) to be bounded without approaching the zero matrix for small values of* ε, *it is necessary that the characteristic equation of the matrix* $X(2\pi, 0)$ *be reciprocal. If this condition is satisfied and Eq. (42.9), which is set up for (44.5) (the characteristic equation of the matrix* $X(2\pi, \varepsilon)$*), has m distinct real roots y such that* $|y| < 1$, *then the matrix (44.2) will be bounded without approaching the zero matrix as* $t \to \infty$.

Remark 44.1. All other possible cases in which we have the matrix (44.2) are considered in Sect. 43.

45. A Sufficient Condition for the Integral Matrix of the Noncanonical System (44.1) to Possess the Property that $X(t, \varepsilon) \to \|0\|$ as $t \to \infty$

In order for

$$X(t, \varepsilon) \to \|0\| \quad \text{as} \quad t \to \infty, \tag{45.1}$$

it is necessary and sufficient (as was shown after (44.4)) that all the characteristic numbers x of the matrix $X(2\pi, \varepsilon)$ be of absolute value less than unity. Let us note first of all that if the characteristic numbers x of the matrix $X(2\pi, 0)$ are of absolute value less than unity, they will remain so for all sufficiently small ε. This is obvious. Consequently, we need to find those conditions under which the characteristic numbers x of the matrix $X(2\pi, 0)$ will be of absolute value less than unity. We proceed as follows.

Let us write the characteristic equation for the matrix $X(2\pi, 0)$ in the form

$$(-1)^n D(X(2\pi, 0) - xI) = P(x) = 0, \tag{45.2}$$

where $P(x)$ is a polynomial of the form (42.1). Now, we can use the methods expounded in [71] to show whether all the roots x are less than unity in absolute value. However, it will probably be more convenient here to use the method proposed by Arzhanykh [70]. Specifically, he obtains equations characterizing the conditions under which $|x| < 1$ for all roots of Eq. (45.2). This is equivalent to Hurwitz' equations for the matrix $\ln X(2\pi, 0)$, which ensure that the real parts of the characteristic numbers of this matrix are negative. But it is more convenient since we do not need to find the matrix $\ln X(2\pi, 0)$. These conditions obtained by Arzhanykh are both necessary and sufficient for $|x|$ to be less than unity for all roots of Eq. (45.2). Altogether, for an nth-order matrix $X(2\pi, 0)$, there are n of these conditions of Arzhanykh. We write them momentarily in the form

$$\Delta_1 > 0, \quad \Delta_2 > 0, \ldots, \quad \Delta_n > 0. \tag{45.3}$$

These inequalities will be satisfied for *all* sufficiently small real values of ε if they are satisfied for $\varepsilon = 0$. Specifically, we shall have

$$\Delta_1(\varepsilon) > 0, \ldots, \quad \Delta_n(\varepsilon) > 0, \tag{45.4}$$

if we have

$$\Delta_1(0) > 0, \ldots, \quad \Delta_n(0) > 0.$$

We may go further and say that Arzhanykh's inequalities are always satisfied for those values of ε that are less in absolute value than ε_0, where ε_0 is the smallest of those real numbers ε_1 for which we have* (by Sect. 43)

$$[P^{(n)}(y, \varepsilon_0)]^2 + [P^{(n-1)}(y, \varepsilon_0)]^2 = 0 \tag{45.5}$$

for real values of y such that $|y| < 1$; hence,

$$P^{(n)}(\pm 1, \varepsilon_0) = 0. \tag{45.6}$$

Thus, to determine ε_0, we have equations in the form of series that converge for those values of ε for which the series in Eq. (44.1) converges.

Remark 45.1. If it is shown on the basis of Theorem 42.1 that Eq. (45.2) does not have a root x lying on the unit circle, then the number N of roots x such that $|x| < 1$ is easily found from formula (42.12) since we know that this is a nonnegative integer.

46. Another Method of Solving Artem'yev's Problem

Consider again a system of the form (18.1)

$$\frac{dX}{dt} = XP(t, \mu_1, \ldots, \mu_\nu, \varepsilon), \tag{46.1}$$

---

*Since, for such ε_0, the equation

$$(-1)^n D(X(2\pi, \varepsilon_0) - xI) = 0$$

has roots lying on the unit circle.

where the matrix $P(t, \mu_1, \ldots, \mu_\nu, \varepsilon)$ is of order $n = 2m$ and is periodic with respect to t with period 2π and where $\mu_1, \ldots, \mu_\nu$, and ε are parameters. Now, we do not assume the system (46.1) to be canonical. Let us find conditions that the parameters $\mu_1, \ldots, \mu_\nu$, and ε must satisfy to ensure that the integral matrix of the system (46.1) will be bounded and oscillatory (without approaching the zero matrix as $t \to \infty$). In accordance with Theorem 42.2, we must require that the characteristic equation of the matrix $X(2\pi, \mu_1, \ldots, \mu_\nu, \varepsilon)$ be reciprocal. This gives us m equations since these conditions for Eq. (42.1) are

$$a_n = 1, \quad a_{n-k} = a_k \quad (k = 0, 1, \ldots, m-1). \tag{46.2}$$

Then, we require that all the roots of the equation (cf. (42.9))

$$Q_m(y) = 0 \tag{46.3}$$

be real and of absolute value less than 1. If the system (46.1) is canonical, the conditions (46.2) are automatically satisfied and only conditions (46.3) remain.

Thus, if we are given the system (46.1), Artem'yev's problem can be solved immediately on the basis of conditions (46.2) and (46.3) without using the matrix W. This is much simpler and, in addition, we shall be dealing with series that converge for the same values of ε as do the series for the matrix $P(t, \mu_1, \ldots, \mu_\nu, \varepsilon)$ in Eq. (46.1). As we know, the series representing the matrix W converge in a smaller region.

Formula II of Sect. 18 is solved in the same way on the basis of the methods expounded in Sect. 44 directly with the aid of the matrix $X(2\pi; \mu_1, \ldots, \mu_\nu, \varepsilon)$. The problems of Sect. 27 are also solved in this way. We might note that many of the problems that we have considered here are studied in greater detail in the works of Golokvoschus [50] in terms of the exponential matrix.

47. Supplement to the Theory of Implicit Functions as Studied in [32,73,97]

We shall present some results from [32]. We know [72] that if an implicit function y as defined by

$$F(x, y) = ax + by + \ldots = 0, \tag{47.1}$$

where the series $F(x, y)$ with real coefficients $a, b, \ldots$, converges in a neighborhood of the point $x = y = 0$, approaches 0 as $x \to 0$, then, for $b \neq 0$,

$$y=\sum_{k=1}^{\infty} \alpha_k x^k, \quad \alpha_1=-\frac{a}{b} \tag{47.2}$$

and this series converges in a neighborhood of the point $x=0$. Here, $\alpha_1, \alpha_2, \ldots$ are real constants.

If $b=0$ but $a \neq 0$, then

$$x=\sum_{k=m}^{\infty} \beta_k y^k, \; \beta_m=-\frac{b_m}{a}, \tag{47.3}$$

where b_m is the coefficient of the smallest power of y in the series (47.1). From this we have the unique real function

$$y=\sum_{k=1}^{\infty} \alpha_k \tau^k, \quad \tau=x^{1/m}, \quad \alpha_1=\sqrt[-m]{\beta_m}, \tag{47.4}$$

defined throughout a neighborhood of the point $x=0$ if m is odd. On the other hand, if m is even, then, for $\beta_m>0$, the series (47.4) provides two real functions (since $\tau=x^{1/m}$ has two real values differing in sign) but only for small positive x.

On the other hand, if $\beta_m<0$, then (47.4) provides two real functions for negative values of x that are small in absolute value, where $\alpha_1=\sqrt[-m]{-\beta_m}$ and $\tau=(-x)^{1/m}$.

Now, let us consider an equation of the form

$$\begin{aligned}&\alpha_1 x^2+\alpha_2 xy+\alpha_3 y^2+\alpha_4 x^3+\alpha_5 x^2y+\alpha_6 xy^2+\\&+\alpha_7 y^3+\alpha_8 x^4+\alpha_9 x^3y+\alpha_{10} x^2y^2+\alpha_{11} xy^3+\alpha_{12} y^4+\ldots=0,\end{aligned} \tag{47.5}$$

where the coefficients α are real constants, where the series converges in a neighborhood of the coordinate origin, and where the terms of degree greater than 4 in x and y are omitted. Let us find conditions under which there is a continuous real solution $y=y(x)$ of Eq. (47.5) possessing the property that

$$y(x) \to 0 \quad \text{as} \quad x \to 0. \tag{47.6}$$

We seek y in the form

$$y=ux. \tag{47.7}$$

Substituting this expression for y into (47.5) and dividing by x^2, we obtain

$$\begin{gathered}\alpha_1 + \alpha_2 u + \alpha_3 u^2 + \alpha_4 x + \alpha_5 xu + \alpha_6 xu^2 + \\ + \alpha_7 xu^3 + \alpha_8 x^2 + \alpha_9 x^2 u + \alpha_{10} x^2 u^2 + \alpha_{11} x^2 u^3 + \\ + \alpha_{12} x^2 u^4 + \alpha_{13} x^3 + \ldots = 0.\end{gathered} \tag{47.8}$$

We denote by a_1 and a_2 the roots of the equation

$$\alpha_1 + \alpha_2 a + \alpha_3 a^2 = 0. \tag{47.9}$$

Let us introduce a new unknown v defined by

$$u = v + a_k \quad (k = 1 \text{ or } k = 2). \tag{47.10}$$

To determine v, we obtain the equation

$$\begin{gathered}(\alpha_2 + 2a_k \alpha_3) v + (\alpha_4 + \alpha_5 a_k + \alpha_6 a_k^2 + \alpha_7 a_k^3) x + \\ + \alpha_3 v^2 + (\alpha_5 + 2\alpha_6 a_k + 3\alpha_7 a_k^2) xv + \\ + (\alpha_8 + \alpha_9 a_k + \alpha_{10} a_k^2 + \alpha_{11} a_k^3 + \alpha_{12} a_k^4) x^2 + \ldots = 0.\end{gathered} \tag{47.11}$$

Here, all the omitted terms are of degree exceeding 2 in x.

If $a_1 \neq a_2$, we have

$$\alpha_2 + 2a_k \alpha_3 \neq 0. \tag{47.12}$$

In this case, we have from (47.11)

$$v = m_l^{(k)} x^l + m_{l+1}^{(k)} x^{l+1} + \ldots \quad (k = 1,2), \tag{47.13}$$

where l is a positive integer,

$$m_l^{(k)} = -\frac{A_l}{\alpha_2 + 2a_k \alpha_3} \quad (k = 1,2) \tag{47.14}$$

and the A_l is the coefficient of the lowest power of x in (47.11).

Consequently,

$$y = x\,(a_k + m_l^{(k)} x^l + m_{l+1}^{(k)} x^{l+1} + \ldots). \tag{47.15}$$

If a_1 and a_2 are real, we have two real functions $y(x)$ that approach 0 as $x \to 0$. There are no other $y(x)$.

If a_1 and a_2 are complex, there are no real functions $y(x)$ that approach 0 as $x \to 0$.

Suppose now that $a_1 = a_2 = a$. Then, the coefficient of the first-degree term in v in Eq. (47.11) is equal to 0; that is,

$$\alpha_2 + 2a\,\alpha_3 = 0, \quad \alpha_2^2 - 4\alpha_1\alpha_3 = 0. \tag{47.16}$$

Under these conditions, the coefficient A of the first-degree term in x in Eq. (47.11) is of the form

$$A=(8\alpha_3^3)^{-1}(8\alpha_4\alpha_3^3-4\alpha_2\alpha_5\alpha_3^2+2\alpha_2^2\alpha_6\alpha_3-\alpha_7\alpha_2^3). \tag{47.17}$$

If $\alpha_3\neq 0$ and $A\neq 0$, then we have from (47.11)

$$x=k_2v^2+k_3v^3+\dots, \tag{47.18}$$

where

$$k_2=-\frac{8\alpha_3^4}{8\alpha_4\alpha_3^3-4\alpha_2\alpha_5\alpha_3^2+2\alpha_2^2\alpha_6\alpha_3-\alpha_7\alpha_2^3}. \tag{47.19}$$

From (47.18), we obtain two real functions y that approach 0 as $x\to 0$ if $k_2>0$:

$$y=x\left(a+\sum_{k=1}^{\infty}A_kx^{k/2}\right),\quad A_1=k_2^{-1/2}. \tag{47.20}$$

Both these y (remember that $x^{1/2}$ has two values differing in sign) are defined in some interval of the form $0\leqslant x<h$.

If $k_2<0$, then, for $x\geqslant 0$,

$$y=x\left(a+\sum_{k=1}^{\infty}A_k(-x)^{k/2}\right),\quad A_1=(-k_2)^{-\frac{1}{2}} \tag{47.20$_1$}$$

has real values. There are no other functions y that approach 0 as $x\to 0$.

Let us consider a few particular cases. If

$$\alpha_1=\alpha_2=0,\quad \alpha_3\neq 0, \tag{47.21}$$

we have $a=0$. Then, for

$$\alpha_4\neq 0 \tag{47.22}$$

we have (47.18).

If

$$\alpha_1=\alpha_3=0,\quad \alpha_2\neq 0, \tag{47.23}$$

then the coefficient of the first-degree term in v in Eq. (47.11) is $\alpha_2\neq 0$. Therefore, we obtain (47.15) ($a_k=0$). But here, we can obtain other functions y that approach 0 as $x \to 0$ as follows: If we make the substitution $x = uy$ in (47.5) and divide by y^2, we obtain

$$\begin{aligned} &\alpha_2 u + \alpha_7 y + \alpha_6 uy + \alpha_{12} y^2 + \alpha_5 u^2 y + \alpha_{11} y^2 u + \\ &+ \alpha_4 u^3 y + \alpha_{10} u^2 y^2 + \alpha_9 y^2 u^3 + \alpha_8 u^4 y^2 + \ldots = 0. \end{aligned} \tag{47.24}$$

Since $\alpha_2 \neq 0$., we obtain

$$u = \sum_{\nu=m}^{\infty} k_\nu y^\nu, \quad k_m = -\frac{A}{\alpha_2}, \tag{47.25}$$

where A is a coefficient of the term in (47.24) of lowest degree in y. If, in particular, $\alpha_7 \neq 0$, then $A = \alpha_7$ and $m = 1$.

On the basis of (47.25), we have

$$x = uy = \sum_{\nu=m}^{\infty} k_\nu y^{\nu+1}. \tag{47.25 1}$$

From this we obtain

$$y = \sum_{k=1}^{\infty} A_k \tau^k. \tag{47.26}$$

Here,

$$\tau = x^{1/(m+1)}, \quad A_1 = k_m^{-1/(m+1)}, \quad \text{if} \quad k_m > 0. \tag{47.27}$$

If $m + 1$ is an odd number in these equations, y is real throughout an entire neighborhood of $x = 0$. On the other hand, if $m + 1$ is an even number, then y will be real only for $x \geqslant 0$. The function τ has two real values differing in sign. Therefore, we have two real y defined for small nonnegative values of x.

If $k_m < 0$ and $m + 1$ is an odd number, then τ and A_1 will again be given by Eqs. (47.27). We have one real y defined in a neighborhood of the point $x = 0$.

On the other hand, if $k_m < 0$ and $m + 1$ is even, then

$$\tau = (-x)^{1/(m+1)}, \quad A_1 = (-k_m)^{-1/(m+1)}. \tag{47.28}$$

We have two real y defined for nonpositive values of x that are small in absolute value.

We have found all real values of y that approach 0 as $x \to 0$ and that satisfy conditions (47.23).

Let us suppose now that

$$\alpha_2 = \alpha_3 = 0, \text{ but } \alpha_1 \neq 0. \tag{47.29}$$

In this case, Eq. (47.9) has no roots.

Let us introduce an unknown u defined by

$$x = uy. \tag{47.30}$$

If we substitute this into (47.5), divide by y^2, and take conditions (47.29) into account, we obtain

$$\begin{aligned}\alpha_1 u^2 + \alpha_4 yu^3 + \alpha_5 u^2 y + \alpha_6 uy + \alpha_7 y + \alpha_8 y^2 u^4 + \\ + \alpha_9 y^2 u^3 + \alpha_{10} y^2 u^2 + \alpha_{11} uy^2 + \alpha_{12} y^2 + \ldots = 0.\end{aligned} \tag{47.31}$$

Here, if

$$\alpha_7 \neq 0, \tag{47.32}$$

we obtain from (47.31)

$$y = k_2 u^2 + k_3 u^3 + \ldots, \quad k_2 = -\frac{\alpha_1}{\alpha_7}. \tag{47.33}$$

Let us suppose that $k_2 > 0$. Then, from (47.33), we have

$$u = \sum_{k=1}^{\infty} A_k y^{k/2}, \quad A_1 = k_2^{-1/2}. \tag{47.34}$$

From (47.34) and (47.30), we obtain

$$y = \left[\sum_{k=1}^{\infty} c_k x^{k/3}\right]^2, \quad c_1 = k_2^{1/6}. \tag{47.35}$$

Thus, if (47.29) and (47.32) hold and if $k_2 > 0$, we have a unique real solution of Eq. (47.5) that approaches 0 as $x \to 0$ and that is defined throughout a neighborhood of the point $x = 0$.

Suppose now that

$$k_2 < 0. \tag{47.36}$$

Then, we have y in the form

$$y = -\left[\sum_{k=1}^{\infty} c_k (-x)^{k/3}\right]^2, \quad c_1 = (-k_2)^{1/6}, \tag{47.37}$$

which is defined for nonpositive x of small absolute value.

Let us suppose now that

$$a_1 = a_2, \tag{47.38}$$

but that the quantity (47.17) is equal to 0:

$$A = 0; \ \alpha_3 \neq 0. \tag{47.39}$$

Then, Eq. (47.11) is of the form (47.5) and we can repeat the preceding line of reasoning for it.

Repeating this reasoning, we can either show that there are no real functions y that approach 0 as $x \to 0$ or we can find them in the form indicated above. But it may happen that we will again arrive at an equation of the form (47.5).

However, it is easy to see that we cannot arrive in this way at an equation of the form

$$P_m(x, y) + P_{m+1}(x, y) + \ldots = 0, \ m \geqslant 3, \tag{47.40}$$

where the $P_k(x, y)$ are all homogeneous kth-degree polynomials, unless $\alpha_1 = \alpha_2 = \alpha_3 = 0$.

It may turn out that no matter how many times we repeat this procedure, we always obtain an equation of the form (47.5). Then, as was shown in [32], we have one y that approaches zero as $x \to 0$ and it can be represented in the form of the convergent series

$$y = \sum_{k=1}^{\infty} c_k x^k, \tag{47.41}$$

where all the c_k are unique (or multiple) roots of equations of the form (47.9).

If we can show that there are real functions y that approach zero as $x \to 0$ (we are thinking of the case in which a multiple root a of Eq. (47.9) $\neq 0$), then all these functions have the same principal part (infinitesimal of lowest order)

$$y \approx ax. \tag{47.42}$$

Let us now consider Eq. (47.40), where $m \geqslant 3$.

If we substitute y = 2x (cf. (47.7)) into (47.40) and divide by x^m, we obtain

$$P_m(1, u) + P_{m+1}(1, u)x + P_{m+2}(1, u)x^2 + \ldots = 0. \tag{47.43}$$

Let us denote by a the roots of the equation

$$P_m(1, a) = 0. \tag{47.44}$$

If we set

$$u = v + a, \tag{47.45}$$

we obtain

$$P_m(1, v + a) + P_{m+1}(1, v + a)x + \dots = 0. \tag{47.46}$$

If we expand this in a series of powers of v, we obtain*

$$\begin{aligned} &P_{m+1}(1, a)x + P_{m+2}(1, a)x^2 + P_{m+3}(1, a)x^3 + \dots + \\ &+ [P'_m(1, a) + P'_{m+1}(1, a)x + P'_{m+2}(1, a)x^2 + \dots]v + \\ &+ \frac{1}{2!}[P''_m(1, a) + P''_{m+1}(1, a)x + \\ &+ P''_{m+2}(1, a)x^2 + \dots]v^2 + \dots = 0. \end{aligned} \tag{47.47}$$

Let us suppose that a is a simple root of Eq. (47.44). Then, $P'_m(1, a) \neq 0$ and, from (47.47), we have

$$v = k_n x^n + k_{n+1}x^{n+1} + \dots, \quad k_n = -\frac{P_n(1, a)}{P'_m(1, a)}, \tag{47.48}$$

where $P_n(1, a)$ is the first of the quantities $P_{m+1}(1, a), P_{m+2}(1, a), \dots$ that is nonzero. On the basis of (47.7), (47.45) and (47.48), we find

$$y = x(a + k_n x^n + k_{n+1} x^{n+1} + \dots). \tag{47.49}$$

If a is real, then the function (47.49) is real. Conversely, if a is complex, then the function (47.49) will also be complex.

If all roots $a_1, a_2, \dots, a_m$ of Eq. (47.44) are real and simple, then we obtain m real solutions y of Eq. (47.40) in the form (47.49) that approach zero as $x \to 0$, and there are no other such solutions.

If all roots of Eq. (47.44) are complex simple roots $a_1, \dots, a_m$, then there is no function y that approaches 0 as $x \to 0$.

Suppose now that a is a ν-multiple root of Eq. (47.44). Then, we have

$$\begin{aligned} &P_m(1, a) = P'_m(1, a) = \dots = P_m^{(\nu-1)}(1, a) = 0, \\ &P_m^{(\nu)}(1, a) \neq 0. \end{aligned} \tag{47.50}$$

Suppose also that

$$P_{m+1}(1, a) \neq 0. \tag{47.51}$$

---

*In this equation, $P_l^{(k)}(1, a)$ denotes the kth derivative with respect to a.

Then, from (47.47), we have

$$x = k_\nu v^\nu + k_{\nu+1} v^{\nu+1} + \ldots, \tag{47.52}$$

where

$$k_\nu = -\frac{1}{\nu!} \frac{P_m^{(\nu)}(1, a)}{P_{m+1}(1, a)}.$$

Taking into account the sign of k_ν and the evenness or oddness of the number ν, we find real functions y that approach 0 as $x \to 0$ by a line of reasoning analogous to that above if a is a real number. On the other hand, if a is complex, these formulas will not give us a real y corresponding to this root a that approaches 0 as x approaches 0.

Let us suppose now that, instead of (47.51), we have

$$P_{m+1}(1, a) = 0. \tag{47.53}$$

Then, Eq. (47.47) takes the form

$$P_{m+2}(1, a)\, x^2 + P'_{m+1}(1, a)\, xv + \frac{1}{2} P''_m(1, a)\, v^2 + \\ + P(x, v) = 0, \tag{47.54}$$

where $P(x, v)$ contains terms of degree exceeding 2 in x and v. Let us note now that the polynomial $L(v)$ in Eq. (47.47), which is made up of terms not containing x, is of degree no greater than m and no less than ν since

$$P_m^{(k)}(1, v + a) \equiv 0 \text{ for } k > m, \text{ and } P_m^{(\nu)}(1, a) \neq 0.$$

If (47.54) does not have second-degree terms, that is, if we do not have

$$P_{m+2}(1, a) = P'_{m+1}(1, a) = P''_m(1, a) = 0),$$

then we have an equation of the form (47.5), which we examined above. Of course, it may happen that the set of terms of lower degree in Eq. (47.54) constitute a form of third or even higher degree. But since, in accordance with the remark made above, the polynomial $L(v)$ is of degree not exceeding m, either we obtain an equation containing linear terms (with the aid of not more than m successive transformations) or we run into the case in which these transformations, no matter how many times we perform them, lead to an equation with the lowest form of the same degree p. In the latter case, the equation corresponding to (47.44) will each time have only one p-multiple root. In that case, as was shown in [32], Eq. (47.40) is of the form

$$[a_1x + b_1y + P(x, y)]^p \Phi(x, y) = 0,$$

where $b_1 \neq 0$, where $P(x, y)$ is a convergent series in positive powers of x and y that does not contain a free term or a first-degree term in x or y, and where $\Phi(x, y)$ is a convergent series possessing a free term.

Thus, if a is a ν-multiple root of Eq. (47.44) that is real, we have a p-multiple real holomorphic solution y of Eq. (47.40) in a neighborhood of the point $x = 0$ that approaches 0 as $x \to 0$. To get all real solutions y of Eq. (47.44) that approach 0 as $x \to 0$, we need to reason along the same lines, making the substitution $x = uy$. But this should be done only in the case in which the polynomial $P_m(x, y)$ does not contain the term βy^m because, if $\beta \neq 0$ in this case, the transformation $x = uy$ does not lead to a new solution.

Here, we have given the results of [32], which contains detailed proofs. Reference [32] also examines systems of equations containing nonholomorphic functions. It is also shown there that analytic continuation of these implicit functions cannot lead to singular points $x = \overset{*}{x}$ such that the function $y = y(x)$ fails to have a limit as $x \to \overset{*}{x}$ and the infinite set of values of $y(x)$ fall in a finite closed region D embedded in the domain of definition of the function $F(x, y)$. In other words, there is no sequence of points $(x_k, y_k) \to (\overset{*}{x}, \overset{*}{y}) \in D$, where D is the domain of definition of the function $F(x, y)$. It is also shown how one may determine the entire domain of definition of an implicit function and the radius of convergence of series representing an implicit function in a neighborhood of the point $x = 0$.

Example: Suppose that $b \neq 0$ in (47.1) and that we have the function

$$y = \sum_{k=1}^{\infty} c_k x^k, \tag{47.55}$$

defined by Eq. (47.1). The point $\overset{*}{x}$ can be a singular point of this analytic function only when

$$F(\overset{*}{x}, \overset{*}{y}) = 0, F'_y(\overset{*}{x}, \overset{*}{y}) = 0. \tag{47.56}$$

This condition is necessary but not sufficient. For the point $\overset{*}{x}$ defined by Eqs. (47.56) to be a singular point, it is sufficient, for example, that, in addition,

$$F'_x(\overset{*}{x}, \overset{*}{y}) \neq 0. \tag{47.57}$$

On the other hand, if (47.56) is satisfied but

$$F'_x(\overset{*}{x}, \overset{*}{y}) = 0, \tag{47.58}$$

then the point $\overset{*}{x}$ cannot be a singular point. For example, if (47.56) and (47.58) are satisfied and the roots of the equation

$$\frac{\partial^2 F(\overset{*}{x}, \overset{*}{y})}{\partial x^2} + 2\frac{\partial^2 F(\overset{*}{x}, \overset{*}{y})}{\partial x \partial y} a + \frac{\partial^2 F(\overset{*}{x}, \overset{*}{y})}{\partial y^2} a^2 = 0$$

are real and simple, then the point $\overset{*}{x}$ cannot be a singular point of the function (47.55).

However, let us suppose that (47.56) and (47.58) are satisfied. Then, the point $\overset{*}{x}$ is a singular point. But here it may turn out that a real function (47.55) exists even when $|x| \geqslant \overset{*}{x}$. But for $x > \overset{*}{x}$ (with $\overset{*}{x}$ real), for example, this function cannot, by virtue of what was said above, be represented by a series in powers of $(x - \overset{*}{x})^{1/p}$, where p is an even positive integer.

If in the domain of definition of the function (47.1) there are no real $\overset{*}{x}$ that satisfy Eqs. (47.56), then the domain of definition of the function $F(x, y)$ contains no real singular points $\overset{*}{x}$. Then, the real function (47.1) will be defined for all real values of x in the domain of definition of the function $F(x, y)$ although the radius of convergence of the series (47.55) can be bounded by a singular value $\overset{*}{x}$ which is complex.

Example. Let y be defined by the equation

$$\Phi(x, y) = e^{ny} + e^{(n-1)y} - 2 - x = 0.$$

Here, Eqs. (47.56) have the solutions

$$e^{y_1} = 0, \ x_1 = -2 \text{ and } ne^{y_2} + n - 1 = 0,$$

$$x_2 = \left(\frac{1}{n} - 1\right)^n + \left(\frac{1}{n} - 1\right)^{n-1} - 2.$$

For the series

$$y = \sum_{k=1}^{\infty} a_k x^k = \varphi(x),$$

which is a solution of the equation $\Phi(x, y) = 0$, the points x_1 and x_2 are singular points since condition (47.57) is now satisfied (in view of the fact that $\frac{\partial \Phi(x, y)}{\partial x} = -2$). If n is positive and even, then $x_2 < 0$ and $|x_1| < |x_2|$. Therefore, the function $y = \varphi(x)$ is real in the region $-2 < x < \infty$ and the series written will converge in the region $|x| < 2$. On the other hand, if n is positive and odd, then $|x_2| < |x_1|$ and the series $\varphi(x)$ converges for $|x| < |x_2|$.

48. Two Implicit Functions

Theorem (Weierstrass) [32, 72]. *Suppose that a function $F(x_1, \ldots, x_m, y)$ is holomorphic in a neighborhood of the coordinate origin:*

$$F(x_1, \ldots, x_m, y) = \sum_{p_1+\ldots+p_m+q=1}^{\infty} a_{p_1\ldots p_m q} x_1^{p_1} \ldots x_m^{p_m} y^q, \qquad (48.1)$$

where $a_{p_1\ldots p_m q}$ are constants and the series shown converges for $|x_k| < r$, $|y| < r$ (for $k = 1, \ldots, m$). Here, r is a positive number. Suppose also that the power-series expansion of the function $F(0, \ldots, 0, y)$ begins with the nth-degree term in y:

$$F(0, \ldots, 0, y) = A_n y^n + A_{n+1} y^{n+1} + \ldots \qquad (48.2)$$

where $A_n \neq 0$. Then,

$$F(x_1, \ldots, x_m, y) \equiv (y^n + a_1 y^{n-1} + \ldots + a_{n-1} y + a_n) \Phi(x_1, \ldots x_m, y), \qquad (48.3)$$

where $a_1, \ldots, a_n$ are functions of $x_1, \ldots, x_m$ that are holomorphic at the point $x_1 = \ldots x_m = 0$ and that vanish at that point and where $\Phi(x_1, \ldots, x_m, y)$ is holomorphic at the point $x_1 = \ldots = x_m = y = 0$ but does not vanish at that point.

Suppose now that we are given the two equations

$$P(x, y, z) = \sum_{k=m}^{\infty} P_k(x, y, z) = 0, \qquad (48.4)$$

$$Q(x, y, z) = \sum_{k=n}^{\infty} Q_k(x, y, z) = 0, \qquad (48.5)$$

where $P(x, y, z)$ and $Q(x, y, z)$ are holomorphic in a neighborhood of the point $x = y = z = 0$ and the functions $P_k(x, y, z)$ and $Q_k(x, y, z)$ are homogeneous polynomials of degree k.

Theorem 48.1 [73]. *If Eqs. (48.4) and (48.5) define functions*

$$y = y(z) \to 0 \text{ and } x = x(z) \to 0 \quad \text{as} \quad z \to 0, \qquad (*)$$

*then these functions can be represented in the forms**

$$y = \sum_{k=1}^{\infty} \alpha_k z^{\frac{k}{\nu}}, \tag{48.6}$$

$$x = \sum_{k=1}^{\infty} \beta_k z^{\frac{k}{\mu}}, \tag{48.7}$$

except in the case in which Eqs. (48.4) and (48.5) have a common root $x = x(y, z)$ for *arbitrary* y *and* z.

Proof: Suppose that

$$P(x, 0, 0) = A_p x^p + A_{p+1} x^{p+1} + \dots, \tag{48.8}$$

$$Q(x, 0, 0) = B_q x^q + B_{q+1} x^{q+1} + \dots, \tag{48.9}$$

where

$$A_p \neq 0 \text{ and } B_q \neq 0. \tag{48.10}$$

Then, on the basis of Weierstrass' theorem, Eqs. (48.4) and (48.5) can also be written

$$P(x, y, z) = [x^p + \varphi_1(y, z) x^{p-1} + \dots + \varphi_p(y, z)] \Phi(x, y, z) = 0, \tag{48.11}$$

$$Q(x, y, z) = [x^q + \psi_1(y, z) x^{q-1} + \dots + \psi_q(y, z)] \Psi(x, y, z) = 0, \tag{48.12}$$

where $\varphi_k(y, z)$ and $\psi_k(y, z)$ are functions that are holomorphic at the point $y = z = 0$ and that vanish at that point and where $\Phi(0, 0, 0) \neq 0$ and $\Psi(0, 0, 0) \neq 0$. From this it follows that, to determine the functions

$$x = x(z), \quad y = y(z), \tag{48.13}$$

that satisfy Eqs. (48.4) and (48.5) in a neighborhood of the point $x = y = z = 0$, we may write

$$L_1(x) = x^p + \varphi_1(y, z) x^{p-1} + \dots + \varphi_n(y, z) = 0, \tag{48.14}$$

*In [74], see N. Chebotarev's survey of the methods of obtaining formal expansions (48.6) and (48.7) by Newton's method. Unfortunately, this work was not known to us at the time of writing [32]. Therefore, it was not cited in that work. However, [74] does not change [32].

$$L_2(x) = x^q + \psi_1(y, z) x^{q-1} + \ldots + \psi_q(y, z) = 0. \qquad (48.15)$$

If we eliminate x from these equations, we find the following necessary and sufficient condition for compatibility of Eqs. (48.14) and (48.15):

$$\Phi(\varphi_1, \ldots, \varphi_p, \psi_1, \ldots, \psi_q) = Z(y, z) = \sum_{k=1}^{\infty} Z_k(y, z) = 0, \qquad (48.16)$$

where Φ is a known polynomial [35] in $\varphi_1, \ldots, \varphi_p, \psi_1, \ldots, \psi_q$, where $Z(y, z)$ is a holomorphic function in a neighborhood of the point $y = z = 0$, and where the $Z_k(y, z)$ are homogeneous polynomials of degree k.

With regard to Eq. (48.16), we may encounter the following cases:

Case I. $\Phi(\varphi_1, \ldots, \varphi_p, \psi_1, \ldots, \psi_q) \equiv 0$. Then, Eqs. (48.14) and (48.15) and hence (48.4) and (48.5) will have common roots

$$x = x_\nu(y, z) \quad (\nu = 1, 2, \ldots) \qquad (48.17)$$

for arbitrary y and z. Consequently, we can take an arbitrary function

$$y = y(z) \to 0 \quad \text{as} \quad z \to 0, \qquad (48.18)$$

and find $x(z)$ in the form

$$x = x_\nu[y(z), z] \quad (\nu = 1, 2, \ldots). \qquad (48.19)$$

However, it may happen that $x_\nu(y, z) \nrightarrow 0$ as $y \to 0$ and $z \to 0$. Then, (48.18) and (48.19) will not be a solution of the desired form (*).

Remark: When Case I holds, Eqs. (48.14) and (48.15) can be written in the form

$$L_1(x) L(x) = 0, \quad L_2(x) L(x) = 0,$$

where L_1, L_2 and L are polynomials in x with coefficients depending on y and z. In this case, we shall also seek a solution of (48.14), (48.15) from the equations

$$L_1(x) = 0, \quad L(x) = 0$$

or

$$L(x) = 0, \quad L_2(x) = 0$$

or

$$L_1(x) = 0, \quad L_2(x) = 0,$$

which returns us to equations of the form (48.14), (48.15).

Case II. Equation (48.16) is not solvable in the form $y = \varphi(z) \to 0$ as $z \to 0$. Then, Eqs. (48.4) and (48.5) do not have solutions of the required form (*).

Case III. Equation (48.16) gives us the solution

$$y = y(z) \to 0 \quad \text{as} \quad z \to 0. \tag{48.20}$$

This solution may not be unique but it can always be represented in the form (see Sect. 47)

$$y = \sum_{k=1}^{\infty} \alpha_k z^{\frac{k}{\nu}} \tag{48.21}$$

From Eqs. (48.14) and (48.15), we see that we can obtain $x = x(z)$ in the form

$$x = \sum_{k=1}^{\infty} \beta_k z^{\frac{k}{\mu}} \tag{48.22}$$

Here, the α_k and β_k are constants and ν and μ are positive integers.

It may also happen that Eq. (48.16) does not contain y (Case II) but has the solution $z = 0$. Then, (48.4) and (48.5) can have the solution

$$z = 0, \quad x = x(y) \to 0 \quad \text{as} \quad y \to 0 \tag{48.23}$$

and $x(y)$ can be represented in the form

$$x = \sum_{k=1}^{\infty} \gamma_k y^{\frac{k}{\delta}}, \tag{48.24}$$

where the γ_k are constants and δ is a positive integer.

Suppose now that we have (48.8), (48.9), that is, that we have either

$$P(x, 0, 0) \equiv 0 \quad \text{or} \quad Q(x, 0, 0) \equiv 0.$$

Then, we shall not have (48.11) and (48.12) simultaneously. But, in this case, Eqs. (48.4) and (48.5) can be reduced to a form such that (48.8) and (48.9) hold. To do this, we introduce new variables defined by

$$\left.\begin{aligned} x &= a_1 u + b_1 v + c_1 w \\ y &= a_2 u + b_2 v + c_2 w \\ z &= a_3 u + b_3 v + c_3 w \end{aligned}\right\}. \tag{48.25}$$

Let us substitute these values of x, y and z into Eqs. (48.4) and (48.5). Then, we obtain

$$P(x, y, z) = \sum_{k+l+\nu=m}^{\infty} \alpha_{kl\nu} u^k v^l w^\nu = 0, \tag{48.26}$$

$$Q(x, y, z) = \sum_{k+l+\nu=n}^{\infty} \beta_{kl\nu} u^k v^l w^\nu = 0. \tag{48.27}$$

These series converge in a neighborhood of the point $u = v = w = 0$. It is easy to see that the coefficeints of u^m and u^n in Eqs. (48.26) and (48.27) are, respectively, equal to

$$P = P_m(a_1, a_2, a_3), \tag{48.28}$$

$$Q = Q_n(a_1, a_2, a_3). \tag{48.29}$$

Let us choose constants a_1, a_2 and a_3 such that

$$P \neq 0 \text{ and } Q \neq 0. \tag{48.30}$$

We choose the remaining coefficients in the transformation (48.25) in such a way that the determinant composed of them will be nonzero. When conditions (48.30) hold, we have, on the basis of Weierstrass' theorem, from (48.26) and (48.27)

$$\begin{aligned} P(x, y, z) = [u^m + \varphi_1(v, w)u^{m-1} + \ldots + \varphi_m(v, w)] \times \\ \times \Phi(u, v, w) = 0, \end{aligned} \tag{48.31}$$

$$\begin{aligned} Q(x, y, z) = [u^n + \psi_1(v, w)u^{n-1} + \ldots + \psi_n(v, w)] \times \\ \times \Psi(u, v, w) = 0, \end{aligned} \tag{48.32}$$

where the $\varphi_k(v, w)$ and $\psi_k(v, w)$ are holomorphic functions at the point $v = w = 0$ and vanish at that point and where $\Phi(u, v, w)$ and $\Psi(u, v, w)$ are holomorphic functions at the point $u = v = w = 0$ but do not vanish at that point.

If Cases I and II above do not hold, we obtain a solution of Eqs. (48.31), (48.32) in the form

$$u=\sum_{k=1}^{\infty}\alpha_k w^{\frac{k}{\nu}}, \tag{48.33}$$

$$v=\sum_{k=1}^{\infty}\beta_k w^{\frac{k}{\mu}}, \tag{48.34}$$

where the α_k and β_k are constants and ν and μ are positive integers. When we substitute these values of u and v into the last of Eqs. (48.25), we obtain

$$z=\sum_{k=1}^{\infty}\gamma_k w^{\frac{k}{l}} \tag{48.35}$$

where the γ_k are constants and l is a positive integer.

On the basis of (48.25), we again obtain x and y in the form (48.6), (48.7). This completes the proof of Theorem 48.1.*

In [75], a study is made of an implicit function of k variables.

49. The Construction of Functions (*) Defined by Equations (48.4) and (48.5)

Suppose that we are given two equations of the form

$$Az+By+Mx+P(x,\ y,\ z)=0, \tag{49.1}$$

$$Cz+Dy+Nx+Q(x,\ y,\ z)=0, \tag{49.2}$$

where A, B, M, C, D, and N are constants and $P(x, y, z)$ and $Q(x, y, z)$ are power series with constant coefficients not possessing free or first-degree terms in x, y, or z. These series converge in a neighborhood of the coordinate origin. Let us seek solutions $y=y(z)$, $x=x(z)$ of Eqs. (49.1) and (49.2) possessing the properties

$$x(z)\to 0,\quad \text{and}\quad y(z)\to 0\quad \text{as}\quad z\to 0, \tag{49.3}$$

---

*The question of the existence of a solution $y_1(z)\to 0,\dots,y_m(z)\to 0$ as $z\to 0$ of the equations

$$F_k(y_1, y_2,\dots, y_m, z)=\sum_{p_1+\dots+p_m+q=1}^{\infty}\alpha^{(k)}_{p_1\cdots p_m q}\, y_1^{p_1}\dots y_m^{p_m} z^q=0\quad (k=1,\dots, m)$$

is investigated in an analogous manner.

or, in general, such that

$$x(z_1),\quad x(z_2),\ldots \to 0 \text{ and } y(z_1),\quad y(z_2),\ldots \to 0 \text{ as } z_1, z_2, \ldots \to 0. \quad (49.4)$$

First of all, we note that if the rank of the matrix composed of the coefficients of the first-degree terms is equal to 2, we can immediately answer the question of the existence of such a solution. For $BN - MD \neq 0$, such a solution exists, is unique, and is easily found.

Suppose now that $AD - BC \neq 0$. Then, we have a solution of the form

$$z = \sum_{k=m}^{\infty} \alpha_k x^k, \qquad y = \sum_{k=n}^{\infty} \beta_k x^k, \quad (49.5)$$

where the α_k and β_k are constant coefficients. We see from this that the desired solutions exist and we can find all of them. We know sufficient conditions (depending on the signs of α_m and β_n and the evenness or oddness of the numbers m and n) under which these real solutions are defined for both $z > 0$ and $z < 0$ or in only one of these regions.

Let us suppose now that the rank of the matrix of the coefficients of the first-degree terms is equal to unity, that is, that at least one of the coefficients A, B, M, C, D and N is nonzero. For example, let us suppose that $A \neq 0$. Then, from Eq. (49.1), we find

$$z = \varphi(x, y), \quad (49.6)$$

where $\varphi(x, y)$ is a series that converges in a neighborhood of the coordinate origin. If we substitute this value of z into Eq. (49.2), we obtain an equation of the form

$$F(x, y) = 0.$$

Consequently, the question that we posed will be solved if we do not consider the case in which

$$F(x, y) = (ax + by + cx^2 + dxy + \varepsilon y^2 + \ldots)^2.$$

In this case, the process of determining the function $y = y(x)$ is transcendental and difficult to find (see Sect. 6 [32]).

Suppose now that $A = B = M = C = D = N = 0$. Then, Eqs. (49.1) and (49.2) can be written

$$F = P_m(x, y, z) + P_{m+1}(x, y, z) + \ldots = 0, \quad (49.7)$$

$$\Phi = Q_n(x, y, z) + Q_{n+1}(x, y, z) + \ldots = 0, \tag{49.8}$$

where $P_k(x, y, z)$ and $Q_k(x, y, z)$ are homogeneous polynomials of degree k. To answer the question posed, we introduce new functions u and v defined by*

$$x = uz, \quad y = vz \tag{49.9}$$

and assume that the sequences

$$\left.\begin{array}{l} u(z_1),\; u(z_2),\ldots, \\ v(z_1),\; v(z_2),\ldots \end{array}\right\} \tag{49.10}$$

remain bounded as $z_1, z_2, \ldots \to 0$.

If we substitute the values of x and y given by (49.9) into (49.7) and (49.8) and divide by z^m, we obtain

$$\left.\begin{array}{l} P_m(u, v, 1) + P_{m+1}(u, v, 1)z + P_{m+2}(u, v, 1)z^2 + \ldots = 0 \\ Q_n(u, v, 1) + Q_{n+1}(u, v, 1)z + Q_{n+2}(u, v, 1)z^2 + \ldots = 0 \end{array}\right\}. \tag{49.11}$$

Since $z_1, z_2, \ldots \to 0$ and the sequences (49.10) are bounded, we must have

$$u_1, u_2, \ldots \to a \text{ and } v_1, v_2, \ldots \to b, \tag{49.12}$$

where a and b are solutions of the equations

$$P_m(a, b, 1) = 0, \quad Q_n(a, b, 1) = 0. \tag{49.13}$$

In Eqs. (49.9), let us make the substitution

$$u = \tau + a, \quad v = \theta + b, \tag{49.14}$$

where τ and θ are new unknowns possessing the properties that

$$\tau(z_1),\; \tau(z_2), \ldots \to 0, \quad \theta(z_1),\; \theta(z_2), \ldots \to 0 \tag{49.15}$$

as $z_1, z_2, \ldots \to 0$.

If we substitute the values of u and v given by (49.14) into (49.11) we find

$$\begin{array}{l} P_m(\tau + a, \theta + b, 1) + P_{m+1}(\tau + a, \theta + b, 1)z + \\ \quad + P_{m+2}(\tau + a, \theta + b, 1)z^2 + \ldots = 0, \end{array} \tag{49.16}$$

*We first used this substitution in [32].

$$\begin{aligned} &Q_n(\tau+a, \theta+b, 1)+Q_{n+1}(\tau+a, \theta+b, 1)z+ \\ &+Q_{n+2}(\tau+a, \theta+b, 1)z^2+\ldots=0. \end{aligned} \tag{49.17}$$

If we expand (49.16) and (49.17) in series of powers of τ and θ, we obtain

$$\begin{aligned} &\sum_{k=1}^{\infty} P_{m+k}(a, b, 1)z^k+\sum_{k=0}^{\infty}\frac{\partial P_{m+k}(a, b, 1)}{\partial a}z^k\tau+ \\ &+\sum_{k=0}^{\infty}\frac{\partial P_{m+k}(a, b, 1)}{\partial b}z^k\theta+ \\ &+\sum_{\nu+l=2}^{\infty}\sum_{k=0}^{\infty}\frac{\partial^{\nu+l}P_{m+k}(a, b, 1)}{\partial a^\nu\,\partial b^l}z^k\tau^\nu\theta^l=0, \end{aligned} \tag{49.18}$$

$$\begin{aligned} &\sum_{k=1}^{\infty} Q_{n+k}(a, b, 1)z^k+\sum_{k=0}^{\infty}\frac{\partial Q_{n+k}(a, b, 1)}{\partial a}z^k\tau+ \\ &+\sum_{k=0}^{\infty}\frac{\partial Q_{n+k}(a, b, 1)}{\partial b}z^k\theta+ \\ &+\sum_{\nu+l=2}^{\infty}\sum_{k=0}^{\infty}\frac{\partial^{\nu+l}Q_{n+k}(a, b, 1)}{\partial a^\nu\,\partial b^l}z^k\tau^\nu\theta^l=0. \end{aligned} \tag{49.19}$$

We again have equations of the form (49.7) and (49.8). Here, the numbers m and n will not exceed the preceding ones. In general, they will be less.

If

$$\frac{\partial P_m(a, b, 1)}{\partial a}\frac{\partial Q_n(a, b, 1)}{\partial b}-\frac{\partial P_m(a, b, 1)}{\partial b}\frac{\partial Q_n(a, b, 1)}{\partial a}\neq 0.$$

in (49.18) and (49.19), then

$$\left.\begin{aligned} \tau&=a_pz^p+a_{p+1}z^{p+1}+\ldots \\ \theta&=b_qz^q+b_{q+1}z^{q+1}+\ldots \end{aligned}\right\}. \tag{49.20}$$

On the basis of (49.14), we obtain

$$\left.\begin{aligned} x&=z(a+a_pz^p+a_{p+1}z^{p+1}+\ldots) \\ y&=z(b+b_qz^q+b_{q+1}z^{q+1}+\ldots) \end{aligned}\right\}. \tag{49.21}$$

Here p and q are positive integers. If a and b are real numbers, the solution (49.21) is real.

At the beginning of this section, we saw how the question may be answered as to the existence of the required solution if at least one of the quantities

$$\left.\begin{array}{lll} P_{m+1}(a, b, 1), & \dfrac{\partial P_m(a, b, 1)}{\partial a}, & \dfrac{\partial P_m(a, b, 1)}{\partial b} \\ Q_{n+1}(a, b, 1), & \dfrac{\partial Q_n(a, b, 1)}{\partial a}, & \dfrac{\partial Q_n(a, b, 1)}{\partial b} \end{array}\right\} \qquad (49.22)$$

is nonzero. Specifically, in this case, the matter reduces to the case of a single equation in two variables.

Let us suppose that all successive transformations of the form (49.9) and (49.14) give us Eqs. (49.7) and (49.8) with $m > 1$. Then, we cannot find the desired solution.* Of course, it may happen that Eqs. (49.13) are incompatible,** which will prove that a solution possessing properties (49.4) and (49.10) does not exist.

We may seek a solution u in the form

$$x = uz, \quad z = vy, \qquad (49.23)$$

where

$$u(z_1),\ u(z_2), \dots \text{ and } v(z_1),\ v(z_2), \dots \qquad (49.24)$$

are bounded. Here, we have

$$x = p(z)\, y, \ p(z) = u(z)\, v(z),$$

where the sequence $p(z_1)$, $p(z_2), \dots$ is bounded. Thus, we have the case

$$x = p(z)\, y, \ z = q(z)\, y, \qquad (49.25)$$

where the sequences

$$p(z_1),\ p(z_2), \dots \text{ and } q(z_1),\ q(z_2), \dots \qquad (49.26)$$

are bounded. We may then proceed just as in the case of (49.9).

Theorem 49.1. *If the system (49.7), (49.8) has a solution*

$$x = x(z), \ y = y(z), \qquad (49.27)$$

*Cf. p. 40 of [32].

**Or have solution $b = \varphi(a)$.

such that $x \to 0$ *and* $y \to 0$ *as* $z \to 0$, *then, for such a solution one of the following three cases holds:*

$$\left.\begin{array}{ll} \text{I.} & x = u(z)\,z,\ \ y = v(z)\,z \\ \text{II.} & x = u(y)\,y,\ \ z = v(y)\,y \\ \text{III.} & z = u(x)\,x,\ \ y = v(x)\,x \end{array}\right\}, \tag{49.28}$$

where the sequences $u_1, u_2, \ldots$ *and* $v_1, v_2, \ldots$, *corresponding to* $z_1, z_2, \ldots$ *are bounded.**

Proof: If $v \to \infty$ in (49.9) as $z \to 0$, then $v(z) \to 0$ in (49.23). If the sequence $u(z_1), u(z_2), \ldots$ in (49.23) is bounded, we have (49.25). On the other hand, if $u(z) \longrightarrow \infty$ in (49.23) as $z \to 0$, consider

$$x = p(z)\,y. \tag{49.29}$$

If the sequence $p(y_1), p(y_2), \ldots$ is bounded, we have (49.25) and (49.26). On the other hand, if $p(z) \longrightarrow \infty$ in (49.29) as $y \to 0$, we set

$$y = p_1(x)\,x, \tag{49.30}$$

where $p_1(x) \longrightarrow 0$ as $x \to 0$.

Since $z = v(y)\,y$, where $v \to 0$ as $y \to 0$, we have, on the basis of (49.23),

$$z = q(x)\,x, \tag{49.31}$$

where $q = vp_1 \to 0$ as $x \to 0$; that is, we again have

$$z = q(x)\,x,\ \ y = p_1(x)\,x, \tag{49.32}$$

where $q(x) \to 0$ and $p_1(x) \to 0$ as $x \to 0$. This completes the proof of Theorem 49.1.

---

*Of course, all three of these cases may hold simultaneously.

Appendix

TABLE OF LAPPO-DANILEVSKIY'S COEFFICIENTS*

p_1	$\alpha^{(1)}_{p_1}$
-1	1
0	0
-2	0

p_1	p_2	$\alpha^{(1)}_{p_1p_2}$
0	-2	1
-1	-1	0
-2	0	-1

p_1	p_2	p_3	$\alpha^{(1)}_{p_1p_2p_3}$
0	-1	-2	1
0	-2	-1	0
-1	0	-2	-1
-1	-1	-1	0
-1	-2	0	-1
-2	0	-1	0
-2	-1	0	1

p_1	p_2	p_3	p_4	$\alpha^{(1)}_{p_1p_2p_3p_4}$
0	0	-2	-2	$\frac{1}{2}$
0	-1	-1	-2	1
0	-1	-2	-1	0
0	-2	0	-2	-1
0	-2	-1	-1	0
0	-2	-2	0	-1
-1	0	-1	-2	-2
-1	0	-2	-1	0
-1	-1	0	-2	1
-1	-1	-1	-1	0
-1	-1	-2	0	-1
-1	-2	0	-1	0
-1	-2	-1	0	2
-2	0	0	-2	1
-2	0	-1	-1	0
-2	0	-2	0	1
-2	-1	0	-1	0
-2	-1	-1	0	-1
-2	-2	0	0	$-\frac{1}{2}$

p_1	p_2	p_3	p_4	p_5	$\alpha^{(1)}_{p_1p_2\cdots p_3}$
0	0	-1	-2	-2	$\frac{1}{4}$
0	0	-2	-1	-2	$\frac{1}{2}$
0	0	-2	-2	-1	0
0	-1	0	-2	-2	$\frac{1}{2}$

p_1	p_2	p_3	p_4	p_5	$\alpha^{(1)}_{p_1p_2\cdots p_5}$
0	-1	-1	-1	-2	1
0	-1	-1	-2	-1	0
0	-1	-2	-0	-2	-1
0	-1	-2	-1	-1	0
0	-1	-2	-2	-0	-1
0	-2	0	-1	-2	-2
0	-2	0	-2	-1	0
0	-2	-1	0	-2	1

[1] This table was prepared by the author's colleagues at the Leningrad division of the mathematics institute of the Academy of Sciences of the USSR, O. A. Fedorova, and I. M. Varentsova, under the direction of Candidate of the Physical-Mathematical Sciences K. E. Chernin.

Table of Lappo-Danilevskiy's Coefficients (continued)

p_1	p_2	p_3	p_4	p_5	$\alpha^{(1)}_{p_1p_2\dots p_5}$
0	-2	-1	-1	-1	0
0	-2	-1	-2	0	- 1
0	-2	-2	0	-1	0
0	-2	-2	-1	0	2
-1	0	0	-2	-2	$-\frac{5}{4}$
-1	0	-1	-1	-2	- 3
-1	0	-1	-2	-1	0
-1	0	-2	0	-2	2
-1	0	-2	-1	-1	0
-1	0	-2	-2	0	0
-1	-1	0	-1	-2	3
-1	-1	0	-2	-1	0
-1	-1	-1	0	-2	- 1
-1	-1	-1	-1	-1	0
-1	-1	-1	-2	0	- 1
-1	-1	-2	0	-1	0
-1	-1	-2	-1	0	3
-1	-2	0	0	-2	0
-1	-2	0	-1	-1	0
-1	-2	0	-2	0	2
-1	-2	-1	0	-1	0

p_1	p_2	p_3	p_4	p_5	$\alpha^{(1)}_{p_1p_2\dots p_5}$
-1	-2	-1	-1	0	- 3
-1	-2	-2	0	0	$-\frac{5}{4}$
-2	0	0	-1	-2	2
-2	0	0	-2	-1	0
-2	0	-1	0	-2	- 1
-2	0	-1	-1	-1	0
-2	0	-1	-2	0	1
-2	0	-2	0	-1	0
-2	0	-2	-1	0	- 2
-2	-1	0	0	-2	- 1
-2	-1	0	-1	-1	0
-2	-1	0	-2	0	- 1
-2	-1	-1	0	-1	0
-2	-1	-1	-1	0	1
-2	-1	-2	0	0	$\frac{1}{2}$
-2	-2	0	0	-1	0
-2	-2	0	-1	0	$\frac{1}{2}$
-2	-2	-1	0	0	$\frac{1}{4}$

p_1	p_2	p_3	p_4	p_5	p_6	$\alpha^{(1)}_{p_1p_2\dots p_6}$
0	0	0	-2	-2	-2	$\frac{1}{12}$
0	0	-1	-1	-2	-2	$\frac{1}{8}$
0	0	-1	-2	-1	-2	$\frac{1}{4}$
0	0	-1	-2	-2	-1	0
0	0	-2	0	-2	-2	$\frac{1}{4}$
0	0	-2	-1	-1	-2	$\frac{1}{2}$
0	0	-2	-1	-2	-1	0
0	0	-2	-2	0	-2	$-\frac{1}{2}$
0	0	-2	-2	-1	-1	0
0	0	-2	-2	-2	0	$-\frac{1}{2}$
0	-1	0	-1	-2	-2	$\frac{1}{4}$
0	-1	0	-2	-1	-2	$\frac{1}{2}$
0	-1	0	-2	-2	-1	0
0	-1	-1	0	-2	-2	$\frac{1}{2}$
0	-1	-1	-1	-1	-2	1
0	-1	-1	-1	-2	-1	0
0	-1	-1	-2	0	-2	- 1

p_1	p_2	p_3	p_4	p_5	p_6	$\alpha^{(1)}_{p_1p_2\dots p_6}$
0	-1	-1	-2	-1	-1	0
0	-1	-1	-2	-2	0	1
0	-1	-2	0	-1	-2	- 2
0	-1	-2	0	-2	-1	0
0	-1	-2	-1	0	-2	1
0	-1	-2	-1	-1	-1	0
0	-1	-2	-1	-2	0	- 1
0	-1	-2	-2	0	-1	0
0	-1	-2	-2	-1	0	2
0	-2	0	0	-2	-2	$-\frac{5}{4}$
0	-2	0	-1	-1	-2	- 3
0	-2	0	-1	-2	-1	0
0	-2	0	-2	0	-2	2
0	-2	0	-2	-1	-1	0
0	-2	0	-2	-2	0	0
0	-2	-1	0	-1	-2	3
0	-2	-1	0	-2	-1	0
0	-2	-1	-1	-0	-2	- 1
0	-2	-1	-1	-1	-1	0
0	-2	-1	-1	-2	0	- 1
0	-2	-1	-2	0	-1	0
0	-2	-1	-2	-1	0	3
0	-2	-2	0	0	-2	0
0	-2	-2	0	-1	-1	0
0	-2	-2	0	-2	0	2
0	-2	-2	-1	0	-1	0

Table of Lappo-Danilevskiy's Coefficients (continued)

p_1	p_2	p_3	p_4	p_5	p_6	$\alpha^{(1)}_{p_1p_2\cdots p_6}$
0	-2	-2	-1	-1	0	-3
0	-2	-2	-2	0	0	$-\frac{5}{4}$
-1	0	0	-1	-2	-2	$-\frac{3}{4}$
-1	0	0	-2	-1	-2	$-\frac{7}{4}$
-1	0	0	-2	-2	-1	0
-1	0	-1	0	-2	-2	$-\frac{7}{4}$
-1	0	-1	-1	-1	-2	-4
-1	0	-1	-1	-2	-1	0
-1	0	-1	-2	0	-2	3
-1	0	-1	-2	-1	-1	0
-1	0	-1	-2	-2	0	1
-1	0	-2	0	-1	-2	5
-1	0	-2	0	-2	-1	0
-1	0	-2	-1	0	-2	-2
-1	0	-2	-1	-1	-1	0
-1	0	-2	-1	-2	0	0
-1	0	-2	-2	0	-1	0
-1	0	-2	-2	-1	0	1
-1	-1	0	0	-2	-2	$\frac{17}{8}$
-1	-1	0	-1	-1	-2	6
-1	-1	0	-1	-2	-1	0
-1	-1	0	-2	0	-2	-3
-1	-1	0	-2	-1	-1	0
-1	-1	0	-2	-2	0	-1
-1	-1	-1	0	-1	-2	-4
-1	-1	-1	0	-2	-1	0
-1	-1	-1	-1	0	-2	1
-1	-1	-1	-1	-1	-1	0
-1	-1	-1	-1	-2	0	-1
-1	-1	-1	-2	0	-1	0
-1	-1	-1	-2	-1	0	4
-1	-1	-2	0	0	-2	1
-1	-1	-2	0	-1	-1	0
-1	-1	-2	0	-2	0	3
-1	-1	-2	-1	0	-1	0
-1	-1	-2	-1	-1	0	-6
-1	-1	-2	-2	0	0	$-\frac{17}{8}$
-1	-2	0	0	-1	-2	-1
-1	-2	0	0	-2	-1	0
-1	-2	0	-1	0	-2	0
-1	-2	0	-1	-1	-1	0
-1	-2	0	-1	-2	0	2
-1	-2	0	-2	0	-1	0
-1	-2	0	-2	-1	0	-5
-1	-2	-1	0	0	-2	-1
-1	-2	-1	0	-1	-1	0

p_1	p_2	p_3	p_4	p_5	p_6	$\alpha^{(1)}_{p_1p_2\cdots p_6}$
-1	-2	-1	0	-2	0	-3
-1	-2	-1	-1	0	-1	0
-1	-2	-1	-1	-1	0	4
-1	-2	-1	-2	0	0	$\frac{7}{4}$
-1	-2	-2	0	0	-1	0
-1	-2	-2	0	-1	0	$\frac{7}{4}$
-1	-2	-2	-1	0	0	$\frac{3}{4}$
-2	0	0	0	-2	-1	$\frac{5}{4}$
-2	0	0	-1	-1	-2	3
-2	0	0	-1	-2	-1	0
-2	0	0	-2	0	-2	-2
-2	0	0	-2	-1	-1	0
-2	0	0	-2	-2	0	0
-2	0	-1	0	-1	-2	-3
-2	0	-1	0	-2	-1	0
-2	0	-1	-1	0	-2	1
-2	0	-1	-1	-1	-1	0
-2	0	-1	-1	-2	0	1
-2	0	-1	-2	0	-1	0
-2	0	-1	-2	-1	0	-3
-2	0	-2	0	0	-2	0
-2	0	-2	0	-1	-1	0
-2	0	-2	0	-2	0	-2
-2	0	-2	-1	0	-1	0
-2	0	-2	-1	-1	0	3
-2	0	-2	-2	0	0	$\frac{5}{4}$
-2	-1	0	0	-1	-2	-2
-2	-1	0	0	-2	-1	0
-2	-1	0	-1	0	-2	1
-2	-1	0	-1	-1	-1	0
-2	-1	0	-1	-2	0	-1
-2	-1	0	-2	0	-1	0
-2	-1	0	-2	-1	0	2
-2	-1	-1	0	0	-2	1
-2	-1	-1	0	-1	-1	0
-2	-1	-1	0	-2	0	1
-2	-1	-1	-1	0	-1	0
-2	-1	-1	-1	-1	0	-1
-2	-1	-1	-2	0	0	$-\frac{1}{2}$
-2	-1	-2	0	0	-1	0
-2	-1	-2	0	-1	0	$-\frac{1}{2}$
-2	-1	-2	-1	0	0	$-\frac{1}{4}$
-2	-2	0	0	0	-2	$\frac{1}{2}$

Table of Lappo-Danilevskiy's Coefficients (continued)

p_1	p_2	p_3	p_4	p_5	p_6	$\alpha^{(1)}_{p_1 p_2 \ldots p_6}$
-2	-2	0	0	-1	-1	0
-2	-2	0	0	-2	0	$\frac{1}{2}$
-2	-2	0	-1	0	-1	0
-2	-2	0	-1	-1	0	$-\frac{1}{2}$
-2	-2	0	-2	0	0	$-\frac{1}{4}$

p_1	p_2	p_3	p_4	p_5	p_6	$\alpha^{(1)}_{p_1 p_2 \ldots p_6}$
-2	-2	-1	0	0	-1	0
-2	-2	-1	0	-1	0	$-\frac{1}{4}$
-2	-2	-1	-1	0	0	$-\frac{1}{8}$
-2	-2	-2	0	0	0	$-\frac{1}{12}$

p_1	p_2	p_3	p_4	p_5	p_6	p_7	$\alpha^{(1)}_{p_1 p_2 \ldots p_7}$
0	0	0	-1	-2	-2	-2	$\frac{1}{36}$
0	0	0	-2	-1	-2	-2	$\frac{1}{24}$
0	0	0	-2	-2	-1	-2	$\frac{1}{12}$
0	0	0	-2	-2	-2	-1	0
0	0	-1	0	-2	-2	-2	$\frac{1}{24}$
0	0	-1	-1	-1	-2	-2	$\frac{1}{16}$
0	0	-1	-1	-2	-1	-2	$\frac{1}{8}$
0	0	-1	-1	-2	-2	-1	0
0	0	-1	-2	0	-2	-2	$\frac{1}{8}$
0	0	-1	-2	-1	-1	-2	$\frac{1}{4}$
0	0	-1	-2	-1	-2	-1	0
0	0	-1	-2	-2	0	-2	$-\frac{1}{4}$
0	0	-1	-2	-2	-1	-1	0
0	0	-1	-2	-2	-2	0	$-\frac{1}{4}$
0	0	-2	0	-1	-2	-2	$\frac{1}{8}$
0	0	-2	0	-2	-1	-2	$\frac{1}{4}$
0	0	-2	0	-2	-2	-1	0
0	0	-2	-1	0	-2	-2	$\frac{1}{4}$
0	0	-2	-1	-1	-1	-2	$\frac{1}{2}$
0	0	-2	-1	-1	-2	-1	0
0	0	-2	-1	-2	0	-2	$-\frac{1}{2}$
0	0	-2	-1	-2	-1	-1	0
0	0	-2	-1	-2	-2	0	$-\frac{1}{2}$
0	0	-2	-2	0	-1	-2	- 1

p_1	p_2	p_3	p_4	p_5	p_6	p_7	$\alpha^{(1)}_{p_1 p_2 \ldots p_7}$
0	0	-2	-2	0	-2	-1	0
0	0	-2	-2	-1	0	-2	$\frac{1}{2}$
0	0	-2	-2	-1	-1	-1	0
0	0	-2	-2	-2	-2	0	$-\frac{1}{2}$
0	0	-2	-2	-2	0	-1	0
0	0	-2	-2	-2	-1	0	1
0	-1	0	0	-2	-2	-2	$\frac{1}{12}$
0	-1	0	-1	-1	-2	-2	$\frac{1}{8}$
0	-1	0	-1	-2	-1	-2	$\frac{1}{4}$
0	-1	0	-1	-2	-2	-1	0
0	-1	0	-2	0	-2	-1	$\frac{1}{4}$
0	-1	0	-2	-1	-1	-2	$\frac{1}{2}$
0	-1	0	-2	-1	-2	-1	0
0	-1	0	-2	-2	0	-2	$-\frac{1}{2}$
0	-1	0	-2	-2	-1	-1	0
0	-1	0	-2	-2	-2	0	$-\frac{1}{2}$
0	-1	-1	0	-1	-2	-2	$\frac{1}{4}$
0	-1	-1	0	-2	-1	-2	$\frac{1}{2}$
0	-1	-1	0	-2	-2	-1	0
0	-1	-1	-1	0	-2	-2	$\frac{1}{2}$
0	-1	-1	-1	-1	-1	-2	1
0	-1	-1	-1	-1	-2	-1	0
0	-1	-1	-1	-2	0	-2	- 1
0	-1	-1	-1	-2	-1	-1	0
0	-1	-1	-1	-2	-2	0	- 1
0	-1	-1	-2	0	-1	-2	- 2
0	-1	-1	-2	0	-2	-1	0
0	-1	-1	-2	-1	0	-2	1
0	-1	-1	-2	-1	-1	-1	0
0	-1	-1	-2	-1	-2	0	- 1

Table of Lappo-Danilevskiy's Coefficients (continued)

p_1	p_2	p_3	p_4	p_5	p_6	p_7	$\alpha^{(1)}_{p_1 p_2 \dots p_7}$
0	-1	-1	-2	-2	0	-1	0
0	-1	-1	-2	-2	-1	0	2
0	-1	-2	0	0	-2	-2	$-\frac{5}{4}$
0	-1	-2	0	-1	-1	-2	-3
0	-1	-2	0	-1	-2	-1	0
0	-1	-2	0	-2	0	-2	2
0	-1	-2	0	-2	-1	-1	0
0	-1	-2	0	-2	-2	0	0
0	-1	-2	-1	0	-1	-2	3
0	-1	-2	-1	0	-2	-1	0
0	-1	-2	-1	-1	0	-2	-1
0	-1	-2	-1	-1	-1	-1	0
0	-1	-2	-1	-1	-2	0	-1
0	-1	-2	-1	-2	0	-1	0
0	-1	-2	-1	-2	-1	0	3
0	-1	-2	-2	0	0	-2	0
0	-1	-2	-2	0	-1	-1	0
0	-1	-2	-2	0	-2	0	2
0	-1	-2	-2	-1	0	-1	0
0	-1	-2	-2	-1	-1	0	-3
0	-1	-2	-2	-2	0	0	$-\frac{5}{4}$
0	-2	0	0	-1	-2	-2	$-\frac{3}{4}$
0	-2	0	0	-2	-1	-2	$-\frac{7}{4}$
0	-2	0	0	-2	-2	-1	0
0	-2	0	-1	0	-2	-2	$-\frac{7}{4}$
0	-2	0	-1	-1	-1	-2	-4
0	-2	0	-1	-1	-2	-1	0
0	-2	0	-1	-2	0	-2	3
0	-2	0	-1	-2	-1	-1	0
0	-2	0	-1	-2	-2	0	1
0	-2	0	-2	0	-1	-2	5
0	-2	0	-2	0	-2	-1	0
0	-2	0	-2	-1	0	-2	-2
0	-2	0	-2	-1	-1	-1	0
0	-2	0	-2	-1	-2	0	0
0	-2	0	-2	-2	0	-1	0
0	-2	0	-2	-2	-1	0	1
0	-2	-1	0	0	-2	-2	$\frac{17}{8}$
0	-2	-1	0	-1	-1	-2	6
0	-2	-1	0	-1	-2	-1	0
0	-2	-1	0	-2	0	-2	-3
0	-2	-1	0	-2	-1	-1	0
0	-2	-1	0	-2	-2	0	-1
0	-2	-1	-1	0	-1	-2	-4
0	-2	-1	-1	0	-2	-1	0
0	-2	-1	-1	-1	-1	-2	1

p_1	p_2	p_3	p_4	p_5	p_6	p_7	$\alpha^{(1)}_{p_1 p_2 \dots p_7}$
0	-2	-1	-1	-1	-1	-1	0
0	-2	-1	-1	-1	-2	0	-1
0	-2	-1	-1	-2	0	-1	0
0	-2	-1	-2	-2	-1	0	4
0	-2	-1	-2	0	0	-2	1
0	-2	-1	-2	0	-1	-1	0
0	-2	-1	-2	0	-2	0	3
0	-2	-1	-2	-1	0	-1	0
0	-2	-1	-2	-1	-1	0	-6
0	-2	-1	-2	-2	0	0	$\frac{17}{8}$
0	-2	-2	0	0	-1	-2	-1
0	-2	-2	0	0	-2	-1	0
0	-2	-2	0	-1	0	-2	0
0	-2	-2	0	-1	-1	-1	0
0	-2	-2	0	-1	-2	0	0
0	-2	-2	0	-2	0	-1	0
0	-2	-2	0	-2	-1	0	-5
0	-2	-2	-1	0	0	-2	-1
0	-2	-2	-1	0	-1	-1	0
0	-2	-2	-1	0	-2	0	-3
0	-2	-2	-1	-1	0	-1	0
0	-2	-2	-1	-1	-1	0	4
0	-2	-2	-1	-2	0	0	$\frac{7}{4}$
0	-2	-2	-2	0	0	-1	0
0	-2	-2	-2	0	-1	0	$\frac{7}{4}$
0	-2	-2	-2	-1	0	0	$\frac{3}{4}$
-1	0	0	0	-2	-2	-2	$-\frac{5}{18}$
-1	0	0	-1	-1	-2	-2	$-\frac{7}{16}$
-1	0	0	-1	-2	-1	-2	-1
-1	0	0	-1	-2	-2	-1	0
-1	0	0	-2	0	-2	-2	-1
-1	0	0	-2	-1	-1	-2	$-\frac{9}{4}$
-1	0	0	-2	-1	-2	-1	0
-1	0	0	-2	-2	0	-2	$\frac{7}{4}$
-1	0	0	-2	-2	-1	-1	0
-1	0	0	-2	-2	-2	0	$\frac{3}{4}$
-1	0	-1	0	-1	-2	-2	-1
-1	0	-1	0	-2	-1	-2	$-\frac{9}{4}$
-1	0	-1	0	-2	-2	-1	0
-1	0	-1	-1	0	-2	-2	$-\frac{9}{4}$
-1	0	-1	-1	-1	-1	-2	-5

Table of Lappo-Danilevskiy's Coefficients (continued)

p_1	p_2	p_3	p_4	p_5	p_6	p_7	$\alpha^{(1)}_{p_1 p_2 \ldots p_7}$
-1	0	-1	-1	-1	-2	-1	0
-1	0	-1	-1	-2	0	-2	4
-1	0	-1	-1	-2	-1	-1	0
-1	0	-1	-1	-2	-2	0	2
-1	0	-1	-2	0	-1	-2	7
-1	0	-1	-2	0	-2	-1	0
-1	0	-1	-2	-1	0	-2	- 3
-1	0	-1	-2	-1	-1	-1	0
-1	0	-1	-2	-1	-2	0	1
-1	0	-1	-2	-2	0	-1	0
-1	0	-1	-2	-2	-1	0	- 1
-1	0	-2	0	0	-2	-2	$\frac{27}{8}$
-1	0	-2	0	-1	-1	-2	9
-1	0	-2	0	-1	-2	-1	0
-1	0	-2	0	-2	0	-2	- 5
-1	0	-2	0	-2	-1	-1	0
-1	0	-2	0	-2	-2	0	- 1
-1	0	-2	-1	0	-1	-2	- 7
-1	0	-2	-1	0	-2	-1	0
-1	0	-2	-1	-1	0	-2	2
-1	0	-2	-1	-1	-1	-1	0
-1	0	-2	-1	-1	-2	0	0
-1	0	-2	-1	-2	0	-1	0
-1	0	-2	-1	-2	-1	0	1
-1	0	-2	-2	0	0	-2	1
-1	0	-2	-2	0	-1	-1	0
-1	0	-2	-2	0	-2	0	1
-1	0	-2	-2	-1	0	-1	0
-1	0	-2	-2	-1	-1	0	- 3
-1	0	-2	-2	-2	0	0	$-\frac{7}{8}$
-1	-1	0	0	-1	-2	-2	$\frac{23}{16}$
-1	-1	0	0	-2	-1	-2	$\frac{31}{8}$
-1	-1	0	0	-2	-2	-1	0
-1	-1	0	-1	0	-2	-2	$\frac{31}{8}$
-1	-1	0	-1	-1	-1	-2	10
-1	-1	0	-1	-1	-2	-1	0
-1	-1	0	-1	-2	0	-2	- 6
-1	-1	0	-1	-2	-1	-1	0
-1	-1	0	-1	-2	-2	0	- 2
-1	-1	0	-2	0	-1	-2	- 9
-1	-1	0	-2	0	-2	-1	0
-1	-1	0	-2	-1	0	-2	3
-1	-1	0	-2	-1	-1	-1	0
-1	-1	0	-2	-1	-2	0	- 1
-1	-1	0	-2	-2	0	-1	0
-1	-1	0	-2	-2	-1	0	3

p_1	p_2	p_3	p_4	p_5	p_6	p_7	$\alpha^{(1)}_{p_1 p_2 \ldots p_7}$
-1	-1	-1	0	0	-2	-2	$\frac{49}{16}$
-1	-1	-1	0	-1	-1	-2	-10
-1	-1	-1	0	-1	-2	-1	0
-1	-1	-1	0	-2	0	-2	4
-1	-1	-1	0	-2	-1	-1	0
-1	-1	-1	0	-2	-2	0	0
-1	-1	-1	-1	0	-1	-2	5
-1	-1	-1	-1	0	-2	-1	0
-1	-1	-1	-1	-1	0	-2	- 1
-1	-1	-1	-1	-1	-1	-1	0
-1	-1	-1	-1	-1	-2	0	- 1
-1	-1	-1	-1	-2	0	-1	0
-1	-1	-1	-1	-2	-1	0	5
-1	-1	-1	-2	0	0	-2	0
-1	-1	-1	-2	0	-1	-1	0
-1	-1	-1	-2	0	-2	0	4
-1	-1	-1	-2	-1	0	-1	0
-1	-1	-1	-2	-1	-1	0	-10
-1	-1	-1	-2	-2	0	0	$-\frac{49}{16}$
-1	-1	-2	0	0	-1	-2	3
-1	-1	-2	0	0	-2	-1	0
-1	-1	-2	0	-1	0	-2	- 1
-1	-1	-2	0	-1	-1	-1	0
-1	-1	-2	0	-1	-2	0	3
-1	-1	-2	0	-2	0	-1	0
-1	-1	-2	0	-2	-1	0	- 9
-1	-1	-2	-1	0	0	-2	- 2
-1	-1	-2	-1	0	-1	-1	0
-1	-1	-2	-1	0	-2	0	- 6
-1	-1	-2	-1	-1	0	-1	0
-1	-1	-2	-1	-1	-1	0	10
-1	-1	-2	-1	-2	0	0	$\frac{31}{8}$
-1	-1	-2	-2	0	0	-1	0
-1	-1	-2	-2	0	-1	0	$\frac{31}{8}$
-1	-1	-2	-2	-1	0	0	$\frac{23}{16}$
-1	-2	0	0	0	-2	-2	$-\frac{7}{8}$
-1	-2	0	0	-1	-1	-2	- 3
-1	-2	0	0	-1	-2	-1	0
-1	-2	0	0	-2	0	-2	1
-1	-2	0	0	-2	-1	-1	0
-1	-2	0	0	-2	-2	0	1
-1	-2	0	-1	0	-1	-2	1
-1	-2	0	-1	0	-2	-1	0
-1	-2	0	-1	-1	0	-2	0
-1	-2	0	-1	-2	0	-1	0

Table of Lappo-Danilevskiy's Coefficients (continued)

p_1	p_2	p_3	p_4	p_5	p_6	p_7	$\alpha^{(1)}_{p_1 p_2 \ldots p_7}$
-1	-2	0	-1	-1	-2	0	2
-1	-2	0	-1	-2	0	-1	0
-1	-2	0	-1	-2	-1	0	-7
-1	-2	0	-2	0	0	-2	-1
-1	-2	0	-2	0	-1	-1	0
-1	-2	0	-2	0	-2	0	-5
-1	-2	0	-2	-1	0	-1	0
-1	-2	0	-2	-1	-1	0	9
-1	-2	0	-2	-2	0	0	$\frac{27}{8}$
-1	-2	-1	0	0	-1	-2	-1
-1	-2	-1	0	0	-2	-1	0
-1	-2	-1	0	-1	0	-2	1
-1	-2	-1	0	-1	-1	-1	0
-1	-2	-1	0	-1	-2	0	-3
-1	-2	-1	0	-2	0	-1	0
-1	-2	-1	0	-2	-1	0	7
-1	-2	-1	-1	0	0	-2	2
-1	-2	-1	-1	0	-1	-1	0
-1	-2	-1	-1	0	-2	0	4
-1	-2	-1	-1	-1	0	-1	0
-1	-2	-1	-1	-1	-1	0	-5
-1	-2	-1	-1	-2	0	0	$-\frac{9}{4}$
-1	-2	-1	-2	0	0	-1	0
-1	-2	-1	-2	0	-1	0	$-\frac{9}{4}$
-1	-2	-1	-2	-1	0	0	-1
-1	-2	-2	0	0	0	-2	$\frac{3}{4}$
-1	-2	-2	0	0	-1	-1	0
-1	-2	-2	0	0	-2	0	$\frac{7}{4}$
-1	-2	-2	0	-1	0	-1	0
-1	-2	-2	0	-1	-1	0	$-\frac{9}{4}$
-1	-2	-2	0	-2	0	0	-1
-1	-2	-2	-1	0	0	-1	0
-1	-2	-2	-1	0	-1	0	-1
-1	-2	-2	-1	-1	0	0	$-\frac{1}{16}$
-1	-2	-2	-2	0	0	0	$-\frac{5}{18}$
-2	0	0	0	-1	-2	-2	$\frac{3}{4}$
-2	0	0	0	-2	-1	-2	$\frac{7}{4}$
-2	0	0	0	-2	-2	-1	0
-2	0	0	-1	0	-2	-2	$\frac{7}{4}$
-2	0	0	-1	-1	-1	-2	4

p_1	p_2	p_3	p_4	p_5	p_6	p_7	$\alpha^{(1)}_{p_1 p_2 \ldots p_7}$
-2	0	0	-1	-1	-2	-1	0
-2	0	0	-1	-2	0	-2	-3
-2	0	0	-1	-2	-1	-1	0
-2	0	0	-1	-2	-2	0	-1
-2	0	0	-2	0	-1	-2	-5
-2	0	0	-2	0	-2	-1	0
-2	0	0	-2	-1	0	-2	0
-2	0	0	-2	-1	-1	-1	0
-2	0	0	-2	-1	-2	0	0
-2	0	0	-2	-2	0	-1	0
-2	0	0	-2	-2	-1	0	-1
-2	0	-1	0	0	-2	-2	$-\frac{17}{8}$
-2	0	-1	0	-1	-1	-2	-6
-2	0	-1	0	-1	-2	-1	0
-2	0	-1	0	-2	0	-2	3
-2	0	-1	0	-2	-1	-1	0
-2	0	-1	0	-2	-2	0	1
-2	0	-1	-1	0	-1	-2	4
-2	0	-1	-1	0	-2	-1	0
-2	0	-1	-1	-1	0	-2	-1
-2	0	-1	-1	-1	-1	-1	0
-2	0	-1	-1	-1	-2	0	1
-2	0	-1	-1	-2	0	-1	0
-2	0	-1	-1	-2	-1	0	-4
-2	0	-1	-2	0	0	-2	-1
-2	0	-1	-2	0	-1	-1	0
-2	0	-1	-2	0	-2	0	-3
-2	0	-1	-2	-1	0	-1	0
-2	0	-1	-2	-1	-1	0	6
-2	0	-1	-2	-2	0	0	$\frac{17}{8}$
-2	0	-2	0	0	-1	-2	1
-2	0	-2	0	0	-2	-1	0
-2	0	-2	0	-1	0	-2	0
-2	0	-2	0	-1	-1	-1	0
-2	0	-2	0	-1	-2	0	-2
-2	0	-2	0	-2	0	-1	0
-2	0	-2	0	-2	-1	0	5
-2	0	-2	-1	0	0	-2	1
-2	0	-2	-1	0	-1	-1	0
-2	0	-2	-1	0	-2	0	3
-2	0	-2	-1	-1	0	-1	0
-2	0	-2	-1	-1	-1	0	-4
-2	0	-2	-1	-2	0	0	$-\frac{7}{4}$
-2	0	-2	-2	0	0	-1	0
-2	0	-2	-2	0	-1	0	$-\frac{7}{4}$
-2	0	-2	-2	-1	0	0	$-\frac{3}{4}$

Table of Lappo-Danilevskiy's Coefficients (continued)

p_1	p_2	p_3	p_4	p_5	p_6	p_7	$\alpha^{(1)}_{p_1 p_2 \ldots p_7}$
-2	-1	0	0	0	-2	-2	$-\frac{5}{4}$
-2	-1	0	0	-1	-1	-2	-3
-2	-1	0	0	-1	-2	-1	0
-2	-1	0	0	-2	0	-2	2
-2	-1	0	0	-2	-1	-1	0
-2	-1	0	0	-2	-2	0	0
-2	-1	0	-1	0	-1	-2	3
-2	-1	0	-1	0	-2	-1	0
-2	-1	0	-1	-1	0	-2	-1
-2	-1	0	-1	-1	-1	-1	0
-2	-1	0	-1	-1	-2	0	-1
-2	-1	0	-1	-2	0	-1	0
-2	-1	0	-1	-2	-1	0	3
-2	-1	0	-2	0	0	-2	0
-2	-1	0	-2	0	-1	-1	0
-2	-1	0	-2	0	-2	0	2
-2	-1	0	-2	-1	0	-1	0
-2	-1	0	-2	-1	-1	0	-3
-2	-1	0	-2	-2	0	0	$-\frac{5}{4}$
-2	-1	-1	0	0	-1	-2	2
-2	-1	-1	0	0	-2	-1	0
-2	-1	-1	0	-1	0	-2	-1
-2	-1	-1	0	-1	-1	-1	0
-2	-1	-1	0	-1	-2	0	1
-2	-1	-1	0	-2	0	-1	0
-2	-1	-1	0	-2	-1	0	-1
-2	-1	-1	-1	0	0	-1	-1
-2	-1	-1	-1	0	-1	-1	0
-2	-1	-1	-1	0	-2	0	-1
-2	-1	-1	-1	-1	0	-1	0
-2	-1	-1	-1	-1	-1	0	1
-2	-1	-1	-1	-2	0	0	$\frac{1}{2}$
-2	-1	-1	-2	0	0	-1	0
-2	-1	-1	-2	0	-1	0	$\frac{1}{2}$
-2	-1	-1	-2	-1	0	0	$\frac{1}{4}$
-2	-1	-2	0	0	0	-1	$-\frac{1}{2}$
-2	-1	-2	0	0	-1	-2	0
-2	-1	-2	0	0	-2	0	$-\frac{1}{2}$
-2	-1	-2	0	-1	0	-1	0
-2	-1	-2	0	-1	-1	0	$\frac{1}{2}$
-2	-1	-2	0	-2	0	0	$\frac{1}{4}$
-2	-1	-2	-1	0	0	-1	0

p_1	p_2	p_3	p_4	p_5	p_6	p_7	$\alpha^{(1)}_{p_1 p_2 \ldots p_7}$
-2	-1	-2	-1	0	-1	0	$\frac{1}{4}$
-2	-1	-2	-1	-1	0	0	$\frac{1}{8}$
-2	-1	-2	-2	0	0	0	$\frac{1}{12}$
-2	-2	0	0	0	-1	-2	1
-2	-2	0	0	0	-2	-1	0
-2	-2	0	0	-1	0	-2	$-\frac{1}{2}$
-2	-2	0	0	-1	-1	-1	0
-2	-2	0	0	-1	-2	0	$\frac{1}{2}$
-2	-2	0	0	-2	0	-1	0
-2	-2	0	0	-2	-1	0	-1
-2	-2	0	-1	0	0	-2	$-\frac{1}{2}$
-2	-2	0	-1	0	-1	-1	0
-2	-2	0	-1	0	-2	0	$-\frac{1}{2}$
-2	-2	0	-1	-1	0	-1	0
-2	-2	0	-1	-1	-1	0	$\frac{1}{2}$
-2	-2	0	-1	-2	0	0	$\frac{1}{4}$
-2	-2	0	-2	0	0	-1	0
-2	-2	0	-2	0	-1	0	$\frac{1}{4}$
-2	-2	0	-2	-1	0	0	$\frac{1}{8}$
-2	-2	-1	0	0	0	-2	$-\frac{1}{4}$
-2	-2	-1	0	0	-1	-1	0
-2	-2	-1	0	0	-2	0	$-\frac{1}{4}$
-2	-2	-1	0	-1	0	-1	0
-2	-2	-1	0	-1	-1	0	$\frac{1}{4}$
-2	-2	-1	0	-2	0	0	$\frac{1}{8}$
-2	-2	-1	-1	0	0	-1	0
-2	-2	-1	-1	0	-1	0	$\frac{1}{8}$
-2	-2	-1	-1	-1	0	0	$\frac{1}{16}$
-2	-2	-1	-2	0	0	0	$\frac{1}{24}$
-2	-2	-2	0	0	0	-1	0
-2	-2	-2	0	0	-1	0	$\frac{1}{12}$
-2	-2	-2	0	-1	0	0	$\frac{1}{24}$
-2	-2	-2	-1	0	0	0	$\frac{1}{36}$

Bibliography

1. Lappo-Danilevskiy, I. A., *Primeneniye funktsiy ot matrits k teorii lineynykh sistem obyknovennykh differentsial'nykh uravneniy* (Application of functions of matrices to the theory of linear systems of ordinary differential equations), GITTL, 1957.
2. Smirnov, V. I., *A Course of Higher Mathematics*, Vol. III, Reading, Massachusetts, Addison-Wesley, 1964.
3. Gantmakher, F. R., *The Theory of Matrices*, New York, Chelsea, 1959.
4. Erugin, N. P., *Metod Lappo-Danilevskogo v teorii lineynykh differentsial'nykh uravneniy*. (Lappo-Danilevskiy's method in the theory of linear differential equations), Leningrad University Press, 1956.
5. Erugin, N. P., "O pokazatel'noy podstanovke sistemy lineynykh differentsial'nykh uravneniy" (problema Puankare) (On the exponential substitution of a system of linear differential equations (the Poincaré problem)), *Matem. sb.*, 3 (45), No. 3, 1938.
6. Goursat, E., *Cours d'Analyse mathématique*, 7th ed., vol. II, Paris, Gauthier-Villars.
7. Hukuhara, M., Tokyo Daigaku ruga Kubu Kuë., S. Fac. Sci. Univ. Tokyo. Sec. 1, 7, No. 1, 1954.
8. Artem'yev, N. A., "Issledovaniye osushchestvimosti periodicheskikh dvizheniy" (An investigation of the attainability of periodic motions), *Izv. Akad. nauk*, USSR, Seriya matem., 5, No. 2, 1941.
9. Artem'yev, N. A., "Metod opredeleniya kharakteristicheskikh pokazateley i prilozheniye ego k dvum zadacham nebesnoy mekhaniki" (A method of determining characteristic exponents and its application to two problems in celestial mechanics), *Izv. Akad. nauk*, USSR, seriya matem., 8, No. 2, 1944.
10. Shtokalo, I. Z., "Kriteriy ustoychivosti i neustoychivosti" (Stability and instability tests), *Matem. sb.*, 19 (61), 263-286, 1946.
11. Erugin, N. P., "Nekotoryye obshchiye problemy kachestvennoy i analiticheskoy teorii differentsial'nykh uravneniy" (Some general problems in the qualitative and analytic theory of differential equations), *Priklad. mat. mekh*, 19, No. 2, 1955.
12. Yakubovich, V. A., "Metod malogo parametra dlya kanonicheskikh sistem s periodicheskimi koeffitsiyentami" (The small-

parameter method for canonical systems with periodic coefficients), *Priklad. mat. mekh*, XXIII, no. 1, 1959.
13. Erugin, N. P., "Metody issledovaniya voprosa ustoychivosti resheniy lineynykh sistem differentsial'nykh uravneniy s periodicheskimi koeffitsiyentami, soderzhashchimi malyy parametr (zamechaniya k rabote Yakubovicha)" (Methods of investigating the stability of solutions of linear systems of differential equations with periodic coefficients that contain a small parameter (comments on Yakubovich's work)), *Inst. Fiz. Zhurnal*, III, No. 2, 1960.
14. Erugin, N. P., "Privodimyye sistemy" (Reduced systems), *Trudy Fiziko- matematicheskogo instituta im. V. A. Steklova*, XIII, 1946.
15. Bogdanov, Yu. S., and G. N. Chebotarev, "O matritsakh, kommutiruyushchikh so svoyey proizvodnoy" (Matrices that commute with their derivatives), *Izv. vysshikh uchebnykh zavedeniy. Matem.*, No. 4 (11), 1959.
16. Amato, V., "Sull'integrazione immediata di un sistema di equazioni differenziali lineari omogenee a matrice circolante," *Giorn. di mat. di Battaglini*, 82, No. 1, 1954.
17. Shenitrer Abe (to 57) Bernstein, B. Truesdell, c(9968), Magnus Wilhelm (2181).
18. Cherubino, S., *Zentralblatt für Mathematik*. 17, 209, 1937-1938.
19. Cherubino, S., *Atti Accad. naz. Lincei Rend.* VI, 25, 1937, 541-547, 686-690.
20. Fedorov, F. I., "Ob odnom obobshchenii kriteriya Lappo-Danilevskogo" (A generalization of Lappo-Danilevskiy's test), *Doklady Akad. nauk*, Belorussian SSR, 4, No. 11, 1960.
21. Mal'tsev, A. M., *Osnovy lineynoy algebry* (Fundamentals of linear algebra), OGIZ, 1948.
22. Erugin, N. P., "Zamechaniye k stat'ye Shifnera" (A remark of Shifner's article), *Izv. Akad. nauk*, USSR, seriya matem., No. 5, 1941.
23. Fedorov, G. F., "Nekotoryye novyye sluchai resheniya sistemy dvukh lineynykh uravneniy v konechnom vide" (Certain new cases of solution of a system of two linear equations in closed form), *Vestnik*, Leningrad State University, No. 11, 1953.
24. Morozov, V. V., "Ob odnoy zadache N. P. Yerugina" (On a problem of N. P. Erugin), *Izv. vysshikh uchebnykh zavedeniy*, Matem., No. 5, 1959.
25. Salakhova, I. M., and G. N. Chebotarev, "O razreshimosti v konechnom vide nekotorykh sistem lineynykh differentsial'nykh uravneniy" (Closed-form solvability of certain systems of linear differential equations), *Izv. vysshikh uchebnykh zavedeniy*, Matem., No. 3, 230-234, 1960.

26. Lyapunov, A. M., "Obshchaya zadacha ob ustoychivosti dvizheniya" (A general problem on the stability of motion), *Sobraniye sochineniy* (Collected works), Vol. II, Akad. nauk press, USSR, 1956.
27. Donskaya, L. I., "Postroyeniye resheniya lineynoy sistemy v okrestnosti regulyarnoy osoboy tochki v osobykh sluchayakh" (The construction of a solution of a linear system in a neighborhood of a regular singular point in special cases), *Vestnik*, Leningrad State University, No. 6, 1952.
28. Donskaya, L. I., "O strukture resheniy sistemy lineynykh differentsial'nykh uravneniy v okrestnosti regulyarnoy osoboy tochki" (On the structure of solutions of a system of linear differential equations in a neighborhood of regular singular points), *Vestnik*, Leningrad State University, No. 8, 1954.
29. Erouguine, N., "Sur la substitution exposante pour quelques sistèmes irrégulières," *Matem. sb.* m. 42:6, 745-753, 1935.
30. Erugin, N. P., "Ob asimptoticheskoy ustoychivosti resheniya nekotoroy sistemy differentsial'nykh uravneniy" (On the asymptotic stability of a solution of a certain system of differential equations), *Priklad. mat. mekh*, XII, No. 2, 1948.
31. Erugin, N. P., *Priklad. mat. mekh*, XXIII, no. 5, 1959.
32. Erugin, N. P., "Neyavnyye funktsii" (Implicit functions), Leningrad University press, 1956.
33. Breus, K. A., "O privodimosti kanonicheskoy sistemy differentsial'nykh uravneniy s periodicheskimi koeffitsiyentami" (The reducibility of a canonical system of differential equations with periodic coefficients), *Doklady Akad. nauk*, USSR, 123, No. 1, 1958.
34. Krein, M. G., "Osnovnyye polozheniya teorii λ-zon ustoychivosti kanonicheskoy sistemy lineynykh differentsial'nykh uravneniy s periodicheskimi koeffitsiyentami" (Fundamentals of the theory of λ-zones of stability of a canonical system of linear differential equations with periodic coefficients), *Sb. "Pamyati A. A. Andronova,"* Izd. Akad. Nauk, USSR, 1955.
35. Kurosh, A. G., *Kurs vysshey algebry* (A course in higher algebra), 1946.
36. Chetayev, N. G., *Priklad. mat. mekh.*, IX, no. 2, 1945.
37. Chetayev, N. G., *Ustoychivost' dvizheniya* (Stability of motion), OGIZ, 1946.
38. Shtokalo, I. Z., "Lineynyye differentsial'nyye uravneniya s peremennymi koeffitsiyentami" (Linear differential equations with variable coefficients), *Izd. Akad. nauk*, Ukr. SSR, Kiev, 1960.
39. Levitan, B. M., *Pochti-periodicheskiye funktsii* (Almost-periodic functions), GITTL, 1953.
40. Gel'man, A. Ye., *Doklady Akad. nauk*, USSR, 116, no. 4, 1957.

41. Shtelik, V. G., "K voprosu o resheniyakh lineynoy sistemy differential'nykh uravneniy s pochti-periodicheskimi koeffitsiyentami" (On the question of solutions of a linear system of differential equations with almost-periodic coefficients), *Ukr. matem. zhurnal*, 10, No. 3, 1958.
42. Ivanov, V. N., *Doklady Akad. nauk*, 109, No. 5, 902-905, 1956.
43. Khalanay, A., *Doklady Akad. nauk*, USSR, 88, No. 3, 419-422, 1953.
44. Şandor, Şt., *Bul. St. Akad. R. P. R.*, sec. de Şt. mat. şi fiz., XII, No. 2, 339, 1955.
45. Lyashchenko, N. Ya., *Doklady Akad. nauk*, SSSR, 111, No. 2, 295-298, 1956.
46. Bogolyubov, N. N., and Yu. A. Mitropol'skiy, *Asymptotic Methods in the Theory of Nonlinear Oscillations*, 2nd ed., Delhi, Hindustan Publishing Corporation, 1961.
47. Vinogradov, I. M., "Obshchiye teoremy o verkhney granitse modulya trigonometricheskoy summy" (General theorems on an upper bound of the absolute value of a trigonometric sum). *Izv. Akad. nauk*, USSR, seriya matem., 15, No. 2, 1951.
48. Vinogradov, I. M., "Osobyye sluchai otsenok trigonometricheskikh summ" (Special cases of bounds for trigonometric sums), *Izv. Akad. nauk*, USSR, seriya matem., 20, No. 3, 1956.
49. Yakubovich, V. A., *Vestnik*, Leningrad University, seriya matem., mekhan. i. astr., 13, No. 3, 1958.
50. Golokvoschus, P. B., "Neobkhodimyye i dostatochnyye usloviya periodichnosti fundamental'noy sistemy resheniy nekotorykh lineynykh sistem differentsial'nykh uravneniy" (Necessary and sufficient conditions for periodicity of a fundamental system of solutions of certain linear systems of differential equations), *Doklady Akad. nauk*, Belorussian SSR, 3, No. 7, 1959.
51. Golokvoschus, P. B., "Otyskaniye kharakteristicheskikh pokazateley sistem dvukh lineynykh odnorodnykh differentsial'nykh uravneniy s periodicheskimi koeffitsiyentami, soderzhashchimi malyy parametr" (The finding of characteristic exponents of systems of two linear homogeneous differential equations with periodic coefficients containing a small parameter), *Doklady Akad. nauk*, Belorussian SSR, 3, No. 9, 1959.
52. Golokvoschus, P. B., "Otyskaniye kharakteristicheskikh pokazateley sistemy dvukh differentsial'nykh uravneniy s periodicheskimi koeffitsiyentami, analiticheskimi otnositel'no malogo parametra" (The finding of characteristic exponents of a system of two differential equations with periodic coefficients that are analytic with respect to a small parameter), *Doklady Akad. nauk*, Belorussian SSR, 4, No. 6, 1960.
53. Golokvoschus, P. B., "Zamechaniya ob ogranichennykh i periodicheskikh resheniyakh sistemy dvukh lineynykh

differential'nykh uravneniy s periodicheskimi koeffitsiyentami, integriruyemoy v zamknutoy forme'' (Remarks on bounded and periodic solutions of a system of two linear differential equations with periodic coefficients that is solvable in closed form), *Izv. vysshikh uchebnykh zavedeniy, Matem.* No. 3, 1960.
54. Golokvoschus, P. B., ''Ob ogranichennykh i periodicheskikh resheniyakh nekotoroy sistemy dvukh lineynykh differentsial'nykh uravneniy s periodicheskimi koeffitsiyentami'' (On bounded and periodic solutions of a certain system of two linear differential equations with periodic coefficients), *Ucheniyye zapiski Vil'nyusskogo gos. universiteta im. V. Kapsukasa*, 9, seriya matem., i fiz. nauk, 1960.
55. Golokvoschus, P. B., ''Dostatochnyye usloviya ogranichennosti vsekh resheniy sistemy dvukh uravneniy, soderzhashchikh malyy parametr'' (Sufficient conditions for boundedness of all solutions of a system of two equations that contain a small parameter), *Ibid.*
56. Gremyachenskiy, A. P., ''Obobshcheniye odnoy teoremy Lyapunova'' (A generalization of a theorem of Lyapunov), *Priklad. mat. mekh.*, XII, no. 5, 1948.
57. Lyapunov, A. M., ''Sur une série dans la théorie, linéaire du second ordre a coefficients periodiques,'' *Zapiski Akademii nauk po fiz.-matem. otd. seriya*, 8, 13, No. 2, 1902.
58. Erugin, N. P., ''Obobshcheniye odnoy teoremy Lyapunova'' (A generalization of a theorem of Lyapunov), *Priklad. mat. mekh.* XII, No. 5, 1948.
59. Morozov, V. V., ''O kommutativnykh matritsakh'' (On commutative matrices), *Uchenyye zapiski*, Kiev State University, 112, book 9, 1952.
60. Erugin, N. P., ''O periodicheskikh resheniyakh differentsial'nykh uravneniy'' (On periodic solutions of differential equations), *Priklad. mat. mekh.*, 20, No. 1, 1956.
61. Vinogradov, I. M., *Elements of Number Theory*, New York, Dover, 1954.
62. Zhukovskiy, N. Ye., *Matem. sb.*, XVI, 3, 1892.
63. Burdina, V. I., ''Ob ogranichennykh resheniyakh sistemy dvukh lineynykh differentsial'nykh uravneniy'' (On bounded solutions of a system of two linear differential equations), *Doklady Akad. nauk*, USSR, XCIII, No. 4, 1953.
64. Kusarova, R. S., ''Ob ogranichennosti resheniy lineynogo differential'nogo uravneniya s periodicheskimi koeffitsiyentami'' (On bounded solutions of a linear differential equation with periodic coefficients), *Priklad. mat. mekh.* 14, No. 3, 1950.
65. Gusarov, L. A., ''Ob ogranichennosti resheniy lineynogo uravneniya vtorogo poryadka'' (On boundedness of solutions of

a linear second-order equation), *Doklady Akad. nauk*, USSR, 17, No. 2, 1949.

66. Starzhinskiy, V. M., "Obzor rabot ob usloviyakh ustoychivosti trivial'nogo resheniya sistemy lineynykh differentsial'nykh uravneniy s periodicheskimi koeffitsiyentami" (A survey of articles on the conditions for stability of a trivial solution of a system of linear differential equations with periodic coefficients), *Priklad. mat. mekh.* 18, No. 4, 1954.
67. Yakubovich, V. A., "Voprosy ustoychivosti resheniya dvukh lineynykh differentsial'nykh uravnenly kanonicheskogo vida s periodicheskimi koeffitsiyentami" (Questions on the stability of a solution of two linear differential equations in canonical form with periodic coefficients), *Matem. sb.*, 37 (79), No. 1, 1955.
68. Starzhinskiy, V. M., "Ob ustoychivosti periodicheskikh dvizheniy" (On the stability of periodic motions), (I) *Izv. Yasskogo politekhn. in-ta.*, Novaya seriya (New series), IV (VIII), No. 3-4, 1958 (II), V (IX), No. 1-2, 1959.
69. Starzhinskiy, V. M., "Zamechaniye k issledovaniyu ustoychivosti periodicheskikh dvizheniy" (A remark on the investigation of stability of periodic motions), *Priklad. mat. mekh.*, 19, No. 1, 1955.
70. Arzhanykh, I. S., "Vsesoyuznaya mezhvuzovskaya konferentsiya po teorii i metodam rascheta nelineynykh elektricheskikh teepey" (All-union inter-university conference on the theory of methods of solving non-linear electric circuits), *Sb. dokladov*, No. 7, Tashkent, 1960.
71. Krein, M., and M. Neimark, *Metod simmetricheskikh i ermitovykh form v teorii otdeleniya korney algebraicheskikh uravneniy* (The method of symmetric and Hermitian forms in the theory of the spacing of roots of algebraic equations), Kharkov, 1936.
72. Markushevich, A. I., *The Theory of Analytic Functions*, Delhi, Hindustan Publishing Corporation, 1963.
73. Erugin, N., "K teorii neyavnykh funktsiy" (On the theory of implicit functions), *Doklady Akad. nauk*, Belorussian SSR, No. 1, 1963.
74. Newton, Isaac.
75. Zanbek, O., *Math. Annalen*, 137, 167-208, 1959, 137, 477, 1959.
76. Feshchenko, S. F., and N. I. Shkil', Asimptoticheskoye resheniye sistemy lineynykh differentsial'nykh uravneniy s malym parametrom pri proizvodnykh (Asymptotic solution of a system of linear differential equations with a small parameter in the coefficients of the derivatives), *Ukr. matem. zhurnal*, XII, No. 4, 1960.

77. Feshchenko, S. F., and L. D. Nikolenko, *Dopovidi, Akad. nauk*, Ukr. SSR, No. 8, 1961. *Ukr. matem. zhurnal*, XIII, No. 3, 1961.
78. Feshchenko, S. F., *Matematika za 40 let* (Mathematics in the past forty years), Moscow, 1957.
79. Bogolyubov, N. N. and Yu. A. Mitropol'skiy, *Asymptotic Methods in the Theory of Nonlinear Oscillations*, 2nd ed., Delhi, Hindustan Publishing Corporation, 1961.
80. Bogolyubov, N. N., "O nekotorykh statisticheskikh metodakh v matematicheskoy fizike" (On certain statistical methods in mathematical physics), *Izd. Akad. nauk*, USSR, 1945.
81. Malkin, I. G., *Teoriya ustoychivosti dvizheniya* (Theory of stability of motion), GITTL, 1952.
82. Lyapunov, A. M., *Izbrannyye trudy* (Collected works), *Izd. Akad. nauk*, USSR, 1948.
83. Yakubovich, V. A., "Rasprostraneniye metoda Lyapunova opredeleniya ogranichennosti resheniy uraveniy $\ddot{y}+p(t)y=0$ na sluchay znakoperemennoy funktsii $p(t+\omega)=p(t)$" (An extension of Lyapunov's method of determining the boundedness of solutions of equations of the form $\ddot{y}+p(t)y=0$ to the case of a sign-alternating function $p(t+\omega)=p(t)$), *Priklad. mat. mekh.*, 18, No. 6, 1954.
84. Demidovich, B. N., "O nekotorykh svoystvakh kharakteristicheskikh pokazateley sistemy obyknovennykh lineynykh differentsial'nykh uravneniy s periodicheskimi koeffitsiyentami," (Certain properties of characteristic exponents of a system of ordinary linear differential equations with periodic coefficients) *Uchenyye zapiski*, Moscow State University, Matem., VI, No. 163, 1952.
85. Makarov, S. M., "Issledovaniye kharakteristicheskogo uravneniya lineynoy sistemy dvukh uravneniy pervogo poryadka s periodicheskimi koeffitsiyentami" (An investigation of the characteristic equation of a linear system of two first-order equations with periodic coefficients), *Priklad. mat. mekh.* 15, No. 3, 1951.
86. Goursat, E., *Cours d'Analyse mathematique*, 7th ed., Vol. II, Paris, Gauthier-Villars.
87. Erugin, N. P., *Doklady Akad. nauk*, Belorussian SSR, 7, No. 2, 1963.
88. Massera, T., Boletin de la Facultad de Ingenieria, IV, No. 1, Mago, 1950.
89. Kurtsvetl', Ya., and O. Voyevoda, *Chekhoslovatskiy matem. zhurnal*, 3, 5(80), 1955.
90. Erugin, N. P., *Vestsi Akad. nauk* Belorussian SSR, ser. fiz.-tekhn. navuk, No. 1, 1962.
91. Breus, K. A., "Pro asymptotychnyi razvyazok lyneinykh differentsyal'nykh rivnyan' z periodychnymy koefitsientamy"

(Asymptotic solutions of linear differential equations with periodic coefficients), *Doklady Akad. nauk*, Ukr. SSR, No. 5, 1955.

92. Tikhonov, A. N., *Uspekhi matem. nauk*, 7, 1 (47), 1952.
93. Erugin, N. P., *Vestsi Akad. nauk*, Belorussian SSSR, ser. fiz.-tekhn. navuk. No. 1, 1962.
94. Erugin, N. P., *Doklady Akad. nauk* Belorussian SSR, 6, No. 7, 1962.
95. Bogdanov, Yu. S., *Doklady Akad. nauk*, Belorussian SSSR, 7, No. 3, 1963.
96. Erugin, N. P., *Vestsi Akad. nauk*, Belorussian SSR, ser. fiz.-tekhn. navuk. No. 1, 1963.
97. Lefschetz, S., *Differential Equations: Geometric Theory*, 2nd ed., New York, Interscience, 1963.

ADDITIONAL REFERENCES

Cesari, L. "Sulla stabilitadelle soluzioni dei sistemi di equazioni differenziali lineari a coefficienti periodici." *Mem. Acad. Italia* (6) 11(1941), 633-695.

Hale, J. K. "Evaluations concerning products of exponential and periodic functions." *Riv. Mat. Univ. Parma* 5(1954), 63-81, "On boundedness of the solution of linear differential systems with periodic coefficients." *Riv. Mat. Univ. Parma* 5(1954), 137-167, "On a class of linear differential equations with periodic coefficients," *Illinois J. Math.*, 1(1957), 98-104, "Linear systems of first and second order differential equations with periodic coefficients."*Illinois J. Math.*, 2(1958), 586-591).

Gambill, R. A. "Stability criteria for linear differential systems with periodic coefficients" *Riv. Mat. Univ. Parma* 5(1954), 169-181, "Criteria for parametric instability for linear differential systems with periodic coefficients." *Riv. Mat. Univ. Parma* 6(1955), 37-43, "A fundamental system of real solutions for linear differential systems with periodic coefficients." *Riv. Mat. Univ. Parma* 7 (1956), 311-319.

Cesari, L. and Bailey, H. R. "Boundedness of solutions of linear differential systems with periodic coefficients." *Archive Rat. Mech. Anal.*, 1(1958), 246-271.

Cesari, L. *Asymptotic Behavior and Stability Problems in Ordinary Differential Equations*, 1959, Springer-Verlag, Berlin-Gottingen-Heidelberg.

Index